Disney

365

Stories

A story a day

PaRRagon

Bath • New York • Cologne • Melbourne • Delhi
Hong Kong • Shenzhen • Singapore

This edition published by Parragon Books Ltd in 2016

Parragon Books Ltd
Chartist House
15–17 Trim Street
Bath BA1 1HA, UK
www.parragon.com

Researched and co-ordinated by Niamh Harkett

New Year's Day

It was the first day of the new year, and Pongo and Perdita were out for a walk with their pets, Roger and Anita. The morning fog was beginning to part, and the air was clear and cold.

"Oh, Pongo," Perdita sighed happily. "What a wonderful year we've just had – 15 puppies to be thankful for!"

"Yes, darling, and just think of all we have to look forward to this year," said Pongo.

"Can you believe they all stayed up till midnight last night to ring in the new year?" Perdita cried. "And still awake when we left! I do hope they don't tire out dear, poor Nanny."

"Yes, that was quite a party we had at the flat last night," Pongo agreed. "And Lucky would have spent the whole night watching television if we had allowed him to."

"Perhaps we should be getting home now," said Perdita. "I am so afraid that Cruella De Vil may come around while we're out. I dread the way she looks at our puppies."

"I suppose we should," said Pongo. "But I'm sure Nanny has been taking good care of them." Pongo and Perdita gently pulled on their leads to let Roger and Anita know it was time to go. The four of them walked towards home just as a sprinkling of rain began to fall.

"Nanny! Puppies! We're home!" called Roger as he and Anita took off their muddy boots and Pongo and Perdy brushed off their paws on the mat in the hall. But no one answered.

"Pongo!" exclaimed Perdita, her panic rising. "Where are the puppies?"

Pongo raced up the stairs and began searching the rooms one by one. Perdita went to check the kitchen. Roger and Anita exchanged concerned looks, but tried to remain calm.

Pongo hurried into the sitting room to rejoin Perdita, who was on the brink of tears.

"Oh, Pongo!" she cried. "Where can –?"

"Hush, darling," said Pongo, his ears pricked intently. The two dogs fell silent. Then they both heard it – a tiny snore coming from the direction of the couch. There, nestled among the cushions, the puppies were sound asleep!

"I found Nanny!" Roger called. "She fell asleep in her chair!"

Perdita was busy counting the sleeping puppies. "... 12, 13, 14.... Oh, Pongo! One of the puppies isn't here!"

But Pongo had trotted into the next room. "Here he is, darling!" he called. "It's Lucky, of course. He's watching the New Year's Day celebration on television."

A Body for All Occasions

With the sky peppered in little white clouds and the air warm and wonderful, the cars of Radiator Springs were having a lovely day ... all of them except Sally.

"Hi, Sally! Why the long hood?" asked Flo.

"Today's just not my day," grumbled Sally. "Tonight I have a date with Lightning and I want to wear something special! I can't find anything I like," Sally explained. "No new accessories or anything pretty I can use."

"Have you tried Sarge's Surplus Store?" asked Flo.

Sally nodded gloomily. "Yes. But I didn't find anything!"

The friends bumped into Ramone as they drove along.

"Sally wants to get dolled up for her date with Lightning tonight. But she can't find anything!" Flo told Ramone.

Ramone moved in closer as if to share a secret. "I may have a solution...."

Moments later, Sally and Flo found themselves at Ramone's body-art shop. Sally was overwhelmed by what was on offer.

"Come on!" Ramone encouraged. "You're in for an all-new look. Lightning McQueen won't believe his headlights!"

"Gee, I had something a little less radical in mind," she admitted nervously.

"Come on! You're gonna love it!" Flo said.

Ramone got to work, masterfully spraying paint in all directions.

When Sally looked in the mirror she was covered from bonnet to bumper in fierce orange and yellow flames. She gulped.

In a second attempt, Ramone covered her body in big, blooming flowers with petals. She gulped again.

And on his third try, Ramone cooked up a picture of wibbly, wobbly splodges in every colour imaginable.

"I think this is a little too special," Sally confessed, feeling silly as she looked at her reflection.

"We need something else," Ramone decided. "Let me think...."

In a burst of vibrant spray and inspiration, Ramone revealed his greatest creation....

"Hey!" Sally exclaimed, as she opened her eyes to see. "It's me again. Back to normal!"

Ramone and Flo smiled widely.

"Because this is the best look for you," said Ramone.

"Yes," agreed Flo. "You're perfect, Sally. And don't ever forget it."

Sally blushed a deep red.

"This evening, Lightning won't be able to take his eyes off you," Ramone said.

Sally left with a spin in her wheels – she didn't need to change who she was inside, or out.

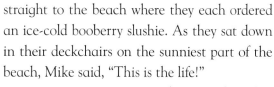

Relaxopolis

It was another cold blustery day in Monstropolis. Sulley and Mike were on their way to work. Mike sighed heavily.

"What's wrong, little buddy?" asked Sulley.

"I'm sick and tired of winter!" Mike replied. "It's cold, it's windy and it gets dark early." He thought for a moment. "Sulley, I think I have the winter blues!"

"Sure sounds like it," said Sulley. "Only a month or so to go, though."

Mike sighed again. A month or two more of winter sounded like an eternity! But a big smile spread across his face when he looked up and saw an advertising board. On it was a big pink monster sitting in a deckchair on the beach, wearing sunglasses and sipping what looked like an ice-cold booberry slushie. In big letters it said: 'Beat Those Winter Blues in Relaxopolis!'

Mike stopped in his tracks and grabbed Sulley's furry arm. He pointed at the sign, too excited to say a word.

"That's a great idea!" Sulley cheered. "A week on a tropical island is just what we need!"

As soon as they got to work, Mike filled in their holiday forms. They would be on their way to Relaxopolis first thing Saturday morning!

When Mike and Sulley arrived, they didn't even unpack their bags. Instead, they went straight to the beach where they each ordered an ice-cold booberry slushie. As they sat down in their deckchairs on the sunniest part of the beach, Mike said, "This is the life!"

"You bet," said Sulley. "Do you think you need some of this Monster Tropic sunscream? You'd better be careful. You don't want to get too much sun on your first day!"

"I'll just soak up the rays for a little while first," said Mike happily. "My winter blues are melting away." He slipped a big mirrored sunglass over his eye and put his arms behind his head. This was paradise!

After a while Sulley got bored of sunbathing and decided to go for a swim. Then he joined in a game of beach monsterball. A couple of hours later, he returned to the deckchairs, where Mike was sound asleep. His green friend had not changed position since Sulley had left. Mike had burned himself in the sun!

Sulley covered Mike with a towel and ran over to get him a refreshing booberry slushie. When he returned to the deckchairs, Mike was just waking up.

"Hey, little buddy," said Sulley. "Guess you chased those winter blues away, huh?"

Mike just looked at Sulley sleepily.

"You aren't blue any more," Sulley explained. "Now you're bright red!"

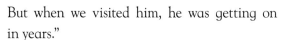

Marlin's Story

"P. Sherman, 42 Wallaby Way, Sydney ... P. Sherman, 42 Wallaby Way, Sydney...." Dory kept repeating the address over and over again. She and Marlin were searching for Marlin's missing son, Nemo. They had just escaped an angry anglerfish, and now they were trying to find someone who could give them directions to Sydney. That's where Nemo probably was. "P. Sherman, 42 Wallaby Way, Sydney ... P. Sherman, 42 Wallaby Way, Sydney...." Dory continued to chant.

Marlin had the address memorized and thought he would go crazy if he had to hear it again. "Dory!" he said with a sigh. "I know you just want to be helpful, but do you really need to keep talking?"

"I love to talk," said Dory. "I'm pretty good at it. Hmm ... what were we talking about?"

"I just want to find Nemo," Marlin said.

"That's right, Chico," said Dory.

"One time, Nemo and I...." Marlin began.

"Go on," Dory said. "Is this going to be exciting?"

"Yes, it's an exciting story," said Marlin, relieved that he had got her to stop reciting the address. "Well," Marlin began, "one time, I took Nemo to the other side of the reef, to visit a relative of mine who was known as the fastest swimmer of all the clownfish, in his day.

But when we visited him, he was getting on in years."

Dory yawned. "When's the good part?"

Marlin sighed. "I was just about to get to it!" he said. "So, anyway, on the way back home, guess what we ran into!"

"What?" asked Dory.

"A huge jellyfish! It was hovering in the water, blocking our way through two big tufts of seagrass."

"Uh-huh," said Dory distractedly. She seemed to be trying to remember something. "P. Sherman...." she muttered softly.

"For a moment there I thought we were goners," said Marlin. "But then ... a huge sea turtle swam up and swallowed the jellyfish in one gulp!"

"Did you say thank you to the sea turtle?" asked Dory, who seemed back on track.

"Well, no," Marlin replied. "I was afraid he would eat us, too, so Nemo and I hurried on our way. But, ever since then, I have been fascinated with sea turtles. And I hope I never have to meet another jellyfish!"

"Say, I've got a story too!" said Dory excitedly. "It takes place at 42 Wallaby Way, Sydney. At P. Sherman. Now, at P. Sherman, 42 Wallaby Way, Sydney, there was this, um, fish ... and ... well...."

Marlin just groaned and kept swimming.

Disney
THE
LION KING

Scaredy Cats

"Nala," Simba whispered. "Are you awake?"

"Yes," Nala replied, stepping out of the dark cave where she slept with her mother. "Why are you here? You're gonna get us in trouble ... again."

Earlier, Simba and Nala had gone to explore the forbidden Elephant's Graveyard, where they'd been trapped by hyenas. Simba's father, Mufasa, had rescued them.

"Come on," Simba hissed. "Follow me."

Soon the two cubs were on the dark savannah near the base of Pride Rock.

"What do you want, anyway?" Nala asked.

"I just wanted to make sure you weren't still scared," Simba said.

Nala scowled at him. "Scared?" she exclaimed. "*I'm* not the one who was scared!"

"What?" Simba cried. "You're not saying *I* was scared, are you? Because there's no way I'd be scared of a few stupid hyenas. I wouldn't have been scared even if we'd run into *10* hyenas."

"Well, I wouldn't have been scared even if we'd found *20* hyenas and an angry water buffalo," said Nala.

"Oh yeah?" Simba said. "Well, I wouldn't have been scared of *30* hyenas, an angry water buffalo and a –"

"FURIOUS HORNBILL?" a new voice squawked from the darkness.

"Ahhhhhh!" Simba and Nala cried, jumping straight up in the air.

Just then, a brightly coloured bird stepped out of the shadows. It was Zazu, Mufasa's most trusted adviser.

"Zazu!" Simba cried. "You scared us!"

"I wasn't scared," Nala snapped indignantly.

"Me neither!" Simba added quickly.

Zazu glared at both of them over his long beak. "Not scared, were you?" he said drily. "That certainly explains the shrieking."

"You just startled us," Nala mumbled, under her breath.

Zazu fluffed his feathers. "Listen up, you two," he said. "There's no shame in admitting you're scared. Even King Mufasa wouldn't deny that he was terrified when he found out you were missing. And, if it's good enough for him, it's good enough for a pair of scrawny cubs like you. Right?"

"I guess so," Simba said as Nala shrugged.

"Everyone gets scared," Zazu went on. "It's how you respond to it that counts. That's where *true* bravery lies. Get it?"

"Got it," Simba and Nala said.

"Good." Zazu marched towards Pride Rock as the sun began to rise. "Now, let's get you back home post-haste ... or I'll *really* give you something to be scared of!"

Red's Tune-Up Blues

One morning, Red the fire engine thought it was the perfect day to plant a garden. He started his engine. *Rrrrrr.* Red's engine sounded funny. *Pop! Pop! Pop!* Now loud noises were coming out of his exhaust pipe.

As his engine spluttered, Red tried to shrug it off. Hopefully, whatever was wrong would go away, because Red did not want to go to Doc's clinic. He sure didn't like the idea of being poked and prodded.

Instead, Red headed into town to work on his garden, and soon passed Lightning McQueen.

"Hey, Red!" Lightning greeted him. "How's it going?"

"Fine," Red replied shyly. *BANG! BANG!*

"Whoa!" exclaimed Lightning. "That can't feel good. You okay?"

"Mmm-hmm," said Red.

Pop! Red continued driving towards town. Lightning headed into town, too, to find his friends. They wouldn't want Red to be sick. Lightning found the others at Flo's V8 Café, filling up on breakfast.

"Red's not running right," Lightning explained as he pointed to the fire engine, who was starting to plant a garden across the street. "But he's afraid to go to the clinic."

"Aw, shucks," said Mater the tow truck.

"I know how the poor fella feels. I was scared my first time, too! But Doc's a pro. He'll have Red fixed up before he knows what hit him!"

The friends tried to convince Red to visit Doc. Ramone offered a new coat of paint at his House of Body Art, but nothing would convince Red to go.

"We had better get over there," Lightning said to Sally, who had just rolled up. The two cars sped over. Mater, Luigi, Guido, Fillmore and Flo followed.

BANG! Pop, pop, pop! Red's engine gurgled and more loud noises came out of his exhaust pipe.

Sally inched forwards. "Listen, Red. We all know going to get a tune-up for the first time can be scary. But whatever is wrong could be easy to fix. If you don't go now, it could turn into a bigger problem later. None of us wants you to need a complete overhaul. We care too much about you."

Red looked back at his friends. He knew what Sally said was true. "Will you go with me?" he asked Sally.

"Of course I will," she replied.

Later that day, Red rolled out of the clinic and all his friends were waiting for him. Red revved his engine. *Vroom!* It sounded smooth as silk. It was great to be running on all cylinders again!

Kung-fu Cowboy

Andy was curled up in bed, reading a comic with Woody by his side. Woody loved hearing the tales of the comic's high-kicking kung-fu hero, and was disappointed when Andy fell asleep.

Still, Woody was pretty sleepy, too. As the little cowboy doll snuggled under the covers, he soon began to dream....

In his dream, Woody found himself back in the old Wild West. He sat behind a desk in the sheriff's office, waiting for trouble to arrive ... and he didn't have to wait too long.

"Sheriff Woody!" cried a townsperson, rushing into the office. "Black Hat and his bandits have shown up!"

"No outlaw's gonna rob the citizens of Ricestone with me here to protect them!" Woody promised, leaping to his feet.

Instead of reaching for his hat, Woody reached for a kung-fu headband! He tied it around his head just as the mean-looking Black Hat and his gang of outlaws arrived.

"Hand over all the money in town, Sheriff!" Black Hat ordered. He and his gang were some of the roughest, toughest villains around.

Woody narrowed his eyes. "I've got one thing to say to you, Black Hat," he said, ducking into a fighting stance. "Take that! Hai-ya!"

With a series of flying kicks and a few well-aimed chops, Woody took down the whole gang. The townspeople cheered. "Thanks, Woody! You're our hero!"

Suddenly, Woody was awoken by a real cry for help. He blinked his eyes open. He'd been so caught up in his dream he hadn't even noticed Andy leaving for school.

"Emergency!" called Slinky from the floor. "Red monkeys on the loose!"

Woody peered over the edge of the bed and saw Rex racing by chased by a gang of crazed red monkeys.

"This is a job for the kung-fu sheriff!" Woody announced, but as he jumped up he tripped on the bedcovers. Flapping his arms, he fell off the bed, bounced on a ball, then smashed into Andy's dressing table with a *thonk!*

"Woody, are you all right?" gasped Bo Peep, rushing to his side.

"Aw, I'm so bad at flying kicks," Woody groaned. The others had no idea what he was talking about. "If bandits come, you'll need a real kung-fu cowboy, and I'm not one of those."

"You don't need flying kicks to be a good cowboy," Bo said, and Woody realized she was right. Snatching up his lasso, he raced to help Rex. He might not be able to do kung-fu, but the other toys knew that when it came to being a sheriff, Woody was the best in the business.

Anything for a Rally

Dusty had been out running some errands, and was racing back home to Propwash Junction. He and Chug had made plans to watch the Interstate Rally on TV together, and as the race was passing right by their home town, Dusty didn't want to miss a minute of it.

But as Dusty flew, the winds grew stronger. Soon, the little plane was being bounced around on the strong gusts, and flying was becoming more and more difficult. "I hope I get back in time for the rally," he said, narrowing his eyes against the storm.

Nearby, two other planes pulled back. The wind was too strong, and continuing would be dangerous. Dusty refused to quit, though. He wasn't about to let a little breeze stop him watching the race.

Far overheard, he spotted a group of other planes. "Those planes up there are still flying," he said, not realizing they were competitors in the rally, or that they were looking for a safe place to land.

The racers looked down at Dusty and gasped. "That plane down there must be crazy! Doesn't he know he's flying straight into a tornado?"

Dusty didn't know, but he found out soon enough. The wind whipped around him, catching his wings and flipping him into a frantic spin. "I can't hold out much longer!" Dusty yelped. "I'm being sucked in."

Using all his skill, Dusty banked steeply around the side of the spinning tornado – and almost flew straight into a rocky cliff face! The tornado was getting more and more dangerous with each second that passed. Dusty was in serious trouble!

But wait! Through the howling wind, Dusty spotted a gap in the rocks. "That's the entrance to Broken Wings Creek," he realized.

He had just one chance. Tilting his flaps, Dusty let the wind push him towards the narrow canyon. At the last moment he twisted sideways, just missing the rock as he swooped into the safety of the creek.

A few minutes later, he emerged near Propwash Junction. He'd never been so happy to see the place, and as he came in for a landing, Chug told him the rally was about to start. Dusty had arrived just in time!

They raced excitedly to the television, only for an announcer to reveal that the race had been cancelled due to the tornado. Dusty groaned. All that work for nothing!

Chug whistled when he saw the tornado on the TV. "Anyone flying in those conditions would have to be crazy!"

"Yeah," agreed Dusty. "You said it!"

A Day in the Pack

Deep in the heart of South America, the wicked explorer, Charles Muntz, was growing excited. He'd been trying to get his hands on a rare tropical bird for years, and today was the day it was finally going to happen.

Muntz had built communication devices which allowed him to talk to his dogs. He assembled the fearless pack in one of the rooms of his airship and began to tell them their mission. The dogs were a scary-looking bunch, with one exception....

"A bird?" panted Dug, a golden retriever.

Muntz rolled his eyes and sighed. How many times did they have to go through this? "Not just any bird," he said, holding up a picture of the rare creature he was looking for. "This bird."

The explorer told the pack the new strategy he'd come up with for luring the bird out of hiding and capturing it. "Follow the plan and bring it to me alive," he told them.

"Don't worry, master!" barked one of the dogs. "We'll be efficient."

"We'll be fast," said another.

"We'll be ruthless!" growled a third.

Meanwhile, Dug happily scratched his ear with his hind leg. It felt good, and it wasn't until he'd finished that he realized everyone was staring at him.

"Oops. Um ... yes, master," he said.

Muntz ordered the dogs to go and bring him the bird. As they raced away, he set about cooking himself a big lunch. He was celebrating. Soon the bird would be his.

Out in the jungle, the dogs stalked quietly through the undergrowth, searching for the creature. The pack leaders, Alpha and Beta, were in front, keeping their noses to the ground. Dug trotted along behind, his tongue hanging out as he admired the pretty plants and trees.

Suddenly, Beta spotted the bird up ahead. It was a tall, elegant creature with colourful feathers. It was happily munching on berries, and had no idea the dogs were nearby.

As the rest of the pack prepared to pounce, Dug sniffed the air. "Wait a second," he whispered. "Do you smell something?"

Alpha groaned as the other dogs raised their noses, sniffed, and then began to drool. "No! Not today!" he pleaded to them. "We have to follow the plan!"

But even Alpha couldn't resist the smell for long. As Charles Muntz sat down to his roast chicken lunch, he saw all four dogs sitting by the table, panting hungrily. Following orders was important, but the smell of chicken – that was irresistible!

Disney·PIXAR

THE INCREDIBLES

Super Mum

As Elastigirl, Helen Parr had fought some of the world's toughest supervillains. Nowadays, though, her biggest challenge was getting her family ready in the morning.

Her husband more or less took care of himself, but their children, Dash and Violet, were always fighting, and often ended up being late for school.

Dash wanted to use his super speed to race to school, but Helen warned him he'd be in big trouble if he did. Like all Supers, they were pretending to be normal people, so showing off their powers was out of the question.

Even Helen had to admit it sometimes wasn't easy, though. After she dropped Dash and Violet at school, baby Jack-Jack started to cry. His dummy had fallen out of his mouth and was lost somewhere in the back of the car.

Without thinking, Helen stretched her arm back over her head and hunted around the back seat. Suddenly, she realized what she was doing, and snapped her arm back to normal just as another car drove past. That was close. She'd almost given away her secret identity!

Back at home, Helen was busy putting the washing away when the doorbell rang. She knew it had to be the postman, and stretched towards the door to open it. Luckily, she stopped herself just in the nick of time and walked to the door instead, doing her best to act naturally.

Later, at the supermarket, Helen tried to push her trolley through the packed aisles. Lots of other shoppers blocked her path, though. She thought how much easier it would be if she could just reach over their heads and grab the items she wanted.

If she did it fast enough, maybe nobody would notice. Glancing around, she flexed her fingers and ... sighed. She couldn't risk anyone seeing her, so she'd just have to wait like everyone else.

As she waited, a trolley bumped into a big stack of oranges. The fruit mountain wobbled then began to fall. It plunged towards Helen's trolley, where Jack-Jack was lying fast asleep.

Instinctively, Helen wrapped her arms around the fruit tower, steadying it and stopping it falling. She shrunk her arms again and turned to see a shocked little boy staring at her. Helen pretended it was just her sleeves that were long, and not her arms, then hurried out of the shop and made her way home.

When Dash and Violet returned from school, they each said the other had used their powers at school. Their mum smiled and pulled them in for a hug. Pretending not to have powers was important, but sometimes they just couldn't hide from who they really were.

Disney
Lady and the TRAMP

Spaghetti and Meatballs

Tramp had just escaped from the dogcatcher – again. He'd taught that dogcatcher who was boss! Tramp could smell wood burning in fireplaces, dinner cooking ... his stomach suddenly rumbled. Escaping from the dogcatcher always made him work up quite an appetite!

But where would he go for dinner tonight? Usually he stopped by the Schultzes for some Wiener schnitzel on Monday, he had corned beef and cabbage with the O'Briens on Tuesday ... but what he was really craving was some spaghetti and meatballs.

So, Tramp headed to Tony's Restaurant. He scratched at the back door, as was his custom.

"I'm coming! I'm coming!" Tony shouted. He appeared at the door wiping his hands on a towel. He pretended not to see Tramp, as he always did.

"Hey, nobody's here!" Tony shouted. "It must be April Fools' Day!" He pretended to think for a moment. "No, it's not the first! It's not even April! It's January!"

Tramp couldn't take it any more. He was so hungry! He barked.

"Oh, there you are, Butch, my friend," said Tony. Tramp, aka Butch, jumped up and down. "I'll get your dinner," said Tony. "Relax, enjoy yourself."

Tramp sat down and looked around the cluttered alleyway. This was the life!

Just then Tony appeared with a plateful of pasta. He had given Tramp two, no, make that *three* meatballs! This was quite a special night.

Tony stood and chatted with Tramp as he ate his meal, telling him about his day – the late delivery of fish, the customer who had complained that the tomato sauce was too garlicky, the trip that he and his wife were planning to take....

Tramp finished eating and gave the plate one last lick. It was sparkling clean.

"That reminds me," said Tony. "There's something I've been meaning to talk to you about. It's time you settled down and got a wife of your own."

Tramp gave Tony a horrified look and began to back out of the alleyway.

Tony laughed so hard his sides shook. "Goodbye, Butch!" he called. "But mark my words, one of these days, you're going to meet the dog you can't resist! And, when you do, I have a good idea – you bring her to Tony's for a nice romantic dinner!"

Tramp barked his thanks to Tony. He walked down the block, shaking his head. He was footloose and collar-free! Settle down? That was never going to happen!

A Never Land Story

It was a cold winter night, and John and Michael just couldn't get to sleep. They climbed onto the bed of their older sister, Wendy.

"Oh, tell us a story, Wendy!" said Michael.

"Yes, please. A Peter Pan story!" pleaded John.

"Certainly," said Wendy. "Have I told you about the time that Peter Pan outsmarted the evil Captain Hook?"

"Yes!" said Michael eagerly. "And we want to hear it again!"

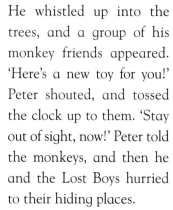

Wendy laughed and began her story. "Well, one night, Captain Hook moored his ship in a secret cove close to the island of Never Land. He and his men rowed ashore quietly, for he was intent on discovering the hiding place of Peter and the Lost Boys. Captain Hook hated Peter Pan because the boy had cut off his hand in a duel and fed it to a large crocodile. And now that crocodile was determined to swallow up the rest of him. Luckily for Captain Hook, however, this crocodile had also swallowed a clock, so the pirate would always be alerted to the crocodile's presence by the sound of the ticking clock.

"Fortunately for Peter Pan," Wendy continued, "his dear friend Tinker Bell learned of Captain Hook's evil plan ahead of time.

She flew to Peter and warned him that the pirate was coming. 'Oh-ho!' laughed Peter. 'Well, we shall be ready for him then!' He found a clock just like the one the crocodile had swallowed.

He whistled up into the trees, and a group of his monkey friends appeared. 'Here's a new toy for you!' Peter shouted, and tossed the clock up to them. 'Stay out of sight, now!' Peter told the monkeys, and then he and the Lost Boys hurried to their hiding places.

"When Hook came to the clearing, the first thing he heard was the ticking clock. The sound seemed to be coming at him from all sides! The monkeys were having a grand time, tossing the clock back and forth, and creeping up behind Hook. Seized with terror, Hook and his men raced to their boat and rowed madly back to their ship."

Just then, the Darling children's parents came in to check on them. "You're not telling more of these poppycock stories about Peter Pan, are you, Wendy?" their father asked.

"Peter Pan is real, Father!" the children cried. "We know he is!"

As the parents kissed their children goodnight, they didn't see that a boy in green was crouching just outside the nursery window. He had been listening to the story, and he would be back again – soon.

A Must-See Event

Radiator Springs was completely empty. It seemed like a ghost town. Spooky and silent. Nothing moved besides a sheet of loose paper, blowing on a breeze as The King slowly drove along the street, all alone.

"Where'd everybody go?" he asked the quiet road, his voice echoing around him. "Hello? Anybody around?"

"I am," came a friendly voice. "Nice to see ya!"

"Lightning!" cried The King, startled. "Good thing I found you."

"Were you looking for someone?" Lightning McQueen asked.

"My wife," explained The King. "She drove into town hours ago, but I haven't seen her since." He tried not to sound too worried.

"I know where she is," Lightning McQueen said confidently. "She had to take a detour. Doc's got a problem!"

"What is it?" asked The King, surprised. He knew Doc liked to practise racing on the outskirts of town and was probably there, warming up those old tyres of his.

"I've always admired Doc's racing. I can't leave him in trouble. Will you take me to him?"

Lightning McQueen nodded and revved his engine in anticipation. "Follow me!"

The King and Lightning drove until they came across a cluster of cars in all shapes, sizes and colours, waiting for them just beyond the mountains.

"Happy Birthday!" they cheered, clutching a colourful banner.

They were all there. Fillmore. Mater. Luigi wearing a bushy wig. Guido. Sarge. Even his wife ... how sneaky! And last but not least ... Doc! All gathered together to throw The King a surprise birthday party.

"How about racing with an ol' timer?" asked Doc, with a growl of his engine and a friendly wink.

The King's wife gave him a little kiss on the cheek. "Are you happy?" she asked. "We've set up a race with your champion."

The King couldn't believe how lucky he was to have his friends and his lovely wife arrange something so special for him.

Guido led the way to the track, with a flag in his grasp and Doc just had time to turn to The King before their tyres bit into the dirt at the starting line, ready to jet them off.

"Happy Birthday!" Doc said. "And may the fastest car win."

"On your marks, get set, go!" Guido yelled, waving his flag joyfully.

And in a screech of tyres and a cloud of billowing dust, the two friends raced, neck and neck, to their hearts' content.

DISNEY·PIXAR

MONSTERS, INC.

Monster Moneymaker

Mike and Sulley walked through the lobby of Monsters, Inc. to the Scare Floor. They passed the Scarer of the Month photos of Sulley hanging on the wall.

Mike suddenly turned to his big blue friend. "Sulley," he said, "do you ever think that we deserve a little more?"

"More?" Sulley asked.

"Oh, you know," Mike continued. "You're the top Scarer month after month. All you get is a lousy picture in the hallway, and I get nothin'. Don't you think we should be famous?"

"What have you got in mind?" Sulley asked.

"A marketing campaign," Mike told him.

"How would we do that?" Sulley asked.

"Well, for starters, we'll get you some new head shots, and not just any old head shots but autographed head shots. And we won't stop there." Mike was on a roll. "We'll make mugs, posters – T-shirts even – with all your best poses." Mike demonstrated a few of his friend's Scarer poses for Sulley, including Sulley's personal favourite – the ol' Waternoose Jump and Growl. "We can set up a gift shop right here in the building featuring 'Sulley the Super Scarer' memorabilia."

"Why would we want to bother with all that?" Sulley wondered.

"Money!" Mike exclaimed, rolling his eye.

"I don't know, Mike," Sulley said. "It just doesn't seem right, us making money off these things. But what if we…? That's it!" Sulley jumped up, nearly knocking Mike over. "We'll donate the money to charity!"

"Who said anything about charity?" asked Mike.

"That's a great idea!" Sulley said, ignoring Mike.

"How will we bask in any glory if we give the money away?" Mike asked.

"Well, we will, sort of," Sulley explained. "We'll make the donation on behalf of Monsters, Inc."

"I don't know about that," Mike said.

"It's a wonderful idea!" Sulley replied. "And when we help the company make a generous donation, Mr Waternoose will be very proud of us!"

Mike was suddenly warming to the idea. "And we'll get lots of press!" he added.

"Sure, why not?" Sulley said with a shrug.

"It's a great idea!" Mike cheered.

"I agree!" Sulley said.

"I'm glad I thought of it!" Mike gave his best friend a huge smile.

"You always have such good ideas," Sulley agreed with a grin.

"It's like I always say," Mike added. "Scaring's important, but it's the brains behind the monster that matter most!"

Pongo Carries a Tune

"I don't know what we're going to do," Roger Radcliffe told his wife, Anita. "We have all these puppies to feed, and I don't have one song to sell!"

"Don't worry," Anita told him. "I'm sure you'll be inspired soon."

"I'm glad *you're* sure!" said Roger. "Because all I've got is a bunch of used paper." He pointed to the overflowing wastebasket.

"Don't give up," said Anita. "I know that you can do it."

After Anita left, Pongo watched his pet pace in front of his piano.

"Pongo, old boy, I must have written 10 songs in 10 days. But they're all terrible," said Roger, pointing to the wastebasket. "What am I going to do?"

Pongo wanted to help his pet, but he didn't know how.

That night, Pongo talked to Perdy about Roger's dilemma. They sat in the middle of the living room, surrounded by puppies.

"Roger has already written 10 songs," explained Pongo. "He just doesn't think they're good enough to sell. But I know they are – I've heard him play them, and you don't have a songwriter for a pet without developing a good ear for hit songs. The songs are right upstairs, stuffed inside his wastebasket."

Perdy saw what he was thinking.

"Do you know the way to the music publisher?" she asked.

Pongo nodded. "I've taken Roger for walks there dozens of times."

"I think you should try it," said Perdy.

After Roger and Anita had gone to sleep, Pongo padded into the music room and gathered up the sheet music from the wastebasket. Then he sneaked out of the house, carrying the music to the publisher's office. Pongo pushed all the pages under the door, then trotted back home.

The next day, the phone rang. Roger answered it.

"You what?" Roger said into the receiver. "You did...? But how did you...? Oh, I see ... well, thank you. Thank you!"

Anita rushed over. "Who was that?"

"My music publisher," said Roger. "He's buying 10 of my songs."

"Ten songs!" cried Anita. "I thought you didn't even have *one* to sell."

Roger scratched his head in confusion. "I didn't think I did."

"So, what happened?" asked Anita.

Perdy looked at Pongo and barked. Her husband could carry a tune too – all the way across town to Roger's publisher!

Space Station High Jinks

Andy gasped in delight. There, standing on his bed, was the latest addition to the Buzz Lightyear toy range – a Star Command space station!

"Thanks, Mum. This is the coolest present ever!" Andy cried, racing over to play with his new toy. Although he couldn't yet show it, Buzz loved it, too.

As soon as Andy left for school the next day, the toys jumped up. Buzz showed off the space station. "Here she is! What do you think?"

Rex and Hamm gazed in wonder.

"Out of this world!" said Rex.

Woody pushed back his hat as he inspected the station. It stood three times taller than he was, with all sorts of gadgets and hidden features. "It'll do," he said, playing it casual.

"It'll do?" Buzz spluttered. He pointed to all the cool features. "It's loaded with laser cannons, a teletransport platform and a turbo-powered emergency capsule. That's way beyond 'it'll do'!"

The station was Buzz's dream come true, and it was a dream he wanted to share with all his friends. "Look, it's big enough for all of us," he said.

Woody's eyes widened. "You mean we're allowed to...?"

"Of course," said Buzz. "From now on you are all honourary space rang–"

The toys didn't wait to hear any more. They barged past Buzz, sending him into a spin, then shoved their way through the door and inside their new playset.

They explored the space station in awe. Even if some of them wouldn't admit it, they'd always wondered what it was like to be a space ranger, and this was their chance.

"Look what I've found," cried Rex. Woody, Hamm and Slinky hurried to join him, and cheered when they spotted a row of Star Command uniforms.

Grabbing a uniform each, they squeezed, squashed and – in Rex's case – ripped their way into the outfits. They ran out of the station to show Buzz their new look. "Ta-dah!"

Woody gave a twirl. "Hey, being a space sheriff ain't bad!"

Buzz watched in shock as the others joined in the fun. "Rex Lightyear to the rescue!" laughed Rex.

"Dog command," barked Slinky. "Do you read me, over?"

Woody struck a heroic pose. "To infinity and beyond!"

"Oh, no!" muttered Buzz, watching his friends dance around in their Star Command uniforms. He had a feeling these new recruits were going to be a lot of hard work!

RATATOUILLE
(rat·a·too·ee)

Happy Birthday

It was his dad's birthday, and Remy had been hard at work preparing a surprise. Before he could unveil it, though, he heard his dad, Django, give a sad sigh.

Remy and his brother, Emile, hurried to their father's side to find out what was wrong. "I know you are a great chef," Django said to Remy. "But are you still a rat?"

"Of course I am," said Remy, taken aback.

"Really? You cook, you read, you have human friends," Django said. "So, make me the best birthday present ever. Show me you are still one of us."

Remy asked how he could prove he was still a rat, and Django led him and Emile down a drain and into the sewers. Django explained that a true rat loved the sewers. "He loves the strong smell," the old rat said. "A perfect mix of garbage, muddy water ..."

"... and rotten stuff," finished Emile, taking a deep sniff.

Remy said that he loved the smell, too, but when his dad saw he was holding his nose, he realized Remy wasn't telling the truth. "Try to smell it, please," Django sighed.

Slowly, Remy uncovered first one nostril, then the other. He sniffed slightly, and the stink wafted up his nose. It wasn't as bad as he'd expected, he had to admit.

"Good!" Django cheered. "Now try to gnaw a wire."

He pointed over to where Emile was already chewing through a cable, and explained that true rats adored the feel of getting their teeth into a wire. As Emile munched, Remy made a dive for him.

"Stop, this is a power cable!" he yelped.

Grabbing his brother by the waist, Remy pulled him back, just as electricity began to spark right where Emile had been chewing.

Django punched the air happily. "True rats help their brothers!" he cheered. "But they walk on all fours, too."

Remy preferred to walk on two legs, but he wanted to make his dad happy, so scurried up and down the sewer pipe on all fours. "This is my son!" Django whooped. Remy had proved he was still a rat at heart.

Back in the restaurant, after Remy had spent almost half an hour scrubbing himself in the sink, Django told him how happy he was, and that he couldn't ask for more.

"But I have something for the truest rat ever," Remy smiled. He unveiled his surprise – a delicious-looking cake that was shaped like a rat, complete with ears and a tail.

"Happy birthday, Daddy!" Emile laughed, and they all tucked into the cake together.

Vita-minamulch Signals

Chug, Dusty, Dottie and Leadbottom were at the airfield when they heard a low droning noise above them. "What's that racket?" asked Chug.

"Sounds like a big plane cruisin' at high altitude," said Dusty.

Dottie gasped. "You're right!" she said. "I've just received a call for help. He's flown off course. His instruments have broken down, and he's running low on fuel!"

The cargo plane would have to make an emergency landing. Leadbottom began to clear the runway, but Dottie stopped him. "Our runway's too short for a plane that size," she said. "Someone's gonna have to go up and guide him towards the city."

Leadbottom creaked his rudder. "I can't fly that high at my age, Dottie. This calls for someone that's young and strong."

Everyone looked at Dusty. "Argh! I'm too small, that cargo jet would never see me," he said. His propeller started to spin. "Besides, I've got a better idea. Luckily I just filled my tank with Vita-minamulch!"

"So what?" cried Chug as Dusty took to the air.

"This is no time for crop dusting!" shouted Dottie, but Dusty was too far away to hear.

They all watched as Dusty levelled off.

He was far too low to guide the cargo plane. What was he thinking?

"I don't need to go that high," Dusty said to himself. "I'll just turn on my sprayers and make a few manoeuvres...."

A white trail sprayed out behind Dusty as he dived and banked through the air. In just a few moments, he'd done what he'd come to do. He just hoped it was going to work!

"Hey, buddy, can you hear me?" he said over the radio. "Take a look below!"

Up above, the worried cargo plane looked down. There, spread out below him, was a series of puffy white arrows pointing off to the left.

"The nearest city is that way," Dusty told him. "They have an airport that's your size."

The cargo plane banked left, following the arrows. Now he knew where to go, he was out of danger. Dusty had saved him!

"Vita-minamulch directional signals! An ingenious idea!" cheered Leadbottom, as Dusty landed beside him.

"Congratulations, Dusty! I have to apologize," said Dottie. "For a second I thought you were trying to avoid flying high, and that maybe you were afraid of heights."

Afraid of heights? "Uh ... you do know I'm a plane, right?" Dusty asked, and the friends all laughed and celebrated another job well done.

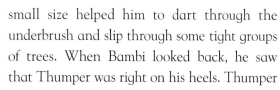

Bambi

The Race

"Good morning, young Prince," Thumper greeted Bambi one bright winter day.

"Good morning, Thumper," Bambi said.

"I have a great idea, Bambi. Let's have a race," Thumper said. "We'll start from here." He drew a line in the dirt. "And whoever makes it to that big pine tree over there first, wins the race."

"But it would be silly for us to race," Bambi told his friend.

"Why's that?" Thumper asked, confused.

"Because I'll win," Bambi told Thumper.

"What makes you so sure?" Thumper challenged, puffing up his chest.

"Because I'm bigger and faster than you," Bambi explained.

"If you're so sure you'll win," Thumper said, "why are you afraid to race me?"

Bambi paused to think about this. He didn't want to hurt the little rabbit's feelings. "Fine," he said at last. "Let's race!"

"Great!" Thumper exclaimed. "Ready?"

"Ready!" Bambi said.

"Okay," Thumper said, crouching down. Bambi crouched down too. "On your marks. Get set. Go!" cried Thumper.

They both took off as fast as they could. Bambi, with his long legs and big, wide stride, immediately took the lead. But Thumper's small size helped him to dart through the underbrush and slip through some tight groups of trees. When Bambi looked back, he saw that Thumper was right on his heels. Thumper took the opportunity to hop past Bambi. Bambi paused to jump over a tree that had been knocked down, blocking the path. Thumper was able to wriggle under it. He popped up in front of Bambi and took the lead.

Bambi took longer and longer strides, running faster and faster. Soon he had passed Thumper. But, in his hurry to go as fast as he could, he got tangled up in a bush. As Bambi struggled to free himself, Thumper hopped past him again.

They were quickly approaching the big pine tree. Bambi was running as fast as he could, jumping over logs and bushes. Thumper hopped as quickly as his bunny legs would carry him, ducking and weaving through whatever obstacles were in his way. As they crossed the finish line, they were in a neck-and-neck tie.

"See!" Thumper said, panting. "Little guys can keep up!"

"You are absolutely right!" Bambi said, also panting.

And the two friends, both winners, sat down together to catch their breath.

Fireproof Flower Patch

The sky was black in Radiator Springs, but not because the clouds were threatening to rain ... Guido and Luigi's pile of old tyres were on fire, filling the town with smoke!

"We've got to put out the flames before they spread!" yelled Lightning McQueen, as the crowds looked on in panic.

Before anyone could budge to help, Red sent a glistening stream of water from his powerful hose, killing the dangerous flames in the rev of an engine.

"Thanks, Red! Radiator Springs sure is lucky to have a fire engine like you," Sarge praised.

"How would we get along without him?" agreed Flo.

Red blushed and returned to his flowers. The crowd watched him proudly water them in the summer sun.

"We should do something to show Red our gratitude," whispered Lightning McQueen to the crowd of grateful cars, who had all witnessed Red's heroic act.

"How about a medal?" suggested The King.

"It might be too embarrassing for him," Sally pointed out, who knew Red better than anyone. "But his equipment is getting a little old," she added thoughtfully.

"Why don't we get him a new part?" Lightning McQueen enthused.

"Excellent idea!" said Doc. "The city's treasury can foot the bill."

"And I know the suppliers of emergency services for the racing circuits," Lightning McQueen insisted.

By the end of the day, Red's friends had rallied together and surrounded him with gifts of new parts. There were so many boxes, Red was overwhelmed.

"I've never seen him so happy," said Sally.

But the next day, Sally and Lightning found Red under a shady tree, looking fed up and washed out.

"What's wrong with Red?" asked Lightning. "Is his new equipment not working?"

Sally smiled. "Oh no! It works fine." They watched Red as he moved from the shadows to tentatively approach his flowers. His gadgets and levers whirred as he prepared to hose them down.

"Red has a hard time telling which lever turns on the water...." Sally explained.

Just then, an explosion of a white gel-like substance jetted from the hose and covered the flowers so only a single petal could be seen.

"... and which one turns on the fire extinguishing foam," Sally giggled.

Red stared at the mess. It seemed there was a lot more practise to be had before he could master his new and improved system!

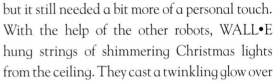

Disney · PIXAR

WALL·E

Home Sweet Home

WALL·E was a robot on a mission. He had spent weeks clearing an area so he could build EVE a house, and now the time had come to get building.

Luckily, he wouldn't have to do it alone. His robot friends from the Axiom spaceship were all keen to help. Working together, they'd get the house built in no time, WALL·E was sure.

The plan was simple. The other robots would bring WALL·E junk, and he'd compress it into building blocks. What could go wrong?

Everything! The other robots were far too enthusiastic. Instead of neatly piling the junk up beside WALL·E, they tossed it towards him at high speed. Cans, scrap metal and even an old fridge rained down on WALL·E, knocking him over – and knocking down the blocks he'd so carefully placed.

When the house was built, the Axiom's painting robot came to give it some colour, but WALL·E ended up being painted, too!

The cleaning robots moved in next. As they worked, they whipped up an enormous dust cloud that covered the whole area, making it difficult for WALL·E to even find where the new house was!

As the dust cloud settled, WALL·E spotted the building and rolled inside. It was looking great,

but it still needed a bit more of a personal touch. With the help of the other robots, WALL·E hung strings of shimmering Christmas lights from the ceiling. They cast a twinkling glow over the whole house, making it look even better.

With a few finishing touches, the house was finished. All that remained was to show EVE.

"Ta-dah!" WALL·E cried. He opened the door and EVE floated inside. She looked around in amazement, barely able to believe her eyes. She'd longed for a home of her own ever since they'd arrived on Earth, and now....

Suddenly, one of the strings of Christmas lights got tangled around EVE's arm. Instinctively, she turned and opened fire with her lasers.

WALL·E ducked for cover as the house exploded around them. He groaned when he finally raised his head and saw that the only part of the house still standing was the fridge. All that work had been for nothing. EVE still didn't have a place she could call home.

Then WALL·E heard EVE gasp with delight. He looked round to find her bobbing happily up and down inside the fridge. "Home!" she said.

WALL·E was happy, too. It might not be the one he'd planned for her, but at least EVE now had a home of her own.

Palindrome Mania!

"Hey, Atta," Flik said. "Did you know that your name is a palindrome?"

Atta gave him a strange look. "What's a palindrome?" she asked.

"It's a word that reads the same forwards and backwards," Flik replied. "Spelled forwards, your name is A-T-T-A. Spelled backwards, your name is also A-T-T-A. See?"

"Oh," Atta said. "That's neat. I've never heard of palindromes before."

"I love them," said Flik. "There are other names that are palindromes, like *Bob*."

"Or *Lil*?" tried Atta.

"Right!" said Flik. "And *Otto*."

"And *Nan*!" added Atta. "This is fun!"

"What's fun?" said Dot, who had just run over to them.

"Thinking of palindromes," Atta replied.

"Huh?" said Dot.

"Exactly!" said Flik. "*Huh* is a palindrome!" Together, Flik and Atta explained to Dot what a palindrome was.

"Oh!" said Dot. "Wait! Let me see if I can think of another one." Dot looked around, hoping that something she saw would spark an idea. She spotted her mother, the Queen, off in the distance, lounging in the shade.

"*Mum!*" cried Dot. "That's one, isn't it?"

"Not bad," said Atta with a wink, "for a *tot* like you!" Atta giggled, pleased that she had fit another palindrome into her sentence.

"Oh, yeah?" replied Dot with a mischievous grin. "Well, you ain't seen nothin' yet, *sis!*"

Taking turns, Dot and Atta challenged one another to think of more and more palindromes. Dot came up with *eye, pop* and *toot*. Atta countered with *gag, noon, did* and *redder*.

"Yes," Flik interjected, "*redder* is a nice, long one! It's harder to think of palindromes that have more than four letters. Believe me, I've spent hours on that. But there's always *Aidemedia* – that's a type of bird. And *Allenella*, of course, which is a category of mollusc...." Flik went on to list a longer palindrome for just about every letter of the alphabet – most of them sciencey words that Atta and Dot had never heard before. As he droned on and on, Dot and Atta looked at each other and rolled their eyes. Now they were both thinking of the same word, and it wasn't a palindrome – B-O-R-I-N-G.

When Flik had finally finished with his list, he looked up at Dot and Atta with a self-satisfied smile. Each of them had a palindrome ready.

"*Wow,*" said Atta flatly, sounding more bored than impressed.

"*Zzz,*" snored Dot, who had drifted off somewhere between *V* and *W*.

A Thorny Rescue

Rex leaned over Andy's video game controller, hitting the buttons as fast as his little arms could. Andy's new video game was great fun, but it sure was tricky!

"Go, buddy! Hit that alien!" Buzz cheered, but Rex knew better.

"No! I'm trying to avoid him. See? It's written here," Rex said, holding up a list of tricks Andy had written down on how to complete the game.

Rex cried out in shock as a sudden gust of wind snatched the page of notes from him and carried it out of the window!

"The notes have blown away!" he yelled.

"Well, shoot my pistols," said Woody, rushing to join Buzz and Rex at the window.

"They've landed in the neighbour's front yard," Buzz said, pointing to the page. "Getting 'em back will be child's play."

But Woody had spotted a problem. The postman was strolling up the path, right towards the instructions! The toys watched in horror as the postman picked up the note, then stuffed it into the neighbours' mailbox.

"Oh no! Now what?" Rex groaned. Without those instructions, he had no hope of completing the game.

"Take it easy," smiled Woody. "We'll get 'em."

Sticking his fingers in his mouth, Woody let out a shrill whistle. A moment later, Buster the dog came running into the room. Woody and Buzz jumped onto Buster's back, then held on tightly as he raced down the stairs and out into the neighbours' garden.

"Up we go," said Woody, as they arrived at the bottom of the mailbox.

Buzz frowned at the spikey thorns which had grown all around the maibox's post. "Those thorns might tear my space suit."

Woody agreed. The thorns were a problem. Luckily, he was an excellent problem-solver.

"Up on your hind legs, Buster!" he cried.

Panting happily, Buster did as he was told. On his back legs, the dog was still not quite tall enough to reach the mailbox, though, which meant it was time for some acrobatics!

Very carefully, Woody and Buzz climbed up onto the pup's head. Woody braced himself as Buzz clambered onto his shoulders.

"Ugh, you weigh more than Hamm with a full belly," Woody gasped. They all wobbled unsteadily as Buzz stretched up and....

Yes! With a final stretch, Buzz caught the edge of the note. They had done it. Woody and Buzz had saved the day. There was no mission they couldn't handle together, but Woody really hoped they wouldn't have to tackle another adventure any time soon!

Mango Hunting

Once upon a time, long before Mowgli came to the jungle, Bagheera the panther met Baloo the bear for the first time.

This is how it happened.

Bagheera was younger then, but no less grave. He took himself very seriously indeed. When Bagheera hunted, he moved silently, with grace and speed. He never tripped, and he certainly never fell. When he slept, he kept one eye open. When he spoke, he chose his words carefully. And he never, ever laughed.

One day, Bagheera was edging along the branch of a mango tree leaning out over a river. There was one perfectly ripe mango right at the end of the branch, and Bagheera loved mangoes. The only problem was that the branch was slender, and when Bagheera moved towards the end of it, the branch began to creak and bend alarmingly. The last thing Bagheera wanted was to break the branch and go for a swim in the river.

So Bagheera, crouched on the middle of the branch, was just coming up with a clever plan when he heard a "harrumph". He looked down and saw a big grey bear. "It looks like you could use a hand," said the bear.

"No, thank you," said Bagheera politely. "I prefer to work on my own." But the bear didn't listen, and began climbing up the tree.

"I'll tell you what," huffed the bear. "I'll just sit at the base of that branch and grab your tail. You can climb out and pluck the mango, and I'll keep a hold of you in case the end of the branch breaks off. Then we can share the mango!"

"No, I don't think that's a good idea," said Bagheera. "I doubt this branch can hold both of us any –"

SNAP!

The bear had ignored Bagheera and climbed onto the branch. And the branch had, of course, snapped under their combined weight. And now a very wet, very unhappy panther sat in the river next to a very wet, very amused bear.

"Ha-ha-ha!" laughed Baloo (for the bear was Baloo). "That was an adventure! Oh, come now," he said, seeing how angry Bagheera was, "it's not a total loss, you know." And Baloo held up the broken branch, with that perfect mango still hanging from the end of it.

"I'll tell you what," said the bear, "let's go climb onto that rock and dry off in the sun while we eat this mango. I'm Baloo. What's your name?"

"Bagheera," said the panther, as they climbed onto the rock. And then, almost despite himself, he smiled. And then, very much despite himself, he laughed.

And Baloo laughed right along with him.

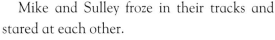

A Monstrous Mix-up

One morning at work, Mike Wazowski opened the door to his locker to find a note taped inside. It said:

Mike, Roses are red. Violets are blue. I have got my eye on you! Sealed with a kiss from.... Your Secret Admirer.

Mike's mouth fell open. He showed the note to his best friend, Sulley.

"Who do you think it could be?" Sulley asked.

"I have no idea!" Mike replied. "You don't think it could be that six-armed cutie down in Purchasing, do you? Or that sassy, one-eyed receptionist, Celia, with the pretty hair?"

"I guess it could be anyone," Sulley said. "But, hey, it's time to get to work."

On the way to the Scare Floor, Mike's mind was racing. Who could his admirer be? Then Mike heard his least favourite voice.

"Wazowski!"

It was Roz, the humourless and strict Dispatch Manager, sliding up behind them. "You owe me some paperwork!" she said.

"Oh ... right," said Mike. "I'll get that to you ASAP, Roz. Promise! See ya." He and Sulley quickly turned on their heels and hurried on down the hallway.

"All right, Wazowski," Roz called out to Mike, shaking her finger. "But remember – I've got my eye on you. I'm always watching...."

Mike and Sulley froze in their tracks and stared at each other.

"Did she just say...?" Sulley began.

"'My *eye* on you'?" Mike said, recalling the wording in the note from his secret admirer.

Sulley gulped. "Your secret admirer is *Roz?*"

"NOOOOOO!" Mike's scream filled the hallway just as Celia came around the corner.

"Hey, Mike," she said batting her eye at him. "Rough morning?"

"Oh. Hey, Celia," Mike replied sullenly, still traumatized by the idea that Roz liked him.

"Gee," said Celia, looking disappointed. "I thought my note would make your day."

Mike stared at her. "Wait a second. *Your* note?" he said, stunned. "Celia, you're my secret admirer?"

She sighed. "Wasn't it obvious? 'I have got my eye on you'? As in, I have one eye, just like you?"

A wave of relief swept across Mike's face.

"I was going to ask you if you wanted to go out sometime," Celia continued. "But if you don't want to...."

Without a word, Mike leaped into Celia's arms and clung to her. "Thank you, thank you, *thank you!*" he exclaimed.

Celia giggled. "So ... I guess that's a yes?"

Wherever You Go, There You Are!

"Oh, dear! Oh, dear!" said Amelia Gabble. The goose and her twin sister, Abigail, had been waddling along the road to Paris, when Amelia suddenly stopped.

"What's wrong?" asked Abigail, bumping into her.

"Just look and you'll see," said Amelia. Stretching out one big white wing, she pointed to the road ahead. Abigail looked, and then the two geese put their heads together and began to argue in low voices.

Behind them, Thomas O'Malley, Duchess and her kittens gathered together.

"I wonder what's wrong," said Duchess.

"Guess I'd better find out," said O'Malley.

He sauntered forward. "Ladies, ladies, what's going on?" he asked the twin geese.

"We know this is the road to Paris," Amelia explained. "But up ahead, the road divides."

Sure enough, the single road split in two.

"I think we should go right," said Amelia.

"And I think we should go left," said Abigail.

The three kittens began to worry.

"Mr O'Malley, are we lost?" asked Marie in a small, frightened voice.

O'Malley smiled down at the little white kitten. "Lost? What's lost? I don't know the meaning of the word."

"I do," said Berlioz. "If you're lost, then you don't know where you are."

"But you know exactly where you are," said O'Malley. "You're right here – with your mother and me and the Gabbles. So how could you be lost?"

Duchess shook her head and said, "Mr O'Malley, if we want to get to Paris and we don't know the way, then I do believe that we are lost."

"But Paris is just a place," said O'Malley. "And places are easy to find."

"Look, Mama, look!" Toulouse shouted. "I see something over that hill. It's the top of the Eiffel Tower!"

"Toulouse, you're right!" said Duchess.

"Nice going, little tiger," said O'Malley. Then he turned to the Gabble sisters. "Well, ladies, looks like Paris is thataway!"

Soon they arrived in Paris, where the Gabble sisters met up with their Uncle Waldo. The geese waved goodbye.

Marie sighed with relief. "I'm glad we're not lost any more."

"Aw, honey," said O'Malley, "someday you'll understand. Places may come and places may go but, when you're a free spirit, you can never be lost."

"Never?" asked Marie.

"Never," said O'Malley. "'Cause wherever you go, there you are!"

Marie nodded. She liked the sound of that!

Pinocchio

Geppetto's Gift

One day, Geppetto was in his workshop painting a clock, when he had an idea. "I know what I will do with that pine log I just found," he told his little cat, Figaro. "I will make a splendid puppet!"

He put down the clock and got to work. When he had finished making the puppet, he got out his jars of paint and some fabric. "Now," he said to Figaro, "should my puppet's eyes be blue or green? Should her hair be yellow or brown or black? Should her dress be red or purple?"

Suddenly, Geppetto heard a noise outside. He went to the window and looked out. He saw groups of children on their way home from school. Geppetto watched them skip past, laughing and shouting and swinging their schoolbooks. He sighed sadly. "How I wish I had a child of my own," he said.

Just then, he noticed a little girl walking quietly with her mother. Like the other girls, she carried a schoolbook under her arm. When a group of girls skipped by her, she just looked at them shyly.

"That little girl must be new in town. She looks like she could use a friend," Geppetto said. Suddenly, he had an idea.

"Excuse me, young miss," he called from the window. "I wonder if you could lend me a hand?"

The girl hurried over, tugging her mother after her. Why, an invitation to Geppetto's workshop – how grand!

"As you can see, my friend here needs some eyes," Geppetto said, pointing to the puppet. "But I don't know what colour her eyes should be."

The girl thought hard. "Green," she decided.

Geppetto picked up his pot of green paint and painted two big green eyes.

"Now, what colour do you suppose her hair should be?" Geppetto asked.

"Brown," the girl said.

Carefully, Geppetto painted brown curls on the puppet's head. "She'll need a dress," he said next. "What do you think? Red? Green?"

"Blue," the girl told Geppetto.

So Geppetto made a little blue dress for the little puppet. Then he added a smiling red mouth to the puppet's face.

"Now there's just one last thing," Geppetto said. "I'm busy in my shop all day long, and I'm afraid this little lady might be lonely. Could you take care of her for me?"

The girl's face lit up with delight. "Thank you!" she cried. Hugging the puppet in her arms, she carried her out of the workshop.

"Thank you," the girl's mother said. "You know, you'd be a wonderful father."

Geppetto smiled. *If only!* he thought.

THE INCREDIBLES

Super Annoying!

Dashiell Robert Parr was bored. It was Saturday afternoon and he had nothing to do. He had already taken a twenty-mile run, but that had only taken about two minutes thanks to his Super speed.

"You know, you could do your maths homework," his mother, Helen, said.

Homework? Now? Dash thought. *I'll do that tomorrow. Right now I want to do something fun.*

BRRRNG!

The telephone rang and Dash's sister, Violet, raced out of her bedroom to answer it. Dash had spotted his target. He grinned slyly and hurried into Violet's room.

Five minutes later, Violet returned. Things were not as she had left them. Her whole room was rearranged! Only one person could have done it.

"Mum!" Violet yelled. "Dash messed up my room!"

As Helen walked down the hall, a breeze whipped through Violet's room. Helen looked inside. "It looks fine to me, honey. Now I've got to get dinner ready," she said. Violet looked at her room again and saw that everything was back in place. Then her eyes fell on the closet door, which was slightly ajar.

"Dash!" Violet exclaimed. "Get out of here, you little insect!"

Dash zoomed around Violet's bedroom at such Super speed that Violet couldn't tell where he was. Dash only came to a halt when he spotted Violet's diary, which had fallen open on her bed.

"Ooooh," Dash said, picking up the diary and taunting his sister. "What have we here?"

That was it. Violet had had enough of Dash. "Give that back!" she yelled.

Dash tried to race out of the room, but Violet threw a force field in front of the door. Dash ran into it head-on and was knocked to the floor. Violet grabbed her diary, but before she knew it Dash had taken it again. Violet turned invisible and lunged at her brother.

Dash and Violet continued to chase each other around Violet's room in a blur of Super powers, until they heard their mum calling.

"Time for dinner!" she cried.

Dash froze. Then, in the blink of an eye, he zipped out through the bedroom door and down the hall to the kitchen table.

"Dash," Helen asked, "did you finish your homework?"

Then Violet appeared at the table. Her hair was all messed up.

"Nah," Dash replied with a smile. "I found something much better to do."

Front-Page Friend

Lightning McQueen whizzed between rocky canyons, his car bonnet sweating. His eyes shifted to his mirrors to check he was in the clear. He needed a plan and he needed one quick.

"Hey, what's the hurry?" called Mater, from across the road.

Lightning McQueen hadn't expected to see his friend so far from Radiator Springs, but he was relieved!

"Mater! I need help!" he said breathlessly. "Chuki's not giving me a moment's peace. Help me lose her!"

Mater giggled.

"She's a reporter. And she wants to do an article on my private life," Lightning sulked. "She's following me everywhere. I was at Flo's V8 café trying to drink one of her infamous Piston Cup beverages when, out of nowhere, a camera flashes! Next thing I know there's a microphone in my face and Chuki asking, 'What do champions drink?'"

Mater nodded in sympathy. He hated being disturbed mid-slurp too.

"Then at Doc's," Lightning continued, "I was just saying goodbye when Chuki was demanding to know if I was under the weather ... because I tend to go to Doc when I need advice."

"Yup. That would be a pain in the bumper," Mater agreed.

"I just told her I was in great shape and took off," Lightning McQueen said. "I can't imagine what would happen if they saw me with Sally."

Mater laughed. "You'd probably wind up in the gossip column!"

Lightning McQueen groaned unhappily.

"Luckily, you ran into me," encouraged Mater. "Grab on to my tow cable."

Mater lowered his friend over the cliff edge onto a road below them – a short cut that would confuse the reporters and therefore give Lightning an easy getaway.

"You've saved my engine!" Lightning shouted up to his friend, his voice echoing off the rocks.

Just then, the reporters almost collided with Mater on the cliff edge. They screeched to a halt and looked at the tow truck in confusion.

"I'm Chuki from OEM news. Have you seen Lightning McQueen?" she asked.

"Yes," said Mater. "But he's long gone now."

Chuki's eyes widened in shock. "How'd he get away?"

"I helped," Mater explained proudly. "I'm his best friend!"

Her eyes flashed with inspiration.

"Really?" asked Chuki. "I've got loads of questions to ask you!"

It took Mater a moment to realize they were after the next big scoop about Lightning McQueen ... from him!

DISNEY·PIXAR MONSTERS, INC.

Mike's Worst Nightmare

"AAAIEEE-AHHH!" Sulley sat bolt upright in bed. The anguished yell was coming from his friend Mike's bedroom. Sulley raced out of his bedroom and threw open Mike's door.

"Hi," said Mike in a shaky voice. "I guess I must have had a bad dream." He swallowed hard, then sat up in bed and gave Sulley a sheepish grin. "I haven't had one since I was little."

Sulley nodded. "Okay, well, goodnight, Mike."

"Don't you want to hear about it?" Mike asked with a hopeful grin.

Sulley came over and sat down on the edge of his friend's bed. "Okay," he said.

"I dreamed...." Mike began. "This is going to sound really, really crazy, I know, but ... I dreamed that there was a kid, a human kid, in my closet over there!" He pointed across the room and laughed nervously.

"Now, now," said Sulley good-naturedly. "Maybe it was the movie you watched tonight."

"*Kidzilla?*" Mike scoffed. "Nah. I've seen it a dozen times and it's never bothered me before."

"Well, why don't you try to go back to sleep?" said Sulley, suppressing a yawn.

Mike cleared his throat shyly. "I remember when I was little, my mum would bring me a sludgesicle when I had a bad dream," he said.

Sulley sighed patiently, then went to get Mike a sludgesicle from the kitchen.

"She would sing me a little lullaby too."

In his low voice, Sulley began to sing.

"*Rock-a-bye, Mikey, Googley-Bear,*

With sharp little fangs and shiny green hair!

Morning will come when the sun starts to rise,

You'll wake up and open those googley eyes!"

"Googley *eye*," Mike corrected his friend.

Sulley finished singing and was just about to leave, when Mike added, "Uh, my mum also always checked the closet."

With another patient sigh, Sulley opened Mike's wardrobe door and stepped inside. "Nope. Nothing in here!" he called. Suddenly, there was a loud clatter and a landslide of junk spilled out of the wardrobe door. A yellow mop fell out. It looked just like blond hair!

"Ahh!" shrieked Mike, leaping out from under the covers. Then he relaxed. "Oh, sorry, pal. In this dim light, I thought that mop was, you know, a human child!" He shuddered and gave Sulley another sheepish smile.

Sulley chuckled at the idea. "Don't be silly, Mike," he said. "A kid will never get loose in Monstropolis – what a disaster that would be!"

"No, you have a point," Mike agreed sleepily. "Goodnight, Sulley."

"Goodnight, Mike."

Where are Buzz and Jessie?

Andy had taken Buzz and Jessie away to play, but now he had gone out for the day and the toys were still nowhere to be seen.

"What happened to those two?" a worried Woody wondered. He called an emergency meeting to let the other toys know that Buzz and Jessie had disappeared.

"So has my ear," said Mr Potato Head, pointing out the empty hole in the side of his head.

Woody told the army men to prepare a search party. "Look everywhere, and keep me informed," he instructed.

"Sir, yes, sir!" called the army sergeant. He and his troops picked up a walkie-talkie, and set off to search the house.

Meanwhile, the other toys got to work searching Andy's bedroom. Slinky explored under the bed, but found only dirty socks.

Woody checked the far corner of the room, but there was no sign of Jessie or Buzz there, either, just a pile of comic books.

From inside the wastepaper basket, Mr Potato Head gave a cheer. Woody looked up, hopefully. Mr Potato Head popped up, smiling happily. He had found his missing ear, but had turned up no trace of the missing toys.

Suddenly, the walkie-talkie crackled noisily into life. "We've found 'em!" announced the sarge. "We're in front of the bathroom door. Bring a rope!"

Woody and the others raced to the scene. As they arrived at the bathroom door, they could hear shouts of panic from inside the bathroom. Lots of tiny bubbles floated through the gap at the side of the door, and a puddle of water had leaked out into the hallway.

"Sounds like they're in trouble!" Woody said.

As another cry rang out from the bathroom, Rex began to panic. "A bubble monster could be eating them alive!"

There was no time to lose. Using a skipping rope as a lasso, Woody snagged the door handle and heaved with all his might. The door opened and the friends raced in.

Jessie and Buzz's cries were coming from the bath, but the sides were too high to see what was happening. "Who's going to save them?" asked one of the army men, but Woody was already leaping into action.

Scampering up a nearby stool, Woody looked into the bath – and couldn't believe his eyes! Jessie and Buzz were in a toy speedboat, cheering and whooping as they zoomed across the bathwater.

"Shall we call in reinforcements, sir?" asked one of the army men.

Woody laughed. "Um, no. Unless they'd like to take a motorboat ride, too!"

101
DALMATIANS

Rolly's Midnight Snack

"Time for bed!" called Pongo.

"Aw, Dad," complained Patch, "we're not tired!"

"No arguments," said Pongo. "Little puppies need their rest."

With a sigh, Patch joined the line of puppies climbing the staircase.

"I'm hungry," Rolly complained as the puppies settled down for the night.

"You're always hungry," said Patch.

"And you always want to stay awake and have adventures," said Rolly.

Patch sighed. "Too bad we never get what we want."

Hours later, Rolly felt a tap on his shoulder. "Is it morning?" he asked with a yawn.

"No," said Patch. "It's midnight. Wanna explore? I'll get you a snack."

"A snack!" cried Rolly excitedly.

"Shhhhh!" said Patch. "Come on."

Rolly followed Patch to the kitchen.

Patch nodded towards the table. "After dinner, I saw Nanny put some juicy bones up there. She's saving them for tomorrow's soup."

"Soup!" cried Rolly. "What a waste! Bones are for chewing on!"

So, Patch and Rolly came up with a plan.

First, Patch climbed onto Rolly's shoulders to reach the table.

Everything went fine until Patch threw down the first bone and it landed in the rubbish bin. Rolly took off after it and leaped inside!

Rolly was stuck. Patch tried hard not to panic. He thought and thought until he came up with another plan – a Rescue Rolly Plan!

Patch went upstairs and woke Lucky and Pepper. The two puppies followed Patch into the kitchen. Then Patch found his father's long lead and tossed one end into the rubbish bin.

"Take hold of the lead!" Patch told Rolly.

"Okay," said Rolly.

Patch turned to the other puppies and said, "Now, let's all pull on this end of the lead, on the count of three."

The three puppies pulled. The rubbish bin fell over and Rolly tumbled out onto the kitchen floor.

"Thanks!" said Rolly.

The puppies licked their brother, and they all returned to bed.

Before Rolly drifted off to sleep, he whispered to Patch, "Guess you finally got your adventure."

"Yeah," said Patch. "But I'm sorry you didn't get your snack."

"Sure, I did," said Rolly. "While I was waiting for you to rescue me, what do you think I was doing? I was eating that juicy bone. And, boy, was it good!"

Emotional Rollercoaster

"Hi, there! I'm Joy. Do you like my blue hair? I'm in charge of being … joyful! And let me tell you, there are a lot of things to be happy about. Like dinosaurs! And sprinkles on cupcakes. And monkeys – it's fun watching them swing. Ooh and bouncy balls! Making goofy faces is great, too. And twirling – you've just got to twirl sometimes. Sunshine is my absolute favourite. Ooh, but rain is my favourite, too! And new adventures are just the best! But most of all, I've found that happiness is being with your friends and family!

Sigh. Hi, I'm Sadness. I usually feel pretty blue. I just don't understand the world sometimes. Like why does ice cream fall off the cone? Or why do pencils break? I do like some things. I like rain – it makes you shivery and droopy. Puppies can be cute … but then they chew on your new jumper. I always seem to lose something. Or, sometimes, I'm the one who's lost. I like crying. It helps me slow down and obsess over the weight of life's problems. Then I feel better. But then I feel sad again.

Hey! What are you looking at? Fine! I'll introduce myself. I'm Anger. Are you really saying you can't tell which one I am? Let me give you a clue – I'm RED! I like to honk my way through the traffic jams of life. But if there's one thing that burns me up – more than sunsets and scented candles – it's putting vegetables where they don't belong! Broccoli on pizza – did you really think I wouldn't notice?

I'm Disgust. I'm the fashionable one in green. There are a lot of gross things out there. Like feet – who decided that people should walk around on smelly blobs with toes sticking out the end? Oh! And socks and shoes? Eww! While we're at it – crabs. Why do they do crawl sideways like that? Creepy-crawly things are so gross. Like spiders, I mean, eww!

H-hello! I'm Fear. I-I'm the shaky one. The world is full of terrifying things – I have a list! – so I consider every day we don't die a success. There's the stairs down to the basement – it's dark down there. And Grandma's vacuum cleaner sounds like a monster. And, dare I say it, clowns. But let me tell you what I do like. Safety. I love to relax in the evenings, sip a cup of tea and watch a peaceful nature show. Until they show the animals. They're so scary.

A Healthy Rally

Dusty, Chug and Dottie were huddled together on the runway, whispering. "So it's all set?" asked Dottie.

"Right, Dottie," replied Dusty. "It'll be our little secret."

Three younger planes had overheard, and came rolling over to find out more. "What's the secret, Dusty?" they asked.

Chug butted in. "Sorry, kids. We can't tell you."

"Come on, Chug," said Dusty. He smiled at the young planes. "The secret is a cool game called the Wings Around Propwash Junction Rally!"

The children chattered excitedly. "If you want, you guys are welcome to join in," Dusty told them, and they cheered.

Dusty announced he would be judging the race. The first stop was the old silo, and on Dusty's orders the three young planes took to the air and flew as fast as they could towards it.

Lydia, a little pink plane, was first to touch down. "Hooray! Did I win the rally?" she asked. Chug, who had been waiting at the silo told her she had won the first leg, but revealed there were more stages still to go.

"Next stop, the landing zone!" Dusty cried.

The planes fired up their engines and lifted off again. They raced hard, whizzing through the air at top speed. Although they all worked hard, there could be only one winner.

"This time Danny's first!" Dusty announced, as a little yellow plane screeched to a stop.

"Any more legs, Dusty?" Danny asked.

"Just one. But it's a mystery," Dusty told him. "Chug's on his way there. To reach the final destination, you'll have to find him."

The youngsters quickly took off again. They banked and curved in the sky, searching for any sign of Chug. At last, they spotted him over by a hangar. They sped after him, with the little blue plane just managing to touch his wheels to the ground first.

"The mystery stop is Dottie's workshop," he realized.

Dottie trundled out. "That's right, and you've all won!"

"Really?" gasped the young planes.

Dottie grinned. "Yes, because you're just in time ... for your annual inspection!"

Chug giggled. "The rally was just a trick to bring you here, because you usually make such a fuss about going to the doctor."

"And true champions need to stay in tip-top shape, all year round," Dusty added.

The young planes smiled. They did hate going to the doctor, but Dusty was right. And besides, getting to their appointment had been a whole lot of fun!

History Repeats Itself

It was a day for remembrance in Radiator Springs. In the gallery, photos of outstanding moments on the racetrack were spread all over the walls.

"Welcome, friends!" greeted Doc, who was parked proudly beneath a cabinet of trophies, most of which he'd won.

"It's always a pleasure for us to admire memorabilia of the great races we've run, Doc!" said The King, with his wife at his side.

"Look, Lightning," said Sheriff, pointing to a frame. "A photo of your most recent challenge!"

The cars admired the picture. Lightning McQueen smiled at the memory.

"My last race too," pointed out The King. "It was a thrilling moment!"

"How about repeating it?" suggested Sheriff.

"Why not? It'll be fun!" The King said.

Later that day, in Ornament Valley, Doc was centre-track with a flag at the ready.

"Start your engines!" he commanded.

Lightning McQueen and The King gave each other a look of encouragement.

"Go!" yelled Doc.

From the hillside, the cars watched their friends race neck and neck across the desert track.

"Who knows which car will win?" Doc wondered in excitement.

But as they were watching, Lightning McQueen suddenly veered off course!

"Why's Lightning braking?" Doc winced.

"He did the same thing in the Piston Cup," Sheriff reminded him. "But that's not what we meant when we said we wanted to repeat the race!"

"He's heading back to town!" Doc cried in alarm.

The King stopped racing, aware that he no longer had anyone to compete against. "What's wrong?" he called to Doc.

"We don't know! Let's follow him!" Doc replied.

The cars headed back into town, tracking the tyre marks that Lightning McQueen had left in the dirt. They found him at the petrol station, looking slightly embarrassed.

"Hey, Lightning, you didn't have to let me win again," said The King.

"I know. I'm sorry!" Lightning McQueen apologized. "I just remembered that I'd promised to pick up Sally and I didn't want to be late!"

Just then, Sally rolled up, looking radiant in the sunshine.

"Keeping her from waiting was more important than any race!" Lightning winked.

"Without a doubt!" The King said.

"That boy sure learned something from you, dear," The King's wife giggled, as she snuggled up to him. The race no longer seemed important.

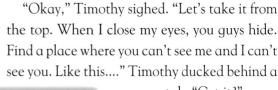

Hide-and-Seek

For quite a while, Dumbo was the newest baby in the circus. But then, one day, the stork arrived with a brand-new delivery – a baby girl giraffe.

"You know, Dumbo," said his friend, Timothy Q. Mouse, "I think we should ask that new baby to play with us."

Dumbo nodded. He loved making new friends!

So together, Timothy and Dumbo made their way to the giraffes' pen.

"Hello, Mrs Giraffe," Timothy said. "Can your lovely new baby come out and play?"

Dumbo gave Mrs Giraffe a big, hopeful smile. "Well ... I suppose so," she said.

She gave her baby a kiss, and sent her off in the care of Timothy Mouse – and Dumbo.

"Okay, kids," said Timothy, standing before the two, "what do you feel like playing?"

Dumbo and the baby giraffe stared back at him blankly.

"I see," said Timothy. "You don't know that many games. May I suggest hide-and-seek?"

Dumbo and the giraffe nodded happily, as Timothy closed his eyes and counted.

"Ready or not," he said finally, opening his eyes, "here I – hang on! Don't you guys know you're supposed to hide?"

No, actually, they did not.

"Okay," Timothy sighed. "Let's take it from the top. When I close my eyes, you guys hide. Find a place where you can't see me and I can't see you. Like this...." Timothy ducked behind a popcorn tub. "Get it?"

Dumbo and the giraffe slowly nodded.

"Okay then, let's try this again. One, two, three...." Timothy counted to 20, then opened his eyes. "No, no!" he groaned. "You can't hide behind the popcorn. You're too big. Let's try this one more time."

Again, he closed his eyes and counted. Then, very slowly, he opened them and looked around. "Much better!" he said, surprised. Of course, it didn't take him long to find Dumbo's wide body behind a narrow tent pole, or the giraffe's tall neck sticking up from behind the clowns' trunk. But they were getting closer!

"This time, guys, try to find a place for your whole body to hide," Timothy said.

So, Dumbo and the giraffe waited for Timothy to close his eyes once more, then they quietly sneaked behind the pole and trunk again. This time, the tall, skinny giraffe hid behind the tall, skinny pole. And short, wide Dumbo hid behind the short, wide trunk. And do you know what? They were hidden so well, Timothy Q. Mouse may still be looking for them to this very day!

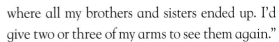

Homesick

Nemo still couldn't believe everything that had happened to him. First, he'd been snatched up by a scuba diver in the ocean. Then, he'd travelled a long way in a big water cooler. Finally, he'd been dumped in a fish tank in a dentist's office. The other fish in the tank seemed nice, but Nemo missed his dad and his home. He couldn't think about anything except getting back to the ocean. But would their plan to escape really work? It seemed hopeless....

"Hey, kid," Bloat the blowfish swam over to him. "Are you okay? You look a little down in the gills."

"I'll say," said Nigel the seagull.

Peach the starfish glanced over from her spot on the tank wall. "He's just upset," she said. "It's only natural." She smiled kindly at Nemo. "It's okay, hon. We know how you feel."

"How could you know?" he muttered, feeling sorry for himself. "You weren't grabbed out of the ocean, away from your dad."

"Well, no," a fish named Gurgle admitted. "But we all had families back where we came from. We all miss them."

"Really?" Nemo blinked in surprise. He hadn't thought about that.

"Sure," Peach said. "The lady who sold me over the Internet kept lots of us starfish in her basement." She sighed sadly. "I still wonder where all my brothers and sisters ended up. I'd give two or three of my arms to see them again."

"I hear you," Bloat agreed. "I was hatched in somebody's garage. They sold me and a whole school of my brothers and sisters to Bob's Fish Mart. Just when we made friends with the other fish there, he came in and bought me." He waved a fin towards the dentist in the office outside the tank. "It could be worse, though," Bloat continued. "You guys are the best friends I've ever had."

A fish named Deb nodded. "I'm lucky he bought me and my sister together. Right, Flo?" She smiled at her own reflection in the glass of the tank. When the reflection didn't answer, Deb shrugged. "I guess Flo is too choked up to talk right now. But I can tell by her smile that she agrees. We don't know what we'd do without each other. But we still miss the rest of our family."

"Wow," Nemo said, looking around at his new tankmates. "I guess you guys *do* know how I feel."

Even though he was sad that the other fish had been taken from their families, it made Nemo feel a little less alone. At least they understood how much he wanted to find his way back to his father. Now, a little braver and more determined than ever, Nemo was ready to escape from the tank – no matter what.

The Haunted Closet

Rex and Slinky were exploring their new home at Sunnyside Daycare. "Isn't this place great?" said Rex, gazing at all the toys and fun things to do.

"You can say that again," Slinky replied. "It's like Andy's room, only bigger!"

As they began to explore, a group of toy dinosaurs suddenly blocked their path. "You can't go down there," said a stegosaurus. "That's the haunted closet!"

Rex's knees began to knock together. "The haunted closet?" he gasped. "Wh-what's that?"

"It's the most dangerous place in Sunnyside," whispered another dinosaur.

"It's super dangerous," agreed a third.

Rex really didn't like the sound of that. He hated anything dangerous. He trembled in fear as the dinosaurs told them more about the closet.

"At night, it captures toys that get too close," they said. "And swallows them up forever!"

"F-for-e-ever?" whimpered Rex.

"No one's ever returned to tell us about it," said one of the dinosaurs, "and it's impossible to open."

Rex backed away, but in his rush he got himself tangled in Slinky's spring. "Hey, watch out, you big lizard," Slinky warned, but it was too late. As the spring got pulled tight, Rex was launched high into the air.

"Help!" he shouted, as he flew upwards.

A piece of thread was strung across the room, for children's paintings to dry on. Rex grabbed for it, and let out a sigh of relief as his stubby arms caught hold.

But his relief didn't last long! The thread snapped, swinging Rex down and sending him hurtling towards the haunted closet!

With a scream, he thudded against the closet door, then fell in a heap on the floor. A moment later, the door began to slowly creak open....

"We're free!" cheered a group of toys, racing out of the closet. They picked Rex up and paraded him above their heads.

"You're a hero, Rex!" cried one of the toys.

"You've beaten the haunted closet," said another.

Rex looked around and smiled. He wasn't used to being a big brave hero, but he had to admit, he quite liked it. "Gee, thanks," he said.

One of the other dinosaurs shot him a worried look. "Now you can help us take on the spooky drawer!"

Rex felt his knees begin to knock once again. "S-spooky? Oh, no!" he whimpered. Maybe he wasn't quite ready to be the fearless hero, after all!

DISNEP
THE
LION KING

Tag!

Early one morning, Simba woke up ready to find Nala and continue their game of Tag. The night before, when their mothers had made them stop ("Time for bed, Simba!" "Time for bed, Nala!"), Simba had been "It" – which is a terrible way to go to bed! – and he was eager to tag Nala and make her "It" as soon as possible. But, when he arrived at the pride's meeting place, everyone, it seemed, was there except for Nala.

"Where's Nala?" he asked his mother.

"Oh, I heard her mother say she wasn't feeling well," she replied. "So they're staying in the cave and resting until she's better."

"But she has to come out," protested Simba. "I'm It and I have to tag somebody!"

His mother smiled. "I'm afraid you'll just have to wait, little Simba," she said.

"But that's so boring!" Simba groaned.

"You can play by yourself, Simba," she reminded him.

"Aw, all right." Simba sighed. First, he tried hunting grasshoppers. But they jumped so high and so far – and so fast! – he soon grew tired and frustrated.

Then he tried climbing trees. But the birds didn't much like a lion cub messing around among their branches and shooed him away.

Finally, he tried just lying down and finding pictures in the clouds. But that was Nala's favourite game, and it made him miss her.

He rolled over and swatted a wild flower with his paw. "Tag, you're "It"," he said half-heartedly. Then, suddenly, an idea popped into his head. What if he picked some wild flowers and took them to his sick friend? It might even make her feel better!

Simba picked as many flowers as he could carry in his mouth and made his way back to the pride's cave.

"Dees ah fur Nana," he said, dropping the flowers at Nala's mother's feet. "These are for Nala," he repeated. "I hope she feels better soon."

"Oh, thank you, Simba," the lioness said. "But why don't you give them to her yourself? She seems to be feeling much better. Nala!" she called. And out came Simba's friend, smiling and looking very glad to see him.

She sniffed at the pretty flowers. "Are these for me? Gee, thanks, Simba." Then she turned to her mother. "Can I go out and play with Simba now, Mama?"

"I don't see why not," said her mother.

"Grrreat!" said Nala.

"Yeah, grrreat!" said Simba. Then he reached out and gently tapped her with his paw. "Tag! You're "It"!"

Law of the Road

On the outskirts of Radiator Springs, the residents gathered. They were annoyed about no longer feeling safe on the roads because a group of rebels were causing trouble.

"You should teach them a lesson," Dustin, the post van, told Sheriff.

Sheriff wasn't sure who the crowd were upset with. There were so many cars tearing up the interstate to keep a close eye on.

"Who are you talking about?" he asked.

"Those rascals who run wild on the roads around town! They bother everybody. Especially us trucks. Just the other day, one of them bashed up against me without warning, called me Gramps and wanted to race!"

"Dustin is right!" declared Doc. "Those tricksters are liable to cause an accident!"

"But they've got powerful engines. I wouldn't be able to catch them," admitted Sheriff.

"I'll volunteer as deputy sheriff," suggested Lightning McQueen.

"Thanks, McQueen," said Sheriff, "but I think I'd rather use Mack for this one."

Mack looked confused. "But I'm not so fast myself, Sheriff...."

"Don't worry!" said Sheriff, with a smile. "We'll show those thugs that the law is always one step ahead!"

Later that day, the rebel race cars were out on the road looking for innocent drivers to challenge.

"Let's give that big guy a hard time!" said Boost, the leader of the gang. The rebels cheered and moved in.

Mack was cruising along the road when the rebels approached fast.

"Hey, you! Come here!" bellowed Boost.

"We're close to town still," warned one of his crew. "I hope Sheriff isn't hiding behind a sign."

"What if he is?" snarled Boost. "We'll out-run him!"

Mack entered a narrow canyon. The rebels followed, laughing at Mack's apparent misfortune. The only way out now was forward! But little did they know ... Mater had barricaded them in with a roadblock! Once the roadblock was in place, no one could reverse out. Not even the bad guys.

Mack braked. The rebels screeched to a halt behind him.

"What's going on?" asked Boost.

Mack's loading door opened, revealing Sheriff, hiding inside, equipped with handcuffs and the power of the law.

"Hello, pranksters!" he called. "Welcome to my new mobile anti-crime unit!"

The rebels groaned. There was no racing out of this one. Sheriff had got the better of them and now they had to deal with the consequences.

A Dory Story

Dory was swimming through the beautiful reef and humming a tune to herself, when she was stopped mid-stroke by a smiling fish.

"Hey, Dory! Happy birthday!" the fish congratulated her.

"Birthday?" she repeated, looking puzzled.

"Surely even you couldn't forget it's your birthday?" the fish said.

"Today is my birthday? Hooray!" Dory cried. "Hey, Marlin! Nemo! Today's my birthday. Oh, and I remember that a birthday means presents."

Nemo and Marlin paled in colour. They'd forgotten! But luckily, Dory was likely to forget any minute too.

"We've just got to go and get your present," Marlin said, backing away slowly.

"Oh, are you going somewhere?" Dory asked excitedly. "Can I come?"

"Oh," Marlin floundered and changed the subject. "Happy birthday, Dory!"

"Today is my birthday?" She seemed surprised. "That means I get a present!"

"That's right," said Marlin, clutching Nemo's fin. "And we'll be right back with it."

Dory cheered. "Birthday present! Burpday pheasant!" she sang. "Gurby peanut. Guppy mean it." She froze. "What did the guppy mean?"

Just then, a massive grey shark blundered towards her.

"Hello, Mister Shark," she greeted. "Do you know what the guppy meant?"

"Erm ... I was looking for my friends," the shark said, baffled by the little fish.

"Lots of my friends are just objects," admitted Dory, handing him a clump of kelp. "Here, have this."

Little tiny fish hiding in the kelp fronds squealed in fear and darted away.

The shark swam after them. "I just want to be friends! I'm a vegetarian!"

Dory turned around to see an orange flicker in the distance. Nemo and Marlin were coming back.

"Here's your present!" said Nemo. "This seaweed is soaked in cuttlefish ink. Now you can write on the rocks if you really need to remember something."

"Wow! You're a genius!" smiled Dory. "Thanks! I'll wear it on my back so I don't forget it." She draped the seaweed over herself like a scarf, but five minutes later she looked bemused. "Why am I wearing filthy algae?"

"Dory!" Nemo sighed.

"Wait! I could wear this as a new fashion trend for my birthday!" she decided, twirling in the water.

Nemo and Marlin shook their heads in defeat. Sometimes Dory could be hard work. But they wouldn't change her for the world.

Simba's Secret

Simba and Nala were best friends. They liked to tell each other secrets.

"I'm scared of mice," Nala told Simba one day. "Don't tell anybody."

"Don't worry, I won't," Simba said.

One day, Simba and his father, Mufasa, were out for a walk. "Look at that mouse stuffing her cheeks with seeds," said Mufasa.

"That's so funny!" said Simba. "I don't know why Nala's scared of mice."

Nala had heard Simba talking with his dad, and she got really mad with Simba.

A few weeks later, Nala said, "I'm going to tell you a secret, but it's a really big one. If you tell this time, I'll be so mad at you."

"I promise I won't say anything!" said Simba.

"Okay," said Nala. "Here's the secret – I found a huge cave yesterday, down in the red cliffs. I'm going back to explore it today."

Simba played all day without Nala. Before dinner he began to wonder when she was coming back.

Nala's mother was worried. "Simba," she asked, "do you know where Nala is?"

"No," he answered. He'd made a promise to Nala, and he didn't want to break it. The sun went down and the moon shone in the sky.

Sarabi, Simba's mother, went to her son. "Do you know where Nala is?" she asked.

"I can't tell," said Simba. "It's a secret. I can't tell, no matter what!"

"Simba," said his mother, "you're a good friend to try not to tell Nala's secret. But there are some secrets that are good to keep and others that are important to tell."

Simba thought about what his mother had said. He decided that he had to tell everyone where Nala was.

The whole pride hurried to the red cliffs. At last, they heard a small voice calling out. "M-mother?" It was Nala!

The lions rushed to the entrance of a cave, but it was almost completely blocked. A rock slide had trapped the little cub! The lions dug and dug, and finally they had cleared the rocks away. Nala rushed out of the cave and ran to her mother.

A few minutes later, Simba walked over and hung his head. "I'm sorry I told your secret, Nala," he said.

"If you hadn't said anything, I'd still be here. It was a stupid secret!" said Nala.

When they got home, it was time for bed. Nala and Simba snuggled together.

"I'm happy you're home," said Simba. "And that's not a secret!"

Nala smiled, she was happy to be home too.

Lady <small>Disney</small>
and the TRAMP

A Lady's Touch

Late one night, Lady's ears perked up and her eyes flew open with a start. The baby was crying! Lady had grown to love the new baby in the house, and she was very protective of him. If he was crying, she was going to find out why. She climbed out of her basket, pushed open the swinging door with her nose and tiptoed up the front stairs.

Meanwhile, Jim Dear and Darling were trying to calm the baby. "Oh, Jim, I just don't know what's the matter with him!" said Darling. She was holding the baby in her arms, trying to rock him and

soothe him, but his little face was a deep red and covered with tears. Jim Dear sat groggily at the edge of the bed and looked at his wife helplessly.

"Well, we know he isn't hungry," said Jim Dear, "since we've just given him a bottle." He massaged his temples as though they hurt. Then he noticed Lady, who had walked tentatively into the bedroom. "Hello, Lady," he said to her.

Lady took a few steps closer to the cradle, where Darling was laying the baby down. His little fists were closed tight, and his shrieks had turned to loud sobs.

"We just don't know what's the matter with the little guy," Jim Dear said wearily to Lady. "We've fed him and changed him, and I've sung him every lullaby I know. Maybe you can figure out what's bothering him!"

That was all the invitation Lady needed. She jumped up onto the bed and peered into the cradle. The baby's eyes were squeezed shut and his cheeks were wet with tears. His little legs were kicking the covers.

Lady reached in and tugged at the covers to smooth them out. The baby opened his eyes and looked at Lady. His cries dropped to a whimper, and he reached out to touch her. His tiny hand grabbed hold of her ear and tugged. Lady winced but held still. With her chin, she began to rock the cradle and, with her furry tail, she beat a rhythmic *THUMP, THUMP, THUMP* on the bedcover.

"Ga!" said the baby as he broke into a gummy smile, his big blue eyes looking like wet forget-me-nots. Still holding Lady's ear, the baby giggled.

"Oh, look, Jim Dear!" cried Darling joyfully. "Lady has got him to stop crying!"

"I just don't know what we'd do without you, Lady!" Jim Dear said gratefully.

Rock, rock, rock, went the baby's cradle.

THUMP, THUMP, THUMP, went Lady's tail on the bed.

Soon the baby's eyelids grew heavy, and then his eyes closed. Tears still streaking his little round cheeks, he relaxed his grip on Lady's ear, smiled and fell asleep.

THE JUNGLE Book

Mowgli Finds a Friend

Bagheera the panther found Mowgli in the jungle when he was just a baby, and decided to take the boy to a wolf family that lived nearby.

The mother wolf agreed to take care of him, and for 10 years she raised him as one of her own. Mowgli was a very happy Man-cub.

One day, bad news arrived in the jungle. Shere Khan the tiger had returned after a long absence. The tiger was mean and hated everything. More than anything though, Shere Khan hated Man. This meant that it was no longer safe for Mowgli to live in the jungle. The wolves decided that he should go to a Man-village at once.

Bagheera had kept watch over Mowgli through the years and volunteered to take him. Later that night, the boy rode on the panther's back as they made their way through the jungle.

But Mowgli did not want to leave the jungle. It was his home. "I don't want to go to the Man-village!" he shouted. Then he added, "I can take care of myself."

Although Bagheera cared a lot for Mowgli, he eventually became tired of the Man-cub's fighting, and walked off into the jungle, leaving Mowgli alone.

Mowgli began to worry that maybe he couldn't take care of himself after all, and wished Bagheera would come back to keep him company.

Before long, a bear named Baloo walked out of the jungle and spotted Mowgli. The bear tried to be friendly, but Mowgli told Baloo to go away and leave him alone. But Baloo did not listen. He decided the little Man-cub needed to have some fun.

"Hey, kid, Baloo's gonna learn you to fight like a bear," he said, jumping around. The bear's silly behaviour made Mowgli laugh and soon he was dancing and boxing just like Baloo.

When they finished, Mowgli jumped up on his new friend's stomach and tickled him. "You're all right, kid," Baloo said gently.

Just then, Bagheera walked over to them. He had returned to make sure Mowgli was okay. The panther told Baloo that he thought Mowgli should go to the Man-village so he'd be safe from Shere Khan.

Baloo didn't want his little buddy to go to a Man-village. "They'll ruin him. They'll make a man out of him," the bear said.

Bagheera sighed. He knew it would be hard to persuade Mowgli to leave now that he had made friends with Baloo.

The panther watched as the pair jumped into the river and floated lazily away.

HERCULES

A True Hero

"Hercules! Slow down!" Amphitryon yelled to his son, who was pulling their cart to the market. His son was headed straight for a marble archway that was under construction. Hercules didn't understand how strong he really was, so his attempts to be helpful often turned into disaster.

Later, Amphitryon and his wife, Alcmene, decided to tell Hercules the truth – they weren't his real parents. They'd discovered him when he was a baby and raised him as their own.

Amphitryon handed Hercules a medallion. "This was around your neck when we found you," he said. It had a thunderbolt on it – the symbol of the gods.

Hercules wanted to know more, so the next morning, he left to visit Zeus. Once he arrived, he stood before the giant statue of Zeus. Suddenly, a great stone hand reached down. "My boy. My little Hercules," Zeus said.

Hercules' eyes widened. Zeus, the most powerful of all gods, was his father! Zeus explained that as a baby Hercules had been stolen and turned into a human. Hercules' super-strength was the only god-like quality he still had.

"If you can prove yourself a true hero on Earth, your godhood will be restored," Zeus told him. "Seek out Philoctetes, the trainer of heroes." With that, Zeus whistled and a winged horse, Pegasus, flew into the temple. Then the statue took its shape once again, and turned back into rigid stone.

That night, Hercules and Pegasus flew to Philoctetes' home. Phil, as Hercules called him, started training him. Hercules succeeded with all of his hero lessons and grew into a strong man.

Finally, Hercules felt he was ready to test his strength in the real world. Phil took him to Thebes, where Hercules heard that two boys were trapped in a rockslide! He and Pegasus flew to the boys. Hercules lifted a giant boulder and freed the trapped children.

There was no time to celebrate, though. A terrible monster called the Hydra was emerging from a nearby cave … and it was hungry. With a massive head and sharp claws, it went after Hercules. Hercules slashed at the monster with his sword. But when he cut off its head, more grew back. The more heads he chopped off, the more appeared!

Then the Hydra trapped Hercules in one of its claws. Hercules slammed his arms against a cliff wall with all his might. Within seconds, the wall broke apart. Huge boulders tumbled down, killing the monster. Hercules was overjoyed. He was well on his way to becoming a true hero.

Mater Stunt Car

Radiator Springs was buzzing about the new open-air cinema. A giant screen had been raised in preparation and the residents made their way to their first outdoor movie feature on a moonlit night.

"We're early. The movie hasn't started yet," said Lightning McQueen to his friends, Mater and Sally.

"Well that's good! We won't have any problems finding a place," said Sally, matter-of-factly.

Mater looked at the movie poster on the fence. "Gosh! This film's starring George Kloonkey!" he said excitedly. "I once acted with him."

Lightning McQueen tried to figure out if Mater was joking. Sally laughed and encouraged Mater to tell them all about it. If it was true, it would be fascinating!

"I was his stunt car," said Mater. "I filled in for George on dangerous scenes … because we're practically lookalikes."

Sally and Lightning McQueen glanced at the poster of George Kloonkey. Honestly, Mater looked nothing like him, but they didn't want to upset his feelings.

Mater pictured George Kloonkey by his side in a stadium.

"Get ready, it's your turn," George said.

"I'm rarin' to go!" Mater boasted.

He imagined the movie was set in the real world of auto-racing – a film he told Sally and Lightning McQueen had been called *Rusty Wheels.*

"Turbo Jack was leading the way and heckling me as I tailed him," Mater continued. "His tyres left flames on the track and he told me I'd never make it to the finish line … but I jumped those flames, only to spy a row of spikes before me!"

"Gee," said Lightning McQueen, humouring him. "How did you get out of that one?"

"Don't you remember?" asked Mater. "You were there!"

Lightning McQueen looked confused.

"You bashed those spikes out of my way and I rushed by, thanking you," Mater prompted.

"Just Hollywood tricks," said Lightning McQueen. "A bit of movie magic."

"What do you mean? It was real!" insisted Mater. "The director figured it would make the movie more realistic."

"No doubt!" Sally laughed. "But I've never heard of a movie called *Rusty Wheels.*"

Mater sighed. "Nope. It never got finished."

"Why's that?" Sally wondered.

"Kloonkey ended up driving off set. He said I was too good and stole the show!"

Sally and Lightning McQueen giggled. Mater had such a vivid imagination.

It's Party Time!

Andy was at school, and the toys had the house to themselves. "Hey, guys, how about an outer space party?" suggested Buzz.

Jessie loved the idea, but Woody wasn't so sure. "I'd prefer a western party," he said.

"Ugh," said Buzz, disappointed. He began to whisper to Jessie.

Jessie giggled. "Good idea," she said.

Before Woody could ask what they were up to, Buzz grabbed him by the arm. "Come on! We're on an intergalactic mission!"

Buzz dragged his friend down to the kitchen. They stood under the table, looking up at its tall legs. "Is this going to be difficult?" Woody asked.

"Difficult, but very important," Buzz nodded. He pointed to a cup filled with straws sitting on the tabletop. "We need to bring back the alien green straws."

Woody gasped. Those straws were awfully high up. "Why alien green?" he wondered.

"We need green straws to make outer space decorations for our party," Buzz announced. Woody groaned. Looked like his dream of a western party wasn't going to happen any time soon.

Working together, the two friends climbed up onto a chair, then hopped onto the table. Woody gathered up the green straws, but before he could start climbing back down, Buzz caught him around the waist.

"To infinity and beyond!" Buzz shouted, leaping off the table. Woody screamed as Buzz opened his wings and swooped down low across the kitchen.

SPLASH!

They crash-landed in Buster's drinking bowl.

"Nice landing," a very wet Woody muttered.

Buzz looked at the bowl next to them, filled with smelly dog food. "It could have been worse," he said.

Carrying the straws under his arm, Woody followed Buzz to Andy's room. "We're back, folks," Buzz announced.

Woody gasped as party-poppers and streamers rained down from above. All his friends were gathered together, dressed in their finest cowboy gear.

"Welcome to our Wild West party, Sheriff Woody!" cheered Jessie.

"This is great!" Woody cried.

"It was tough to pull off the surprise, but we did it!" Buzz said. "But what will I do with these straws?"

Woody had an idea. Bending a straw, he made it into an intergalactic cowboy belt, just for Buzz. The friends laughed. Cowboys and spacemen were both great on their own, but together they were even better!

Disney PLANES
Blind Flight

Skipper was thrilling Dusty and Chug with tales of the olden days. "The night was so dark and foggy we couldn't locate the U.S.S. *Flysenhower*," he said.

"How'd you make it back on board?" Dusty asked. "With your radar?"

Skipper laughed. "No radar back then! We were forced to make a blind flight entry. Luckily, we found our way thanks to a radio beacon."

"What's a radio beacon, Skip?" Dusty asked. Skipper explained it was a device that sends out radio signals from carrier aircraft to guide planes in.

Dusty had never heard of anything like it. He couldn't imagine what it would be like not to be able to see where he was flying.

Before he could think about it too much, Leadbottom called him over. "You promised to dust the crops after training," the old plane reminded him.

Dusty groaned. A promise was a promise, but after the story he'd just heard, dusting crops seemed pretty boring.

"Why not try flying blind?" Chug suggested. "I'll guide you back to the ground! I'll be your radio beacon!"

That put some spin in Dusty's propeller! "Awesome idea!" he cheered. "Let's do it!"

Dusty lifted off and headed for the field.

He closed his eyes tightly and turned on his Vita-minamulch sprayers. "All set, Chug. I can't see a thing," he said.

A moment later, Dusty's radio crackled into life. "Beep! Radio beacon to Dusty," said Chug. "Turn towards 9 o'clock."

Dusty turned, but something didn't feel right. "You sure? The field's in the opposite direction," he said.

"I goofed!" admitted Chug. "I meant to say make a 180° turn right."

Confused, Dusty banked to the right, but Chug's voice came screeching over the radio again. "No, I mean left! I never know which is which!"

"Make up your mind," said Dusty, turning.

"Too far left! Beep! Beep!" cried Chug, doing his best to sound like a real radio beacon.

All those beeps were getting poor Dusty even more confused. Soon, he had no idea which direction he was supposed to be flying in.

Chug's voice crackled over the radio for a final time. "Ugg! You'd better open your eyes, Dusty," he said. "And turn off your Vita-minamulch sprayer!"

Dusty looked down. He had flown back over the airfield, and instead of dusting the crops, was dusting all his friends instead. He blushed. Maybe flying blind wasn't such a good idea, after all!

Bambi

Growing Up

One day, Bambi and Thumper were playing in the snow-covered meadow.

"Look, Bambi!" exclaimed Thumper.

A herd of stags was running towards them.

"I wish I could be a stag!" Bambi exclaimed.

"Well, you know what my father always says," said Thumper.

"I know," said Bambi. "'Eating greens is a special treat. It makes long ears and great big feet.'"

"No, not that!" said Thumper. "I mean, he does say that, but he also says, 'If you want to hop well, but your hop is all wrong, then you have to practise all day long!'"

"I have to hop all day long?" asked Bambi.

"No!" cried Thumper. "If you want to become a stag, you have to practise!"

Bambi glanced back at two big deer. They suddenly ran towards each other, locking horns to test their strength. They looked so powerful and majestic. Bambi wanted to be just like them!

"Okay," Bambi told Thumper.

"Okay," said Thumper. "Follow me."

Thumper hopped to the edge of the meadow. He stopped by a big oak tree. "Lower your head," he told Bambi.

Bambi lowered his head. "Now what?" he asked, staring at the ground.

"Run straight ahead," said Thumper.

Bambi ran straight ahead – towards the trunk of the old oak tree! But, before he got there, a voice cried, "Stop!" Bambi skidded to a halt only a few inches from the tree trunk.

Thumper and Bambi looked up. Friend Owl looked down at them with big curious eyes. "Bambi, why were you going to butt my tree trunk with your head?" asked Friend Owl.

"I'm practising to become a big stag," said Bambi. "Stags butt heads to show their strength."

Friend Owl laughed and said, "Bambi, the stags have antlers to protect their heads! And becoming a stag is not something you can practise. It's something that will happen to you with the passing of time."

"It will?" said Bambi.

"Of course!" Friend Owl assured him. "Next summer, you'll see. You'll be bigger and stronger. You'll also have antlers – and, I hope, enough sense not to butt heads with an oak tree!"

"Yes, sir," said Bambi.

"Now go on, you two," said Friend Owl. "And don't be in too much of a hurry to grow up. You'll get there soon enough!"

"Okay," they replied. Then the two friends returned to the snowy meadow to play.

DISNEY·PIXAR

MONSTERS, INC.

Occupational Hazard

Mike strolled in through the front doors of Monsters, Inc., whistling happily. Today was the anniversary of his first day working for the company, and he was sure his friends would all want to celebrate with him.

But when he arrived, Sulley and the others just looked at him in surprise.

"Everyone forgot?" he gasped. He threw down his lunch box and turned around. "I can see I'm not appreciated here. I quit!"

Sulley tried to stop him, but Mike had made up his mind. He stormed off, determined to find a job where he would be recognized for his hard work and dedication.

As Mike went in search of a new career, he felt excited. The world was full of thrilling new opportunities, and a monster of his talents would have no difficulty finding work.

Even Mike was amazed, though, when he landed a job as a model. He was dressed from head to toe in elegant clothes, and told to parade up and down a catwalk. However, on Mike's stubby frame, the outfit looked anything but stylish, and as Mike flopped around in his too-large shoes his boss called him over to tell him he wasn't working out.

"I'm too handsome, that's it, isn't it?" said Mike. Being a model clearly wasn't for him, but there were plenty of other roles for him to fill.

Next, Mike got a job wrapping parcels at a gift company. On his very first package he managed to completely cocoon himself in tape and wrapping paper. Only his one big eye was visible in the colourful tangle, and when the boss told him he was fired, Mike hopped out of the door.

A little later, Sulley was sitting in a café, wondering how he could get Mike to come back to Monsters, Inc. He accidentally knocked his coffee onto the floor, and the waiter called for a cleaner. The kitchen doors flew open and Mike emerged, running.

He slipped on the floor and slid straight into Sulley's table, smashing it to pieces. This time, he didn't even wait to be told he'd been fired. Instead, he trudged back to Monsters, Inc. with Sulley. Nobody else wanted him, so what other choice did he have?

Mike gasped in surprise as all his co-workers jumped out at him. They handed him an enormous cake, and all hurried to shake his hand. "Happy anniversary!" they cheered.

"You planned a party all along?" Mike said. "Why didn't you tell me?"

Sulley explained that Mike had run off before they could reveal the surprise. Mike smiled happily. His friends did appreciate him, but he appreciated them even more.

A Lucky Move

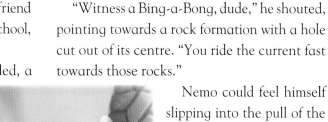

On weekends, Nemo met up with his friend Squirt. Squirt went to a different school, so it was nice to be able to catch up.

As the two friends laughed and giggled, a group of little sea turtles zoomed overhead.

"What's going on, dude?" Squirt called out to them.

"Hi, Squirt," said one of his turtle friends. "We're gonna hit this current for a major Bing-a-Bong run. You coming?"

"Totally!" said Squirt.

Nemo marvelled at the turtles. Once in the current, they could travel really fast and cross the ocean in no time! It was thrilling and fun, but also very dangerous.

"Show me how to go Bingo Bong too," pleaded Nemo.

"Um. It's Bing-a-Bong, Nemo. And that is a screaming current. Do you think you can ride steady with that lucky fin of yours?" Squirt asked, sceptically.

"Please don't leave me behind," said Nemo. "I can do anything a turtle can."

Squirt felt sorry for the little clownfish. "Don't get all bummed out on me, buddy. If you wanna rock, then let's rock."

Squirt led the way, rising in the water until they were at the brink of the current, which cut a choppy path through the ocean.

"Witness a Bing-a-Bong, dude," he shouted, pointing towards a rock formation with a hole cut out of its centre. "You ride the current fast towards those rocks."

Nemo could feel himself slipping into the pull of the current. Squirt was already leading the way, picking up speed....

"Then when you're inside, tuck into your shell and bing-bong-bounce off the sides until you can crank yourself out of the current at the other end."

"What?" Nemo yelled in panic. "I don't have a shell!"

"Oh, yeah," realized Squirt. "Oops. Just hang tight and steer through!" he bellowed as his head disappeared inside his shell and he bounced his way through the rocks.

Nemo accidentally flipped upside down and found himself doing numerous loop-the-loops.

"I can't keep steady!" he wailed. "Aaahh!"

Spiralling through at top speed, he thought he'd never stop spinning....

"Woah! He's got killer moves!" cheered a sea turtle from above.

Nemo managed to slip safely out of the current. The sea turtles patted him on the back and couldn't believe how brave he was. Nemo had invented a new move!

From that point on, the Bing-a-Bong game was known as 'Nemo's Lucky Fin Flop'.

BIG HERO 6

Tech Nightmare

Tadashi's friends had stopped by the garage one evening. Hiro was fast asleep on the couch. "He's been working on his showcase project all day," Tadashi told them.

He showed his friends one of the tiny pieces of metal Hiro had made. "These are microbots," Tadashi explained. "They work together when controlled by a neural transmitter."

Tadashi looked around for the headband controller so his friends could try the microbots themselves, but as he searched, the metal pieces began to buzz furiously.

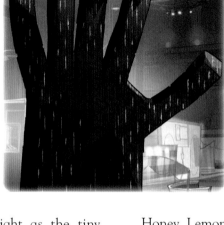

The friends yelped in fright as the tiny microbots all came together to form the shape of an enormous hand. "It's my brother!" cried Tadashi, pointing at Hiro. "He's still wearing the headband!"

The microbots were responding to Hiro's dreams, and whatever he was dreaming about seemed very violent.

The hand formed a fist and smashed towards the friends. They dodged and ran, all screaming in panic except for Fred. "This is epic!" he cheered, ducking another swiping blow from the microbot fist.

They all took cover behind a low wall. "Let's just wake Hiro up," GoGo suggested. She cupped her hands to her mouth and shouted, but Tadashi said Hiro was a heavy sleeper. Besides, if the crashing of the giant fist hadn't disturbed him, a little bit of shouting definitely wouldn't.

The hand appeared over the wall, and the friends turned and ran. They reached a door at the back of the garage and heaved on it. "I can't get it open!" said Wasabi, straining from the effort. The others wrapped their arms around him and all pulled together, but it was no use.

They were trapped, and the microbots were getting closer and closer with every second that passed.

Honey Lemon had an idea. Twirling her handbag, she launched it towards the swarm. The microbots dodged easily, but Honey Lemon hadn't been aiming for them. The bag bounced off Hiro's head and he jumped awake, startled.

At once, the microbots fell to the floor. Hiro blinked, then smiled when he saw the others. "I'm so happy to see you guys," he said. "I want to show you my project!"

Hurriedly, Tadashi's friends all made excuses and raced out of the garage. They'd seen quite enough of the microbots for one night!

Hiro didn't understand what they meant. He looked up at his brother. "I wanted to practise my project with them."

Tadashi smiled. "Trust me, bro, you did," he said. "And it was a great success!"

DISNEY·PIXAR
THE INCREDIBLES

Every Day the Same Old Story

Bob Parr missed the superhero life. As Mr Incredible he'd wrestled robots, smashed supervillains and been a thorn in the side of criminals everywhere.

Now that the Supers had been forced to hide their powers, though, he worked in a boring office doing a job he didn't like.

As Bob squeezed himself into his car one morning, he thought about the Incredicar he'd owned in his previous life. He remembered the roar of its engine and the ping of bullets bouncing off it.

The car he drove now was nothing like that. It was small and noisy, and as Bob chugged through the morning rush hour the engine spluttered and died. Behind Bob, other drivers began to angrily blast their horns.

Bob pressed his foot down on the accelerator pedal, but the car wouldn't start. Getting angry, Bob slammed his foot down hard, and groaned as his leg punched a hole in the bottom of the car.

"Looks like we're going on foot," he sighed, putting both feet through the hole. He began to run, pushing the car all the way to the office.

When he arrived, there was only one parking space left. The cars on either side had been parked badly, so there wasn't enough room for even Bob's little car.

Glancing around to make sure nobody was looking, Bob shoved the cars aside and pushed his own car into the gap.

He ran into work, bracing himself for another boring day. The coffee machine was playing up, as usual, and as Bob filled his mug it began to fizzle and spark.

Bob wrapped his strong arms around the machine, stopping it exploding. Smoke poured out of the dispenser. Bob sighed. Looks like there'd be no coffee today.

After a dull morning of paperwork, Bob had lunch in the park. He munched on his sandwich, remembering the good old days. As he reached for the bin to put his litter in, a fleeing robber slammed into his arm.

Bob didn't notice the man crumple to the ground, winded, or spot the policeman leading him away. When an old woman came to thank him, he only said, "Well, it's everybody's duty to keep the city clean."

At home, Bob kicked one of Dash's footballs, glad another dull day was over. The ball rocketed across the city, before smashing into a runaway truck, bringing it to a stop.

Bob may not have realized it, but even when he was doing a boring office job, he was still pretty incredible!

Off-Track Advice

Lightning McQueen was on a quest for advice! In the centre of town, he spotted his rusty friend Mater and wise old Doc, enjoying the sunshine on their bonnets.

"Hey, Mater!" he called. "Have you seen The King?"

"Nope. Sorry, buddy!" replied Mater.

"Try looking in the museum," suggested Doc.

Lightning McQueen's wheels screeched on the tarmac in his haste to leave. "Good idea!" he cried.

"What's the rush?" Doc wondered. The young cars of Radiator Springs were always bolting around as if they were against the clock.

"I need some advice," Lightning McQueen confessed to him.

Doc frowned. "If you need any driving tips, boy, just ask me."

"Thanks, but I need some different advice," Lightning McQueen said. "Only The King can help me on this."

Doc was left feeling unwanted, as Lightning McQueen sped off. "What could The King know that I don't?" he growled.

"What are you grumbling about, Doc?" asked Sheriff, who had pulled up stealthily. "When McQueen asked you to teach him tricks you were more grumpy than an empty oilcan! You should be glad he went elsewhere."

Doc scowled. "But he always comes to me for advice! I'm gonna go see what The King has to say to the young rookie."

Doc found Lightning McQueen on the roadside with The King. He was thanking The King enthusiastically so Doc performed some impressive stunts to get their attention.

"I've still got a few secret manoeuvres that might be of use, champ!" he yelled.

"Nice command of the road, Doc," said Lightning McQueen in appreciation.

"I can still drive, see," grunted Doc as Lightning McQueen drove off. "But it looks like my advice is not as good as Mister-Know-It-All King's."

The King laughed. "Don't worry, Doc! McQueen still loves your advice! It was just because you're not married. Come and see...."

Doc joined The King in secret pursuit of Lightning McQueen.

"Lightning wanted my opinion on a present," The King whispered to Doc, as they watched Lightning McQueen present a box to Sally.

"For the anniversary of our first meeting," Lightning McQueen announced.

Sally gasped. "Wow! Chrome finishings!"

The King laughed and nudged Doc with a wink. "My wife's always adored them, too."

Doc smiled back, no longer feeling like an unwanted, spare part.

Go Fish!

"Okay, small fry," said Baloo the bear. "Today I'm going to teach you to fish like a bear!"

Mowgli was delighted. He loved his new friend Baloo. Unlike Bagheera the panther, who kept insisting that Mowgli should live in the Man-village for his own protection, Baloo made no such demands on Mowgli. Baloo was much more interested in having a good time living in the jungle, and so was Mowgli.

"Now, watch this, kid," said Baloo as they arrived at the riverbank. "All ya gotta do is wait for a fish to swim by and then...."

WHOOSH! Quick as a flash, Baloo held a wriggling silver fish in his paw. "Now you try it!" he said to Mowgli.

Mowgli sat very still, waiting for a fish to swim by. Then – SPLASH! – he toppled head first into the water.

"Hmm," said Baloo after he had fished Mowgli out and set him down, dripping wet. "Now I'll show you my second technique."

Baloo and Mowgli walked towards another part of the river. This time, the fish could be seen leaping out of the water as they swam down a little waterfall. Baloo waded into the water, waited for a fish to jump, then – WHOOSH! – he swiped it out of the air. "Now you try."

Mowgli waded in just as Baloo had done. He waited for the fish to jump and then leaped for it. SPLASH!

"Okay, Plan C," said Baloo, after he had fished Mowgli out a second time. "I'll take you to the big waterfall. The fish literally fall into your paws. All ya gotta do is reach out and catch one!"

Mowgli followed Baloo to the big waterfall. Sure enough, silvery fish were jumping all the way down the fall. Catching one would be easy!

In the blink of an eye Baloo held up a fish for Mowgli to admire.

"I'm going to do it this time, you watch me, Baloo!" said Mowgli excitedly. He scrunched up his face with concentration. Then – flash! – for an instant, Mowgli actually had a silvery fish in his hands. But, a second later, the fish shot out of his grasp and jumped into the water again. Mowgli looked down at his empty hands with a sigh.

"You know what, kid?" said Baloo, clapping a huge paw on Mowgli's skinny shoulders. "I think you're working too hard. That's not how life in the jungle should be! It should be fun, happy and carefree. So, come on. Let's go shake a banana tree instead!"

And Mowgli cheerfully agreed.

Toy Ghosts

Bonnie was in her bedroom, playing with Woody, Buzz and all her other new toys. The heroes were working together to take on the evil Dr Porkchop, who was causing trouble once again.

"Ghost rangers, ready for action!" cried Buzz, as he, Woody, Rex and Bonnie's toy triceratops, Trixie, raced into Dr Porkchop's pretend lab.

"It's no use," snorted Dr Porkchop. "Nothing can stop my ghost army!"

The no-good villain pulled a lever. With a wailing "*WHOOO!*" three scary ghosts appeared from nowhere.

"Run for your lives!" yelled Trixie. Rex didn't need to be told twice. The two dinosaurs ran for cover, leaving Woody and Buzz to face the spooks on their own.

"N-now what, Buzz?" Woody stammered.

"Keep cool, Woody," said Buzz. He held up a blaster weapon. "I'll just activate my ghost-laser and...."

The gun gave a disappointing click.

"Uh-oh," Buzz gulped. "It looks like I left my batteries at home!"

Woody and Buzz braced themselves as the ghosts floated closer and closer and....

"Bonnie! Lunch is ready," called Bonnie's mum, interrupting the game.

The toys waited until Bonnie had raced out of the room, then jumped to their feet. They were all very excited – it had been years since they'd had this much fun!

"You ain't seen nothin' yet," laughed Trixie. "Wait till Bonnie plays Time Travel!"

Hamm smiled. He loved being the evil Dr Porkchop, but even he had been a little worried by the spooky ghosts. "Luckily the stories she makes up are pure fantasy. Otherwise –" he began, before a voice from nearby stopped him.

"Hi, pal!" it called.

Hamm turned to find a ghost grinning at him. His eyes went wide as he turned and ran as fast as he could. "Ahhh! The ghost!"

"Wait! Don't run away!" the ghost pleaded, but Hamm was already too far away to hear him. "Shucks. Every time a new toy sees me it runs away screaming. It's not my fault if I'm a toy ghost."

Trixie did her best to cheer the little ghost up. "Don't take it personally, Ghosty. You'll see, it'll be better with the other toys," she promised.

Just then, Rex, Woody and Buzz caught sight of the spooky little figure. Like Hamm, they turned and ran off, screaming in fright.

Trixie put her arm around Ghosty and gave a little giggle. "Oops," she said. "Looks like I spoke too soon!"

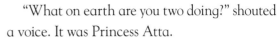

Bird Trouble

It was the height of the rainy season, and the roof of the ant colony had sprung a leak.

"Bucket brigade!" shouted Princess Atta.

The ants obediently lined up and began catching the water in cupped leaves, passing them along the length of the line and dumping them into the stream. It was exhausting, but the ants were used to hard work.

"There's got to be an easier way," Flik said. "Tomorrow I'm going to find a way to fix the roof!"

"What are you doing, Flik?" Dot asked the next morning. The rain had let up and the two were outside. Flik had arranged dozens of torn pieces of leaves along one side of the roof.

"I'm fixing the leak," he said cheerfully. "These leaves act as rain deflectors. Then the water will run into these hollowed-out flower stems that will act as gutters."

"Wow," said Dot. She was the only ant who thought Flik's inventions were worthwhile.

"The only thing I'm missing is some sort of deflection device for the ant hole itself," he said, but then spotted a buttercup. "Aha! That flower should work perfectly. Come on, Dot. Give me a hand. Boy, oh, boy, is this invention ever going to impress the Princess!"

Together, the two ants dragged the buttercup to the top of the anthill.

"What on earth are you two doing?" shouted a voice. It was Princess Atta.

"Flik figured out a way to fix the leak!" shouted Dot triumphantly.

Flik shrugged modestly. "It's very simple, really. What I did was –"

Suddenly, the ant lookout began shouting, "Bird! Bird! Bird coming!"

Flik, Atta and Dot ran for cover. Sure enough, a hummingbird was hovering just above the anthill.

"It's going for the flower!" shouted an ant. The hummingbird pressed its long beak into the buttercup Flik and Dot had dragged over to the anthill.

"Avalanche!" shouted the ants. As the anthill began to collapse, ants scrambled to get out of the way. The bird flew off.

"Nice work, Flik," said Princess Atta. "This is going to take weeks to rebuild."

Flik sighed and hung his head.

"Don't worry, Flik," whispered Dot. "Someday you'll do great things."

"Oh, you're sweet, Dot," Flik said sadly. "If only it hadn't been for that bird. I should have known it would like the flower. Birds are so predictable." Flik looked thoughtful. "Maybe someday I could use that to my advantage."

Flik smiled at Dot. "Imagine that," he said. "An ant using a bird in his plan!"

Disney
Pinocchio
Follow Your Star

Jiminy Cricket was a wanderer. He loved the independence, the excitement and the simplicity of his way of life. For many a season, he had roamed the countryside, stopping to recover in towns along the way, and moving on when he grew restless.

But lately, Jiminy Cricket had noticed that there was one thing missing from his vagabond lifestyle – a purpose. Camping one night by the side of the road, he sat on his sleeping bag and gazed into his campfire.

"I wonder what it would feel like to be really helpful to someone," he said.

Jiminy lay on his sleeping bag and tried to get comfortable on the hard ground as he gazed up into the starry night sky. As his eyes scanned the many tiny points of light, one star to the south jumped out at him and seemed to shine brighter than all the rest.

"Say, is that a Wishing Star?" he wondered aloud. Since he couldn't know for certain, he decided it would be best to make a wish on it, just in case. "Wishing Star," he said, "I wish to find a place where I can make a difference and do a bit of good."

Then, after he made his wish, Jiminy Cricket suddenly felt a strange impulse. He had an urge to get up, gather his things and follow that star – the Wishing Star – to wherever it may lead.

He couldn't quite explain the feeling, but he felt it just the same.

So do you know what Jiminy Cricket did?

He put out the campfire. He gathered his things. And he took to the road. He followed that star all through the night. He walked for miles, until the sun came up and he could no longer see the star to follow it. Then he made a camp and he slept.

He did the same thing for several more nights and several more days.

Then, one night, he came to a village. Looking up at the Wishing Star, Jiminy Cricket noticed that it seemed to hang directly overhead.

It was very late at night as Jiminy Cricket walked into the village. Every window of every house was dark – except for one window at the end of a street. So Jiminy Cricket hopped over to the window. Peering inside, he saw that it was a woodcarver's workshop, dimly lit by the embers of a fire dying in the fireplace. It seemed a warm and pleasant place to stop for the night.

Little did Jiminy Cricket know that it was the home of Geppetto, a kind old woodcarver who had just finished work on a puppet he called Pinocchio.

And little did he know that he had found a place where he would do more than just a bit of good.

Harvest Champ

It was almost harvest time, and Dusty was giving the crops one last dusting. From nowhere, two female fighter jets swooped down and flew alongside him.

"How about some head-to-head aerial acrobatics, ladies?" Dusty suggested.

The jets snorted in disbelief. "You think you can outfly us?"

Dusty grinned and went into a barrel roll. "You bet!" he cried. "Can you do this?"

He began to loop and twirl, but was interrupted by Leadbottom calling him. "Dusty! You were daydreaming again!" the old plane said. Dusty looked around. Sure enough, the fighter jets were nowhere to be seen! "Vita-minamulch needs to be sprayed evenly over the fields, so forget about that corkscrew stuff!"

Dusty apologized and promised to be more careful, but just a few minutes later he was bored again. Dusting crops was so dull! Was this really all he was meant to do?

"Hey, crop duster!" cried a voice from above him. The two fighter jets roared past, speeding through the sky to taunt him. "We've got a challenge to finish!"

Dusty knew he was daydreaming, but he didn't care! This daydream was way better than dusting crops. He set off after the imaginary fighters, his propeller spinning at top speed.

"You may be a whizz at aerial acrobatics," said one of the jets, tilting her wings and speeding into a canyon. "But what about flying through tight spaces?"

"You kiddin'?" laughed Dusty, dodging past them. "Slaloming round obstacles is my speciality!"

Taking the lead, he decided to make things a little more difficult. He flew so low his wheels were almost touching the canyon floor. "You guys into ground hugging?" he asked.

The fighter jets gasped. "Awesome! He's even better than everyone says."

Dusty laughed as he dropped even lower. "Come on! What are you waiting for?" he called, but before he could get an answer, Leadbottom's voice cut in.

"Dusty! Wake up! You're flying too low!"

Leadbottom's cry snapped Dusty out of his daydream. He realized that he was flying straight towards the cornfield! He tried to pull up, but it was too late! His propeller churned up the corn as he came to a bumpy stop in the field.

Soon, Dottie came over to see what was going on. She gasped when she saw the mountain of harvested corn piled up in front of Dusty. "Wow! How did you manage this?" she asked.

Dusty spat out a mouthful of grass and corn. "It's a long story," he sobbed.

Déjà-Vu

Russell and Carl were exploring the South American jungle. The sun was shining, the birds were singing and it would have been a perfect day, if it were not for the fact a hungry jaguar was hunting them down!

As they ran from the big cat, Carl couldn't shake the feeling that he'd been in exactly the same situation before. Then he remembered a day he'd spent playing with Ellie when they were young. They'd pretended to be adventurers racing through the rainforest, and when they'd been chased by an angry dog, Ellie had said it was a jaguar.

Russell flipped through his book, frantically looking for something that might help them. He found pages about pumas, monkeys, parrots and more, but nothing at all about jaguars.

Scrambling up a rock face, Russell reached the top first then bent down and took Carl's hand, just like Ellie had done when they were young. They leaped off the rock and landed with a splash in a river.

Even though he was scared, Carl couldn't help but smile. Everything was happening almost exactly as it had all those years ago. Rather than land in a river, though, he and Ellie had landed in a paddling pool where a confused little girl had been happily playing with a mermaid doll.

There was no little girl in this river – but there was a fearsome-looking crocodile!

"Run, Russell!" Carl cried. The pair jumped out of the water and raced off through the trees.

They could hear the jaguar bounding through the foliage behind them, and the fast *pat-pat-pat* of the crocodile's feet on the grass.

When Carl had run away from the dog with Ellie, he'd been much younger and fitter. Now, he puffed and panted as they hurried on through the jungle. Russell knew his friend couldn't run much farther, and searched around for a place they could hide.

"This way, Mr Fredricksen!" he shouted, clambering up a tree. When Russell had helped Carl up into the branches, the old man told him how much everything reminded him of the day with Ellie. They'd climbed a tree to escape the angry dog in the end, too.

"And how did you get free?" asked Russell, hopefully. If the young Carl managed to escape the dog, maybe they could use the same plan to escape the jaguar and crocodile who had gathered at the bottom of the tree.

"We didn't," Carl admitted. "The next day, firefighters came and saved us."

Russell sighed and got himself comfortable. The nearest fire station was hundreds of miles away. They were in for a long wait!

Race Against Time

On quiet days in Radiator Springs, Lightning McQueen and Mater liked nothing more than to go backwards racing!

"But you can't beat me!" Mater yelled at Lightning McQueen, as he sped past him.

Just as they disappeared round a bend, a messenger car paused in the road. "Wait!" he called, but he'd already lost them. Casting his eyes downwards, he examined the tracks. Fresh tyre marks suggested they'd taken a right turn. He followed them.

Finally, at Mater's tow shop, the messenger found his target. "Lightning McQueen!" he said breathlessly. "I've finally caught you! Aren't you in today's race?"

Lightning McQueen turned to face the messenger, looking shocked. "What are you talking about?" he asked.

"Didn't you know?" the messenger replied. "Chick Hicks was supposed to tell you."

Lightning McQueen simmered with anger. "That cheat! He doesn't want me to race so he can win!"

"The race track has been set up in the desert," the messenger told him. "You think you can make it in time?"

"I know a few shortcuts you could take!" Mater insisted. "But you have to be careful you don't wind up stuck in a gully!"

The cars set off, weaving through wastelands with ditches and sharp drops. There were cacti and roaming lizards and all kinds of obstacles! They had to keep their wits about them. But in no time at all, they were at the track ... and luckily the race hadn't started.

"Hi, Chick Hicks. I made it! Aren't you glad?" Lightning McQueen teased, knowing that Chick Hicks would be very annoyed.

The lights flashed green and the race began. Lightning McQueen shot by an orange car on his left, and with a daring move he drove between a purple car and car number 82. Zooming into the lead, he left Chick Hicks behind him in a cloud of exhaust fumes and with a scream of the klaxon, the stadium cheered for Lightning McQueen's winning moment.

"A champion once again!" bellowed the announcer on the megaphone.

Chick Hicks growled at Lightning McQueen from his second place podium.

"Don't take it hard, Chick," said Lightning McQueen, holding his gleaming trophy. "Maybe next time you'll be able to cheat your way to the top!"

Lightning McQueen knew Chick Hicks couldn't count on it, though. Some cars were just born to be heroes, and cheating Chick wasn't one of them!

Disney·PIXAR

Rex Rules!

One morning, while the other toys were busy playing, Buzz was looking out of Andy's window, watching the world go by. "Look, Woody! There goes the Pizza Planet truck!" he announced.

Buzz loved Pizza Planet, but as he leaned out of the window to get a better look, he slipped and tumbled out!

"Buzz!" cried Woody, rushing to the window ledge. "Everything okay, Buddy?"

From down in the garden, Buzz gave a thumbs up. He had landed safely on a soft bush. "No problem, Woody," he called. "I'm made of tough space ranger plastic!"

Wriggling free of the bush and dusting himself down, Buzz started walking back in the direction of Andy's house.

"I've got to get back up," he began, but then he cried out in shock as a frightening green creature with a long red tongue scurried out of the foliage.

It was a lizard, and as it hissed angrily at him, Buzz realized he was in big trouble!

"I've got to help Buzz," said Woody. The fearless cowboy knew he couldn't leave his friend in danger. Hopping out of the window, he slid swiftly down the drainpipe and landed with a bump on the grass.

Meanwhile, Buzz had hidden behind some flowers, keeping out of the lizard's sight. The scaly creature looked around for him, its tongue flicking in and out. It hadn't spotted him yet, but it was only a matter of time before it did.

"Hide in here, pal," Woody whispered, calling Buzz over to a thick clump of bushes. They ducked down and kept quiet, watching the lizard crawl past.

"He didn't spot us," said Woody. "I think the coast is clear."

They stepped out of the bushes together, then realized they'd made a terrible mistake. The sneaky lizard knew where they were hiding and had been waiting for them. Now they were trapped!

Up at the window, Rex watched on, feeling helpless. "My p-p-poor friends," he stammered worriedly, then he let out a loud gasp as he toppled out of the window and landed with a crash in the shrubbery.

The lizard looked at Rex.

Rex looked at the lizard.

A moment later, they both screamed in fright.

With a final hiss, the lizard ran off. Woody and Buzz had looked like a tasty meal, but Rex was too big and scary to challenge.

"You saved us, Rex!" Woody cheered.

"I was pretty scared," Rex admitted.

Woody and Buzz laughed and put their arms around their trembling friend. "But the lizard was more scared than you!" they cheered.

THE JUNGLE Book

The Den of Doom

"Where are we going, Baloo?" Mowgli asked. He and Baloo had been travelling through the jungle for a while now.

"Have you ever heard of the Den of Doom, Man-cub?" replied Baloo in a hushed voice.

"The Den of Doom?" Mowgli gasped. "They say that the Den of Doom is a giant cave filled with bears who will eat anything – or anyone! They say that those bears can hear for miles and see in the dark! They say that even Shere Khan is afraid of them!"

"Mmm-hmm," said Baloo. "They do say that. They *also* say that all of the bears in the Den of Doom are over eight feet tall, that their teeth are green and razor-sharp, and that their battle cry is so loud that the whales in the ocean hear it and shake with fright. They say all that, and much, much more."

"And we're going there?" Mowgli squeaked, beginning to tremble. "We can't! Baloo, those bears aren't like you! They're dangerous!" He looked at Baloo pleadingly.

"Too late, Man-cub," Baloo said with a grin. "We're already there!" He picked up Mowgli, whose knees were knocking together so hard he could barely stand, and strode right into a thicket. The bear ducked under a huge palm leaf and emerged into a large, sunlit clearing in front of an enormous cave.

Baloo put Mowgli down. The boy looked around in complete and utter surprise.

Mowgli had expected to see hundreds of fierce, angry bears. Instead, he saw hundreds of relaxed, happy bears having a really good time. Bears were swimming in a small pond, splashing and laughing. Bears were resting in the cool shadows of the cave. Bears were playing tag out in the clearing and chomping on piles of ripe, delicious fruit. It was, in short, a bear party.

"I don't understand," Mowgli said to Baloo. "This is the Den of Doom?"

"Yep," Baloo said happily, grabbing a palm frond and fanning himself with it. "It used to be called the Den of Delights, but we had to change the name. Everyone in the jungle knew that the Den of Delights was the most fun place around. We bears never turned anyone away from our party. But then it got so crowded that it just wasn't any fun any more. So we spread a few rumours, changed the name, and presto – it's the Den of Doom! Now no one bothers us bears any more."

"But what about me?" Mowgli said anxiously. "I'm not a bear."

"You're an honorary bear, Mowgli," Baloo replied with a smile. "You sure have enough fun to be one!"

DUMBO
Float Like a Butterfly

One day, Dumbo's best friend, Timothy Q. Mouse, found Dumbo looking sad. "What's the matter, little guy?" the mouse asked the elephant. "Have people been teasing you about your ears again?"

Dumbo nodded sadly. The little elephant looked totally miserable.

Timothy shook his head. The two were very good friends and did everything together. He didn't mind one bit that Dumbo had large ears. In fact, he thought they were great.

Timothy was trying to think of a way to cheer up his dear friend. And then he saw something. "Look, Dumbo!" he cried, racing over to a nearby fence post. Hanging from the fence was a large cocoon. "It's a butterfly cocoon!" Timothy said excitedly.

Dumbo came over to examine it.

"And look – it's about to hatch into a butterfly," said Timothy. He looked thoughtful for a moment, and then he turned to Dumbo. "You know what? You are a lot like the little caterpillar that made this cocoon."

Dumbo looked at Timothy quizzically.

"Yep, it's true. You see, a caterpillar is something nobody really wants around much. They think it's kind of plain-looking, and it can't really do anything very interesting. But then one day, the caterpillar turns into a beautiful butterfly, and everyone loves it. And you know what? I think you're going to be that way, too. When you get older, everyone is going to admire you rather than tease you!"

Dumbo smiled at his friend, and wiped away a tear with one of his long ears.

Suddenly, it started to rain. "Oh no!" cried Timothy. "The butterfly is going to get its new wings all wet. It won't be able to fly if it gets rained on. What'll we do? We need an umbrella!"

As Timothy looked this way and that for an umbrella, Dumbo smiled and unfurled his long ears. He draped them over the fence post so that they made a lovely roof for the insect, protecting it from the falling droplets of rain.

"Great idea!" said Timothy admiringly. The two friends stood there during the downpour, which didn't last very long. While they waited, they watched the beautiful new butterfly emerge from its cocoon. When the rain stopped, the butterfly spread its wings (which were quite dry, thanks to Dumbo) and flew away.

"You know, my friend," said Timothy as they watched it fly away, "I think someday you're going to be a big success. You'll be like that butterfly – happy, carefree and floating along. Well, not floating for real, that's impossible. Imagine that, a flying elephant!"

The Induction

Nemo still had a satisfied smile on his face from the previous night's induction ceremony. *I'm part of the club!* he thought.

"So, Shark Bait, what did you think of the ceremony?" Gill asked.

"It was the best!" Nemo cheered excitedly.

"If only we could get Flo to be part of the ceremony," Deb sighed. "But she never seems to want to come out at night."

"So, kid, what was your favourite part?" Jacques wanted to know.

"I think my favourite part was swimming to the top of Mount Wanna-wannaha-ha...." Nemo tried unsuccessfully to pronounce it.

"Wannahockaloogie," Bloat said.

"Yeah," Peach reminisced. "I have a soft spot for my first climb too."

"I wonder," Nemo said, "who came up with that name?"

Bubbles pointed at Gurgle, who pointed at Bloat, who pointed at Peach, who pointed at Deb, who pointed at Flo.

Deb shrugged. "I guess we came up with it together," she said.

"Okay, so, why do they call it the Ring of Fire if there's no fire, only bubbles?" Nemo asked.

"Well, you see, it's like this ... I don't know," Peach had to admit.

"But who made it up, then?" Nemo asked.

"I think Bubbles came up with the Ring of Fire," Gurgle offered.

"Aren't they beautiful?" Bubbles mused.

"I find it very unsanitary to swim through others' bubbles," Gurgle complained to the others. "Which is why I came up with the chanting part of the ceremony. It's very cleansing both for the body and the mind, and circulates carbon dioxide through the gills."

"That makes sense," Nemo agreed, although it really didn't.

"Don't forget about the kelp fronds," Peach added.

"Oh, there's no big secret there," Deb admitted. "I just like giving a good whack with the old kelp fronds every now and then." And she demonstrated by whacking Bloat, who immediately began to swell up.

"Was that really necessary?" Bloat asked as he floated away.

"What can I do in the next ceremony?" Nemo asked eagerly.

"Hopefully, we won't have another one. Not if we break out of here first, Shark Bait," Gill answered.

"Well, you never know," Deb said forlornly. "Maybe Flo will come around."

Everyone just rolled their eyes and sighed, including Nemo.

Disney
THE ARISTOCATS

Bedtime for Duchess

"Come, my precious ones!" Duchess called to Berlioz, Toulouse and Marie. "It's time to go to sleep."

"Oh, Mother!" Toulouse complained.

"But I'm not tired!" Marie joined in.

"I'm not going to sleep," Berlioz added. "Night-time is just when things start happening for us alley cats." Berlioz crouched down low, with his hindquarters in the air, and pounced on an imaginary opponent.

"Who does he think he's kidding?" Toulouse whispered to Marie, who rolled her eyes in agreement.

"Now, now, it's been a long day," Duchess told them calmly. "I don't want to hear any more protests."

"We need a bedtime story!" Marie insisted.

"A story? My darlings, it's way past your bedtime, and I'm just too tired tonight," replied Duchess, with a yawn.

"Then why don't we tell you a story?" Toulouse offered.

"Yeah!" Berlioz chimed in.

"What a lovely idea," said Duchess.

"Once upon a time –" Marie began.

"There was a big, mean, ferocious alley cat," Berlioz continued.

"Berlioz!" Marie protested. "It's not supposed to be scary. She'll have nightmares!"

"Sorry, Mama," Berlioz said.

"That's quite all right," Duchess told him.

"Now where were we?" Toulouse asked.

"Once upon a time –" Marie said again, prompting her brothers.

"Yeah, once upon a time there was this amazing kitten," Toulouse said. "And he could paint like no other kitten you've ever seen."

"And that's because the model for his paintings was the most beautiful kitten you've ever laid eyes on," Marie added.

"Give me a break!" Berlioz said, grumbling under his breath. He and Toulouse snickered.

"Very funny." Marie was not amused. "Can we get back to the story?"

"This kitten was a painter by day and a smooth-talking, alley-hanging, danger-seeking hepcat by night," Berlioz continued.

Toulouse tapped Berlioz with his paw. He looked up and saw what both Toulouse and Marie were staring at. Duchess herself had fallen asleep!

Berlioz, Toulouse and Marie each gave their mother a kiss goodnight.

"Goodnight, Mama," said Marie.

"Goodnight, Mama," said Toulouse.

"Goodnight, Mama," said Berlioz.

Then all three curled up beside Duchess and promptly fell asleep too.

DISNEP
THE
LION KING

Just Like Dad

"Dad, when I grow up, I want to be just like you," Simba said to his father.

Mufasa nuzzled his son's head gently. "All in good time, son," he said.

Just then, Simba's friend Nala ran up to them. "Come on, Simba!" she called. "Let's go play by the river!"

On their way, Simba stopped abruptly. "Listen to this," he said. He threw back his head and roared as loudly as he could. Then he looked at her expectantly. "Do I sound like my dad?"

Nala tried to suppress a giggle. Simba's roar wasn't very impressive yet. "Not quite," she said.

Soon they reached the river. The waters were high as a result of the recent rains. Simba found a quiet pool at the side and stared down at his reflection. "Do you think my mane is starting to grow?" he asked Nala.

Nala sighed. "Maybe a little," she replied. "But, Simba, what's the big rush? Let's just have fun being young!"

Simba was eyeing a tree branch that extended over the raging river. "Well, I may not be as big as my dad yet, but at least I'm as brave as he is!" he shouted, and raced up to the tree. Climbing its gnarled trunk, he began walking along the branch over the water.

Nala hurried over. "Simba!" she yelled. "Come back here! The branch is going to break!"

But Simba couldn't hear her over the loud waters. Nala bounded away to get help.

Simba felt the branch begin to sag. "Uh-oh," he said to himself.

Suddenly the whole thing broke off and Simba tumbled into the water. The current was strong, and he struggled to swim towards the shore. He was running out of strength, and he realized he might not make it.

Then Simba felt himself being lifted out of the water and tossed onto the bank. Soaked, he looked up ... right into the angry eyes of his father.

"Simba!" thundered Mufasa. "There's a big difference between being brave and being foolish! The sooner you learn that, the better chance you will have of growing old!"

Simba hung his head. Out of the corner of his eye, he saw Nala, pretending not to overhear. "I'm ... sorry, Dad," he said softly. "I just wanted to be brave like you."

His father's gaze softened. "Well," he said, "as we're already soaking wet, why don't we go to a quieter part of the river and do some swimming?" He looked over to where Nala was sitting. "Come on, Nala!" he called. "Come with us!"

"Yippee!" cried the cubs, and they all went off together.

Spring Cleaning

Mickey Mouse hummed as he tidied up his messy house. He swept up some leaves that had blown in through the front door. Then he shook the mud off his doormat.

He was picking up some old magazines when one of them caught his eye.

"'Make a Fresh Start with Spring Cleaning'," Mickey read aloud. "Hmm. Spring cleaning, eh?"

He looked out of the window. It wasn't spring – it was autumn! What was he doing cleaning his house?

"Whew!" he exclaimed as he dropped his broom. "Looks like I have a whole day free now. I think I'll see if Minnie wants to come over!"

A short while later, Minnie Mouse rang the doorbell. "Hi, Mickey!" she said cheerfully. "What do you want to do to –?"

She gasped. Mickey's house was a complete mess! There were leaves and mud all over the floor, dust on the shelves, dirty dishes on the table, laundry piled here and there, books and magazines everywhere....

"What's wrong?" Mickey asked, seeing the shocked expression on Minnie's face.

"Mickey," Minnie said, "when was the last time you cleaned your house?"

Mickey laughed. "What are you talking about, Minnie?" he said. "I don't need to clean this place for months."

"M-m-months?" Minnie gasped. She couldn't believe it. In a few months, Mickey's entire house would be buried in mess!

"Sure!" Mickey shrugged. "Haven't you ever heard of spring cleaning?"

Minnie wasn't sure what to do. She didn't want to be rude, but she had to convince Mickey to clean his house. Looking around, she knew it couldn't wait until spring!

"You know, Mickey," she said casually, "the other day I read something about a fun new trend."

"Really?" Mickey smiled. "What's that, Minnie? Maybe it's something we could do today, since we now have the whole day free!"

"Oh!" Minnie pretended to be surprised at the idea. "Why, I suppose we could! I hadn't thought of that."

"So, what's the trend?" Mickey asked eagerly. "Waterskiing? Rock climbing? Fondue parties?"

"No," Minnie said cheerfully. "Autumn cleaning! It's the newest rage."

"Autumn cleaning?" Mickey said doubtfully. He frowned at the idea, but then he started smiling. "You know, that's so crazy, it sounds like fun! Come on, let's try it!"

Minnie smiled and picked up the magazine with the spring-cleaning article in it. "Good," she said. She stuffed the magazine into the rubbish bin. "I'll start right here!"

And the Winner Is....

Bonnie and her family were off on their summer holidays, and the toys had a whole month to play and have fun.

Today, however, wasn't about fun. Today was about winning! Woody and Mr Pricklepants, Bonnie's cuddly hedgehog, were having an obstacle race around the whole house. While Woody got ready for the race, his friends offered him encouragement.

"Give it everything you've got," urged Buzz.

Mr Pricklepants and Woody took their positions at the starting line. The aliens raised a flag. "Ready ... set ..." The flag dropped. "... Go!" cried the aliens, and the racers sprang forwards in a blur.

"You'll never beat me, cowboy!" laughed the hedgehog, as he zoomed into an early lead.

"We'll see about that, Pricklepants," puffed Woody, working hard to catch up. Mr Pricklepants was a fast runner, but Woody had plenty of tricks up his sleeve.

"Ha-ha!" he whooped, leaping over hurdles. "Obstacles are my speciality, partner!" Woody dashed past Mr Pricklepants.

The hedgehog laughed as one obstacle blasted Woody with a jet of sticky toothpaste.

"Well, my speciality is dodging toothpaste," Mr Pricklepants giggled, ducking safely under the minty goo.

The toys were neck and neck as they raced into the bathroom and climbed up the side of the bath. The finish line was in sight! All they had to do was swim across the bath.

"Last obstacle! Nobody beats Sheriff Woody," Woody said, diving into the cold water. "Victory is –"

"Mine!" announced Mr Pricklepants. He dived below the water and yanked the plug out.

Woody splashed about frantically, but it was no use. The current was too strong. Mr Pricklepants used the bath chain to take the lead, reaching the finish line in first place. "Ha-ha-ha! That'll teach you to challenge me," he chuckled.

Later, Woody sat on the floor, wrapped in a blanket. "I'm telling you, he cheated," he said.

Jessie shrugged sadly. "But you still lost."

As Woody shivered and sneezed, Buzz gave a sigh. "I should've raced him," he said. "Because now, for a whole month, they get to decide what to look at on the Internet!"

"A site about dinosaurs!" laughed Trixie, reaching for the computer mouse.

"No, the one about unicorns," insisted Buttercup, tapping the keys with his hooves.

Mr Pricklepants laughed. "Calm down," he said, grinning at Woody and Buzz. "We've got all the time in the world!"

Hard Work for Nothing

After a long day of training, Dusty wearily came in for a landing. "Ugh! I'm beat!" he grumbled. "Training for a rally is a lot harder than I thought."

Dusty told Chug about how Skipper had made him weave in and out of trees to improve his technique, then forced him to fly towards a powerful turbine to get him used to racing into an oncoming wind.

It had been hard work, but now training was over he was looking forward to a well-deserved rest. Unfortunately, Leadbottom had other ideas.

"Got a full tank of Vita-minamulch?" the old plane chugged. "Those fields can't wait!"

Despite his tiredness, Dusty knew there was work to be done. He took off over the fields, dusting the crops as he went. Leadbottom flew alongside him, using his own sprayer to give the crops a double-coating.

As Dusty grumbled that the fields seemed to be going on forever, Leadbottom frowned. Dark clouds were gathering up ahead of them. A big storm was heading their way.

"We'll never dust all these crops before it hits," the old plane said. He began to pull back. "Might as well call it a day!"

"What? No!" cried Dusty. Skipper had warned him that he'd meet terrible storms when racing over the ocean. How could he fly through those if he was going to let a little country shower stop him?

"I won't give up!" he said, determinedly. "I'll finish this job regardless!"

Down on the ground, Leadbottom and Chug watched Dusty battle through the storm. The wind rocked him from side to side as the rain lashed down on his roof.

"Why isn't he calling it quits?" wondered Chug.

Leadbottom got on the radio to warn Dusty that it wasn't safe, but a flash of lightning and boom of thunder drowned him out. Dusty knew his friend was trying to tell him something, but it would have to wait – he was going to finish the job, first!

To everyone's amazement, Dusty navigated safely through the storm, dusting each and every field along the way. His friends cheered when he touched down safely on the runway.

"Nice goin', Dusty. I'm truly impressed," said Leadbottom, fighting back a smile. "Too bad all that hard work was for nothing."

Dusty was confused. "Huh?"

"The rain washes all the Vita-minamulch away," laughed Skipper.

With a groan, Dusty looked back over the wet fields. "Oh no," he said. "I never thought of that!"

Lady *and the* TRAMP

Don't Mock Jock

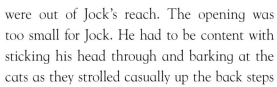

Aunt Sarah had only just arrived to look after the baby while Jim Dear and Darling were away, but already her Siamese cats, Si and Am, had caused nothing but trouble. When they made a huge mess in the living room, Lady had been blamed for it, and Aunt Sarah had taken Lady to be fitted with a muzzle!

Meanwhile, left alone in the house, Si and Am had discovered the doggy door that led out to the garden.

"What works for doggies, works for kitties, too," Si hissed to Am.

They slunk out to the garden. They dug in the flower beds, scared the birds at the birdbath and chased a squirrel up a tree.

Then they found a small hole in the garden fence. They poked their heads through the hole and spied Jock snoozing by his kennel.

"Time for a wake-up call?" said Am.

Si smiled and nodded. They squirmed through the hole and stole silently across the yard until they were sitting on either side of the sleeping Jock. Then, at the same moment, they let loose a shrill, ear-splitting yowl.

Jock awoke with a start. By the time he had identified the culprits, Si and Am were halfway across the lawn, heading for the fence.

Jock tore after them, barking. But, in a flash, the cats squirmed through the small hole and were out of Jock's reach. The opening was too small for Jock. He had to be content with sticking his head through and barking at the cats as they strolled casually up the back steps of Lady's house and through the doggy door. Then they collapsed in a laughing fit on the kitchen floor.

"Dogs are so dim-witted," Si cackled.

They waited a while, then creeped out through the doggy door again, itching to try their trick once more. Peeking through the hole in the fence, they spied Jock, eyes closed, lying in front of his kennel. They squirmed through the hole and creeped towards him.

But, this time, Jock was ready for them. When the cats got within five feet of him, the feisty Scottie leaped to his feet and growled. The cats gave a start, wheeled around and raced for the fence, only to find the way blocked by Jock's friend, Trusty the bloodhound, who stood, growling, between the cats and the hole.

Jock and Trusty chased Si and Am around Jock's garden until Jock was confident they had learned their lesson. Then they allowed the cats to retreat through the hole in the fence.

This time, they didn't stop running until they were up the back steps, through the doggy door, and safely inside.

And inside is where they stayed.

Race to Victory

In a field outside Radiator Springs, Lightning McQueen showed off his best racing moves to his friends.

"Wow, buddy!" said Ramone, in awe.

"It's beginner's luck," grunted Doc.

"Actually it's an old trick a friend taught me," Lightning McQueen laughed, nudging Doc.

"I wish I could drive like you," sighed Ramone.

"I can teach you if you want?" Lightning McQueen offered. He had no problem with sharing a few tricks of the track!

"I want to learn!" came a cry.

The cars turned in surprise to find a breathless Mater joining them.

"I can drive like a race car too!" Mater insisted. He narrowed his eyes to focus his sights on gaining speed, weaving between cacti. But at a sharp turn, his wheels wobbled. Before anyone could stop him, Mater went over the edge of a cliff!

"Mater! Are you okay?" called Doc.

He was dangling from a cactus that had caught him mid-fall.

Dragging their friend to safety, Lightning McQueen tried to cheer Mater up. "Come on, let's practise together," he suggested.

"Forget it! I'm hopeless," Mater said, wandering off in defeat.

Later that day, Lightning McQueen sat with Sally and Doc. "Mater's at Flo's all by himself," he said, concerned. "He needs our help to snap out of the blues."

"Mater's sad because everybody drives better than him. He'd be happy if he could only win a race...." Doc said.

"But that's impossible," said Sally. "Racing just isn't Mater's thing."

Then Doc had an idea. "There is one thing he can do better than anyone else...."

Doc left with a plan brewing in his circuits, finding Mater outside the tyre yard.

"Quick, Mater!" he cried urgently. "We need your help! Guido tried to imitate Lightning and wound up in a ditch."

Mater gulped. "I'm on my way!"

But instead of finding Guido in peril, Mater discovered his friends at the beginning of the racetrack, smiling.

"It's a backwards race," explained Doc.

"A backwards race? Are you sure?" Mater wondered, feeling a little unsure.

"Sure I'm sure! Everybody wants to try, so you have to join us," said Lightning McQueen.

The cars revved their engines and with a wave of the flag, sped off in the wrong direction.

Mater expertly wiggled around corners and, with cheers from the crowd, he won the race!

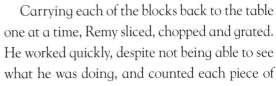

Close Your Eyes

Remy and his older brother, Emile, were in the kitchen having an argument. Remy was insisting he could cook a full meal with his eyes shut, but Emile shook his head in disbelief.

"You can cook without seeing?" he laughed. "I don't believe it!"

Remy didn't like it when anyone doubted his cooking ability, so he passed Emile a strip of white cloth. "Blindfold me with this napkin," he said. He'd show his brother exactly how skilled a chef he was.

Emile tied the napkin around Remy's head, covering his eyes. When Remy was completely in the dark, he asked Emile if he had any requests. Emile thought for a moment.

"Hmm. A four-cheese salad," he suggested, his tummy rumbling hungrily.

With a nod, Remy set to work. He picked up his chef's knife and began to slice up the salad vegetables. It chop-chop-chopped through the crunchy green leaves.

Once the salad vegetables were prepared, Remy flicked them into the bowl Emile had placed beside him.

Remy scampered to the fridge, following his nose. You couldn't make a four-cheese salad without cheese, after all. He sniffed around until he'd found the four different cheeses he was looking for.

Carrying each of the blocks back to the table one at a time, Remy sliced, chopped and grated. He worked quickly, despite not being able to see what he was doing, and counted each piece of cheese he dropped into the bowl to make sure he didn't use too much.

By now, he knew the salad would be coming along nicely. All that remained was to add a little seasoning to taste. Following his nose again, Remy chose the perfect mix of herbs and spices. He sprinkled them into the bowl, along with a little salt, oil and vinegar dressing.

With the meal complete, Remy lifted his blindfold. He expected to see a delicious four-cheese salad filling the bowl, but instead he saw Emile lying at the bottom, licking his lips. The cheeky rat had been in the bowl the whole time, catching every scrap of food Remy had tossed inside!

"But ... a salad has to be mixed!" Remy pointed out.

Emile jumped up. "Of course! Wait a minute...." he cried.

Remy had proved he could make a meal blindfolded, but as his brother shook his bulging belly from side to side, mixing up the salad, Remy couldn't shake the feeling he'd fallen for a trick!

An Afternoon with Zurg

Andy was in his room, having fun playing with his toys. He had dressed Rex as the evil Emperor Zurg, and was making him have an epic battle with Buzz.

"Snack time, Andy," called his mum. Setting the toys safely on the floor, Andy rushed off to get something to eat.

Even though Andy was gone, the toys wanted to keep playing. "Okay, guys, here's the plan," began Woody, calling Slinky and Mr Potato Head over. "We'll attack Zurg by surprise."

"I'll provide a diversion," said Mr Potato Head, putting on his angry eyes.

"And I'll surround him with my spring," announced Slinky.

The three friends tiptoed towards Rex, getting ready to launch their attack.

Rex, meanwhile, was listening to Buzz, who was giving him some tips on how to be a truly terrifying intergalactic villain.

"See, Rex, you've got to learn to walk like a real space emperor," Buzz said, demonstrating a mean and scary stride.

"How's this?" asked Rex, doing his best to copy Buzz's walk.

Buzz gave him a big thumbs up. "Wow! You're great, Rex!"

Rex blushed. "Thanks, Buzz. You've been a big help."

"What are friends for?" asked Buzz, patting his dinosaur pal on the back. "Now show me a super-space-spin!"

Just then, Woody, Slinky and Mr Potato Head began their ambush. "Ready for action!" Woody cheered, leading the others into battle.

"Hey, Buzz! Watch this awesome intergalactic move," said Rex, beginning his spin. He flicked his tail, but then tripped over his Zurg cape.

Rex knocked Woody and Slinky aside, then landed with a crash on top of Mr Potato Head. Ears and eyes and limbs went flying in all directions as Potato Head's parts popped out.

"You won!" said Mr Potato Head, hurriedly pushing his nose back in.

"Nice going, Rex," said Buzz. "You're a true space predator."

Woody agreed. "That was a surprise move worthy of Emperor Zurg."

Rex yelled in panic. "Zurg? Here? Yikes!" he wailed, fleeing as fast as his legs would carry him.

Woody tipped back his hat and laughed. Rex made a pretty good space emperor, but he reckoned the dinosaur probably wouldn't want to set off on any more space missions for a long time to come!

THE JUNGLE Book

Bagheera Bears Up

Mowgli danced around, humming happily to himself.

"What are you doing, Mowgli?" Bagheera asked from his perch in a nearby tree.

"Practising being a bear," Mowgli told him. "You should try it."

"Me?" Bagheera said, stunned. "I couldn't possibly do such a thing."

"Why not?" Mowgli wanted to know.

"Well, I'm a panther and I happen to like being one," Bagheera replied. "Why on earth would I want to be a bear?"

"Are you kidding?" Mowgli exclaimed. "Bears have the life! They hang out all day long, and they eat ants!"

"Eat ants?" Bagheera asked. "And that's a good thing?"

"Sure!" Mowgli said. "Well, truthfully, they tickle your throat at first. But you get used to it soon enough."

"Have you?" Bagheera asked.

"Not yet," Mowgli confessed. "But I will!"

"Whatever you say, Mowgli," said Bagheera.

Mowgli thought for a moment. "And if you were a bear, you would eat fruit and drink coconut juice, and you would relax, just like us!"

"If you ask me," Bagheera said. "I don't see anything so bad about being a panther. In fact, I like it very much."

"I think you're scared," Mowgli told him.

"Absolutely not!" Bagheera protested. "What on earth would I have to be scared of?"

Bagheera stood up, stretched and gracefully jumped out of the tree and onto the ground.

"Exactly," Mowgli said. "So, why not try it?"

"You've got to be kidding me!" Bagheera said.

"You know what your problem is?" Mowgli said.

"I'm afraid to ask," Bagheera said.

"You're like a beehive," Mowgli told him. "You work too hard." He stared at Bagheera pleadingly. "Come on, dance with me!" he cried, grabbing Bagheera's paw and prancing around the panther.

After a bit, Bagheera began to dance too, moving his feet and twitching his tail.

"That's it!" Mowgli cheered.

"You know what?" Bagheera admitted. "This isn't so bad after all."

"Now you're getting it!" Mowgli exclaimed. "Now you see why being a bear is so great!" The Man-cub stopped dancing and threw himself onto a soft patch of moss. "It's not so bad, is it?"

"Actually," Bagheera said, scratching his back against a rock, "it's sort of fun!"

"One more time!" Mowgli cheered, and they began dancing again.

A Perfect Picnic

Mickey Mouse and his friends were planning a picnic!

"We can all make our favourite foods and then swap baskets!" Mickey suggested.

"That sounds like fun. I can't wait!" said Minnie.

The friends raced home and each began to pack their lunch.

Donald made a sandwich and chose a piece of fruit. But as Donald looked at the food, he began to get hungry.

These are my favourite foods, he thought. *I don't want to share them!*

Over at Minnie's house, things were not going well either. Minnie had packed all her favourite foods. But as she got ready to leave, she started to wonder if she would like what her friends had packed.

Meanwhile, Daisy was excited about sharing her lunch. She hummed to herself as she packed her basket. But when Daisy picked up a banana, she began to frown. Maybe she didn't want to share her lunch after all....

Elsewhere, Goofy was making lemonade. He was soaking wet and covered in lemon juice! Goofy tasted his lemonade.

This is my best lemonade ever, Goofy thought. *I want to drink it all myself!*

As Mickey walked to the park, he grew more excited about the picnic. When he got there, Mickey found his friends waiting for him. They all had baskets of food, but they didn't look very happy.

"What's wrong?" Mickey asked his friends.

Donald explained that everyone wanted to eat their own favourite foods.

"Oh," Mickey said, disappointed. "Well, I guess we don't have to share."

Minnie looked at Mickey. He seemed so sad. She didn't want to be the reason he was upset! "I'll trade lunches with you, Mickey," she said.

"Thanks!" Mickey said.

Mickey's friends saw how happy Minnie had made Mickey and swapped baskets, too.

Mickey laid out a blanket, sat down, opened his picnic basket and started to laugh!

"What's so funny, Mickey?" Minnie asked. Then she looked in her basket and laughed, too.

Everyone had packed peanut butter sandwiches and lemonade!

The only difference in the baskets was the fruit. There was an orange, a banana, an apple, some grapes and a pineapple!

Then Mickey had an idea. He cut up the fruit, put it all in a bowl and mixed it together, making a big fruit salad.

As Mickey's friends ate their dessert, they realized that Mickey had been right. Sharing was fun, after all!

Disney
WRECK-IT RALPH

Wrecking Party

The arcade was closed for the day, and Ralph was looking forward to spending some time with his new friends, Felix and the Nicelanders.

Ralph wandered through the tower, searching for Felix and the others. They were nowhere to be seen. He called their names as he made his way up through the different floors, but nobody replied. Everyone had vanished. Ralph was all alone.

Feeling miserable, Ralph made his way back to the dump. He thought the others had abandoned him, but then....

"Surprise!"

Ralph turned and gasped as Felix and the Nicelanders leaped out from behind a pile of bricks. "Happy wrecking party!" they cheered, throwing their arms in the air.

One of the Nicelanders, Gene, handed Ralph a piece of cake. He looked at it, confused. "A party? For me?" No one had ever thrown him a party before.

"Not any old party," Felix laughed. "A wrecking party! We made this just for you!"

Felix gestured to a tall brick wall he and the others had built nearby. They knew how much Ralph loved to wreck things, and they couldn't wait to see him in action.

"Although, come to think of it ..." began Gene, frowning, "... I haven't the foggiest idea how to wreck something."

Ralph handed the little Nicelander a pickaxe. "I'll show you. It's really easy," he said, swinging with his fist. A chunk of the wall broke off, and Gene cheered.

"My turn!" he cried, swinging with the axe. The axe's metal point smashed into one of the bricks. The wall wobbled, then a large block fell off and smashed against the ground.

Gene bounced around happily. "I'm a wrecker! I'm a wrecker!" he cried.

Soon everyone wanted to have a go at wrecking the wall. Ralph munched on his cake and laughed as the Nicelanders took it in turns to break chunks of the stonework away. He realized, though, that there was someone who was missing out on all the fun. Felix hadn't wrecked a thing!

"It's not my style," Felix shrugged. "But I invited someone who can help me."

Ralph turned to see Sergeant Calhoun striding towards them, barking orders at the Nicelanders. "The kitten whispers and tickle fights stop now," she said, drawing her blaster rifle. "Now, where's this evil wall?"

Ralph and the others ducked for cover as Calhoun pulled the trigger and demonstrated how to wreck things, Hero's Duty style!

Disney·PIXAR

MONSTERS UNIVERSITY

Silent Invasion

The members of Oozma Kappa were down in Squishy's basement, practising for the second event in the Scare Games – Avoid the Parent.

To win the event, they'd have to sneak past a robotic librarian and grab a flag, so Mike had come up with a great way for them to train.

"We'll sneak past Squishy's Mum and grab a slice of cake," he said. "Be quiet and slow. Clear?"

"Yes, coach," said the other monsters, but Sulley just rolled his eyes. This was amateur-level stuff, and no challenge for someone like him.

A few minutes later, while Squishy's mum was busy knitting a new scarf for her son, Mike tiptoed into the room. The cake was sitting on a table right next to her. This wasn't going to be easy.

Creeping across the floor, Mike squeezed under the table. He waited until just the right moment, then quickly stretched out an arm and snatched a slice of the cake. Mission accomplished!

After carefully making his way back to the basement, Mike told Terri and Terry to go next. The two-headed monster was too big to fit under the table, but they sneaked silently up behind Mrs Squibbles and grabbed two pieces when she turned to examine the scarf.

Don took a different route to the cake, using his tentacles to climb along the ceiling. Squishy's mum didn't notice him reach down from above and grab his slice. She also didn't spot Squishy popping up from behind her armchair to steal his piece, and even Art managed to collect some cake without being seen.

Then it was Sulley's turn. Mike tried to give advice, but Sulley ignored it. "I can do this blindfolded, Wazowski," he said.

Mike thought it would be good for the other monsters to see how Sulley did it, so they all sneaked up to watch him in action.

Sulley easily made it across the room without alerting Squishy's mum, but as he got closer to the cake one of his big feet tangled in the wool she was using to knit with. Sulley flapped his arms, trying to stay upright, but it was no use. He smashed into the table, sending the rest of the cake flying through the air.

The other monsters shut their eyes as the cake splattered down on them, covering them in sticky green frosting. Mrs Squibbles gasped when she saw the mess. Sulley and the rest of the Oozma Kappa team had been well and truly spotted.

"Well, she caught us," said Squishy. He scooped a lump of cake off his head and ate it. "But at least we got a jumbo portion!"

Disney
Bambi

Spring Has Sprung!

Spring had come at last to the forest. Sniff, sniff – Bambi could smell the change in the air. The days were growing longer. The nights were getting shorter. The ice and snow were quickly melting away. Crocuses and daffodils were pushing new green shoots out of the ground.

And the forest didn't feel quite as lonely as it had during the cold weather. In just the last few days, Bambi had noticed that there were more animals peeking their heads out of their holes and burrows and dens.

As he took a walk through the forest very early one morning on the first day of spring, Bambi came upon Mrs Possum and her children hanging upside down by their tails from a tree branch. She and Bambi had not seen one another in a long while. But Mrs Possum recognized him just the same.

"Well, hello, Bambi," said Mrs Possum.

"Hello, Mrs Possum," Bambi replied. "I haven't seen you since autumn. Where have you and your family been all winter long?"

"Oh, we like to spend most of our winter indoors," Mrs Possum replied. "But now that spring is here, it's so nice to be out in the fresh air again." Then Mrs Possum and the rest of her family closed their eyes and dozed off, because they liked to spend most of their days sleeping, you know.

Walking on through the forest, Bambi stopped by a tree filled with twittering birds.

"Hello, Bambi," one of the birds called down to him.

"Hello," Bambi replied. "And where have you birds been all winter long?"

"Oh, we fly south for the winter, to warmer places where we can find more food," the bird explained. "But we are so happy it is spring once more. It is lovely to be back in the forest."

Then the bird joined her voice with her friends' twittering tunes. After so many months without it, the chirps and tweets were sweet music to Bambi's ears.

Bambi walked farther, meeting old friends at every turn. He came upon mice moving from their winter quarters back into their spring and summer homes. He noticed the squirrels and chipmunks snacking leisurely on nuts, no longer storing them away in their winter stockpiles. He heard a woodpecker rapping at a pine tree. And he spotted the ducks out for a swim on the pond.

Yes, thought Bambi, it had been a long, cold, difficult winter. But somehow the arrival of spring made him feel that everything would be all right. Everywhere he looked there was life, there were new beginnings ... and, most importantly, there was hope.

Red's Surprise

Guido and Luigi desperately needed to clean their shop. There were so many tyres stuffed into it they could barely move. It was becoming ridiculous! The only problem was that there was simply nowhere to put any of them.

"Gee, Luigi!" Lightning McQueen gasped as he entered the shop with Mater. Piled high like the great pyramids, they couldn't believe how many tyres Guido and Luigi actually had.

"Old stuff," said Guido. "I need room, but I don't want to throw them out."

"I think I know how to recycle them," said Mater, smiling.

A little while later, the cars found Mater outside standing proudly beneath a huge tower of tyres with a flag at the top.

"Like it?" Mater asked.

"I dunno," said Guido. "It looks wobbly...."

"Rest assured nothin' will knock this baby down!" Mater told him.

But as soon as the words left his mouth, there came a disturbing rumble. Suddenly, tyres fell like black rain, bouncing along the street.

"This is no good. We've got to come up with something else," Guido said.

Then Lightning McQueen had an idea. "I could use them to build protection barriers along the track!" he suggested.

"Bad idea, rookie" came a disgruntled voice. Doc emerged from a pile of fallen tyres. "Those tyres aren't going to stop you if you crash."

Lightning McQueen pictured himself ploughing into them at top speed. Even in a vision, it didn't go well for him.

"We can't keep these here," Guido groaned. "We need room for new arrivals."

"Maybe Sally could use them at the motel?" said Mater to them.

The cars gathered up the tyres and towed them to Sally's place.

"Thanks!" she said. "But I can't imagine what I would do with them."

"Decorations!" Guido insisted hopefully.

Sally tried to find places she could put the tyres, but everywhere seemed dangerous.

"Sorry, I just can't find the right place for them," she admitted, giving them back.

"I guess I'll just have to throw them out tomorrow," said Guido in defeat.

The cars drove away, leaving the tyres in a pile ready to be discarded.

The following day, however, when Guido was ready to be rid of them for good, the tyres were filled with blooming flowers.

"Flower pots!" cried Guido, as Red the fire engine watered the plants happily. "Nice goin' Red!

Finally, the tyres had been put to good use.

The Mysterious Treasure

Sheriff Woody was playing cards with Jessie and Buzz when Slinky ran up, panting excitedly. "Woody! Come and look!"

Following Slinky, Woody was amazed to find a carefully drawn treasure map!

"Andy drew this a long time ago, after hiding something in the yard," Woody remembered.

"Do you think the treasure is still there?" wondered Slinky.

There was only one way to find out. With Jessie at his side, Woody carefully folded the map then climbed out onto the window ledge. The cowboy and cowgirl slid down the drainpipe as Buzz and Slinky watched from Andy's window.

Down in the garden, Woody unfurled the map. "It should be easy to find this treasure," he said.

Jessie gulped. "I'm not so sure!" she said. "B-behind you!"

Woody spun round to see a large, mean-looking cat approaching. Its eyes were narrow and its fur stood up on end. It was getting ready to pounce!

Woody and Jessie backed up against the wall as the cat let out an angry hiss. Up at the window, Slinky and Buzz watched on.

"What can we do?" Slinky asked.

Luckily, Buzz had a plan. Grabbing a nearby megaphone toy, he held it in front of Slinky's mouth. At once, the stretchy toy dog knew what to do. He barked and growled into the megaphone as loudly as he could.

Startled, the cat let out a loud "Meoooow!" then ran off with its tail between its legs.

After shouting a thank you to their friends, Woody and Jessie set off to find the treasure. With help from the map, they found their way to a pile of bricks. "It must be under here," Woody said.

He and Jessie pushed the bricks out of the way. Beneath them was a hole, and sitting at the bottom was a shiny gold tin.

"Yee-ha! There it is!" Jessie cheered.

Climbing down into the hole, the toys pushed open the tin's lid. Inside was a folded-up piece of paper.

"Huh. What's this?" Jessie wondered.

"We'll soon find out," said Woody, unfolding the paper.

When they saw what was on the paper, Woody and Jessie both gasped. "Oh, it's beautiful!" said Jessie.

Woody looked down at the page, which showed a drawing of him and Andy together, holding hands and having fun in the sunshine. "Now that," said the cowboy, wiping a tear from his eye, "is a real treasure!"

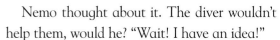

Hide-and-Seek

When Nemo and his friends were bored, they liked to play games. One of the best games at the reef was hide-and-seek, because there were so many places to hide.

They were discussing who would be the seeker when a school of fish ploughed into them screaming, "Swim away!"

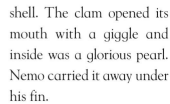

Nemo and his friends turned to see a human invading their world, dressed in a black suit and snorkel.

"We have to stop him!" Sheldon said.

"But we're so small," Pearl reminded him.

"We need big help!" Nemo insisted.

"I'll get the sharks," offered Tad. "They'll soon scare him off!"

In the meantime, Sheldon and Nemo made a plan to distract the diver. Swimming around and around his head, hoping to make him dizzy until – *THWACK!* – the diver's hammer struck the coral, making Sheldon spiral out of control. He fell to the ocean bed in a shower of pebbles.

"Are you okay?" asked Nemo, peeking through a gap in the stones. They had completely covered Sheldon, leaving him with no room to swim out.

"I'm stuck!" Sheldon cried.

Pearl and Nemo tried to budge the stones, but nothing worked. They needed a plan.

"Maybe the diver could dig him out?" Pearl suggested shyly.

Nemo thought about it. The diver wouldn't help them, would he? "Wait! I have an idea!"

Nemo scouted around for something shiny. Anything! He spotted a clam and tickled its shell. The clam opened its mouth with a giggle and inside was a glorious pearl. Nemo carried it away under his fin.

"Here," he said, passing it to a frowning Sheldon. "Keep this close. Humans like to collect shiny things. When the diver sees a sparkle, he'll investigate and set you free."

They waited patiently and as the pearl made lights reflect from Sheldon's enclosure, the diver came over. With curious fingers, he prised apart the heavy stones to grasp the pearl, freeing Sheldon in the process.

"Yes!" his friends cheered, just as Tad returned. Behind Tad was an army of vegetarian sharks but the diver didn't know the truth about their diet. He saw the sharks swimming a mean and scary path in his direction and, with a burst of bubbles from his snorkel, he shot to the surface like his life depended on it.

"That intruder won't show his face around here again," Bruce boasted.

Nemo thanked the sharks and followed his friends back home to safety. One thing was for sure: that had been the most intense game of hide-and-seek they'd ever played!

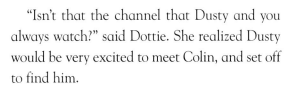

You Blew That One

While Dottie wasn't looking, Dusty was getting in some sneaky race training out over the fields.

Dottie didn't think Dusty was built for racing, and always tried to talk him out of it.

Chug was talking Dusty through some aerobatic moves and giving him lots of encouragement. Neither of them noticed a huge shadow passing overhead.

Back at her workshop, Dottie frowned. "Why has it suddenly gone dark?" she wondered. There hadn't been a cloud in the sky a few moments ago, so Dottie rolled outside to find out what was going on.

She couldn't believe what she saw! It wasn't clouds blocking out the sun, it was an enormous airship!

"I'm short on fuel," the blimp said. "Do you know where I can tank up?"

Dottie knew just how to help. She sent Leadbottom to find Chug and bring him back to fuel the airship. "A stranger needs a full tank," Chug said over the radio. "I'll be back in no time at all."

Dusty continued with his training, while Chug trundled off. The fuel truck recognized the stranger right away.

"It's Colin Cowling from Racing Sports Network!" he gasped.

"Isn't that the channel that Dusty and you always watch?" said Dottie. She realized Dusty would be very excited to meet Colin, and set off to find him.

Dusty knew that Dottie didn't approve of him training to race, so when he saw her approaching he quickly took cover behind the old silo. He stayed very still and kept quiet until Dottie had safely driven by.

"I couldn't find him," Dottie told them, when she'd returned to the hangar.

Chug said. "What a pity! Colin's tank is full now."

The friends asked Colin if he could stay a little longer to meet their friend, but Colin had a race to get to, and couldn't stick around. "Maybe next time," he promised, as he lifted into the air and cruised off on his journey.

Just then, Dusty finished pulling off a tricky flip. He blinked in surprise when he saw the familiar outline of Colin Cowling drifting overhead. "I can't believe it's him!" he cried.

Frantically, Dusty sped over to the airstrip and swooped in to land. "Did you see? Colin Cowling was in town!" he cried. "Why didn't anyone tell me?"

When Dottie explained she'd come looking for him, Dusty realized what had happened. He made a note to himself never to hide from his friends again. Who knew what he might miss?

THE INCREDIBLES

Lethal Fashion

When Mr Incredible visited the infamous Edna Mode to get his damaged costume patched up, she insisted on making him a new one instead.

Once Bob had left, Edna got to work. This would be the greatest costume ever. It would be bold, dramatic ... and indestructible!

After carefully choosing the materials, Edna stitched together the red and black outfit. It looked perfect, but before she could give it to Mr Incredible, she had to test how well it would cope with the type of situations a superhero would face. For that, she'd need some help.

"Rolf, come to the lab, darling," Edna said, pressing an intercom switch.

Her bodyguard, Rolf, appeared at the door just a few moments later. "I need you to test this suit," Edna told him. "Do you feel like helping?"

Rolf was happy to help, and soon he was standing in the middle of the lab wearing the new costume. He jumped with fright as the floor began to move beneath him like a treadmill. It quickly became too fast for him to keep up with, and he was bounced and battered by the moving belt.

"Mr Incredible's suit must be friction-proof," said Edna, ticking a box on her notes.

The floor stopped moving and Rolf stood up, groaning. The suit was undamaged, but he couldn't say the same for himself. Still, at least it was over now. Or so he thought!

"Chill-proof," Edna said, as a blast of frosty cold air hit Rolf, freezing him and making his teeth chatter.

A fountain of flame bloomed up around him next. He hopped about and yelped as his eyebrows began to sizzle.

There were still lots of tests to go. Edna blasted the suit with high-speed chunks of icy hail.

Then she stretched the fabric between two huge robotic hands, giving the bodyguard a painful wedgie.

Poor Rolf was dangled from a high ledge in a howling gale, before finally being electrocuted. Edna nodded approvingly as Rolf buzzed and bounced around the test chamber. The suit was perfect.

When Mr Incredible came to collect it the next day, he quickly tried it on and admired himself in the mirror. "Edna, you're the best," he said, puffing up his chest. "It's bold, dynamic...."

"And indestructible," sighed a battered and bruised Rolf, limping in to join them.

Edna smiled. The suit was as tough as Mr Incredible himself – and far tougher than her bodyguard would ever be!

Disney · PIXAR

WALL·E

W is for WALL·E

Aboard the Axiom space cruiser, no one ever had to do things for themselves. Robots whizzed around the ship, taking care of the passengers' needs, and everything ran perfectly on auto-pilot.

The only thing not on auto-pilot was WALL·E, who roamed around the ship trying to find the little white robot who he'd seen back down on Earth.

As WALL·E rolled around, he spotted a group of human babies in a room. They were all in tiny floating chairs, listening to a Nanny robot teach them the ABCs.

"B is for Buy 'n' Large, your very best friend. C is for consume, your favourite entertainment," the Nannybot chimed. When she reached the letter E, though, WALL·E interrupted her.

"E is for –"

"EEEVE!" WALL·E said. "EEEVE! EEEVE!"

The Nannybot had never been challenged before, and her circuits weren't built to handle it. She buzzed noisily. "E is for.... Malfunction!" she said. She wobbled for a moment, then completely shut down.

All around WALL·E, the children began to cry. They looked so sad, with their pudgy little faces all screwed up and wet with tears. WALL·E wanted to stop them crying, but how?

He had an idea. WALL·E tucked his head and arms back inside his body. The babies fell silent, wondering what was going to happen next, then they giggled as WALL·E popped back up, shouting, "Boo!"

WALL·E soon began to enjoy having fun with the babies. He decided to take them out of the daycare centre, and they all set off to explore the ship.

They spent the day having lots of fun together. WALL·E hooked the babies' floating chairs together and pulled them along behind him in a frantic race against some of the ship's other robots. The children laughed and cheered as they whizzed through the corridors at high speed, weaving like a snake through the robotic traffic.

Next, they headed out to the observation deck to gaze up at the universe outside the ship. The babies gasped as they got their first glimpse of stars and planets.

After having some more fun playing a few tricks on adults, WALL·E took the babies back to the daycare centre. He said his goodbyes just as the Nannybot woke up again.

The poor Nanny's circuits were still confused, and her alphabet was all jumbled up.

"W is for...." she began, and the babies knew just how to respond.

"WALL·E!" they cried, then they giggled as the Nannybot fizzed and sparked in confusion all over again!

Surprise Rodeo

The toys stood at the bottom of Andy's stairs, looking at a weird new addition to the household. It looked like some sort of flower, but where its petals should have been was a mouth!

"What is it?" Buzz asked, staring at the plant.

"It's a tropical plant," Hamm explained. "It hunts for its food."

Jessie laughed. "Oh, please!" she snorted, strolling over for a closer look. "How can a plant catch anything?"

"Watch out!" Woody warned, as the plant's mouth opened. It snapped shut, catching Jessie by the bottom and holding her tightly. The little cowgirl wriggled and fought, but the plant's grip was too strong.

"What are you doing just standing there?" she demanded, glaring down at her friends. "Help me!"

Woody adjusted his hat. "There's only one thing to do," he said, grabbing one of Jessie's legs. "Pull!"

The friends all heaved together, tugging on Jessie's arms and legs with all their strength. No matter how hard they pulled, though, the plant would not let go. As the toys gave a final tug, their grips slipped and they landed in a heap on the carpet.

The situation was worse than they thought.

Woody, Buzz and Rex put their heads together and tried to come up with a plan, while Slinky tried to keep Jessie calm. "Keep your chin up, cowgirl. We'll save you," he promised.

Jessie reached down and patted Slinky's head. "Thanks, pal," she said, and Slinky's tail wagged happily.

As the tail brushed against the exotic plant, its leaves began to shudder and shake. "Hey, this plant's ticklish!" Slinky realized.

As long as Slinky kept tickling, Woody knew the plant would be distracted. "I have a plan," he announced, unravelling his lasso. He tossed the rope, hoping to catch hold of Jessie, but instead it flew past her and looped around the plant.

"Well, not exactly what I had in mind," Woody admitted, but as he pulled the rope tight the plant spat Jessie out!

What's more, Woody realized that with the rope tied around its mouth, the plant looked an awful lot like a bucking bronco! He swung up onto its back and waved his hat in the air. "Who wants the next rodeo ride?" he asked, swinging around on an imaginary saddle.

Most of the other toys made their excuses, riding the plant looked far too dangerous, but one couldn't wait to take his turn.

"Count me in, cowboy," smiled Buzz. "That ride looks wild!"

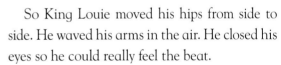

Dance, Daddy-o!

Deep in the jungle at the temple ruins, the monkeys and their ruler, King Louie, were always looking to have a swingin' time.

"Let's have a dance-off!" King Louie suggested to the monkeys one evening.

"Hooray! Hooray!" the monkeys cheered.

"What's a dance-off?" one monkey asked.

"You know, a contest," said King Louie. "An opportunity for everyone to get down, strut their stuff, cut a rug! And whoever lays down the smoothest moves is the winner!"

"Hooray!" cheered the monkeys.

King Louie rubbed his chin. "The first thing we need is some music," he said, pointing at the monkey musicians. "Hit it, fellas!"

The musicians blasted out a jazzy tune by blowing through their hands like horns, knocking out a beat on some coconuts and drumming on a hollow log. Soon, all the monkeys were gathered around the musicians, tapping their toes and shaking their tails.

"Now," said King Louie, "who will dance?"

All the monkeys raised their hands. King Louie looked around. "Let's see," he said, scratching his head. "I choose ... me!"

"Hooray!" the monkeys cheered. They were disappointed not to be chosen. But, after all, King Louie *was* their King.

So King Louie moved his hips from side to side. He waved his arms in the air. He closed his eyes so he could really feel the beat.

"Dance, Daddy-o!" one monkey cried.

King Louie boogied and bopped like he had never boogied and bopped before. Then, when the song was over, King Louie stopped dancing and scrambled onto his throne. "Now it's time to choose the winner!" he said.

"But King Louie...." one monkey began to object. All the other monkeys were thinking the same thing – didn't you need more than one dancer to have a dance-off?

"Oh, silly me," said King Louie with a chuckle. The monkeys looked at each other and smiled, expecting that the king had realized his mistake. But King Louie said, "Of course, we need a judge! Who will judge?"

Everyone raised their hands. King Louie looked around, then said, "I choose ... me!"

"Hooray!" the monkeys cheered.

"And as the judge, I will now choose the winner of the dance-off," King Louie continued on. He looked around at all the monkeys. "Now, let's see," he said, scratching his head. "I choose ... me! Let's hear it for the winner!"

"Hooray!" the monkeys cheered, because, after all, King Louie was their king – and a pretty swingin' dancer, too!

SOS! A New Tyre for Sally

Sally relaxed in the shade on a sunny day, watching Red water his favourite flowers.

"Hi, Sally!" Lightning McQueen greeted. "How about taking a little spin?"

"Sure thing, hotshot!" she agreed. "My tyres need a good warming up!"

She zoomed ahead, glancing in her mirrors to see if he was keeping up. "C'mon, champ! Why are you driving slow?" she teased.

"Ha! Watch out, or you'll hear my engine rumbling from afar!" Lightning McQueen joked, tearing through a cave beneath a glorious waterfall.

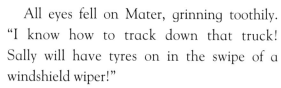

"Let's see how a shower suits you!" Sally said. But she swallowed her words when she drove over a particularly sharp stick. Sally's right wheel flumped and bumped in the dirt. "Oh, no! My tyre is flat!" she sobbed.

Lightning McQueen inspected it closely. "I'll take you to Guido and Luigi's place," he decided. "They'll fix it!"

They drove slowly, so Sally wouldn't hurt herself more.

"Sorry, we're out of tyres!" Guido said, when they arrived. "The supply truck's late. Could even be lost. We don't know how to find him."

Sally fought back tears. "Now what?"

"I'll take care of everything, buddy!" called a voice from the doorway.

All eyes fell on Mater, grinning toothily. "I know how to track down that truck! Sally will have tyres on in the swipe of a windshield wiper!"

Nestled in the hold of a Dinoco helicopter, Mater and his friend flew fearlessly through the air. "We'll find the lost supply truck in no time, pal!" Mater yelled.

High above winding roads, Mater spotted their target. "There it is! Let's go see what's wrong!"

They hovered beside the supply truck. "We've been looking all over for you!" Mater said. "C'mon, we'll show you the way!"

"Phew!" the truck sighed, relieved. "My tracking system broke down. I didn't know which road to follow!"

At the tyre shop, Sally's friends tried hopelessly to make her happy. Then came a familiar sound. *CHOP, CHOP.*

The Dinoco helicopter, Mater and the supply truck arrived with beaming smiles and the cars cheered in delight!

With speed and agility, Guido and Luigi fixed Sally up with a shiny new tyre.

"Now we can hit the road again!" Lightning McQueen sang.

Together they raced off, leaving Mater and his friend, the Dinoco helicopter, to take a ride in the bluest of skies.

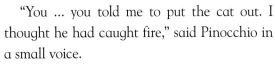

A Helping Hand

"Oh, Pinocchio!" cried Geppetto. "I can hardly believe that my little puppet is alive!" It was the morning after the Blue Fairy had visited Geppetto's house and brought Pinocchio to life. "You must get ready for school, my boy," said Geppetto.

Pinocchio was full of curiosity. "Why must I go to school, Father?" he asked.

"Why, so that you can learn!" Geppetto replied. "Now be a good boy and go make the bed while I clear away these dishes."

Ever eager to help, Pinocchio ran over to Geppetto's workbench. He found a hammer, a nail and a piece of wood, and began to pound loudly with the hammer.

"Pinocchio! Whatever are you doing?" cried Geppetto.

"Well, you asked me to make the bed," said Pinocchio. "So I was starting to make one."

With a little smile, Geppetto patted him on the head and said, "Perhaps it would be better for you to put the cat out."

As Geppetto turned back to the breakfast table, Pinocchio jumped up and grabbed a jug of water. Hurrying over to Figaro, Pinocchio threw the water onto the cat.

"*YEEEEOOWWWW!*" shrieked Figaro.

"Pinocchio!" shouted Geppetto. "Why did you do that?"

"You ... you told me to put the cat out. I thought he had caught fire," said Pinocchio in a small voice.

"Oh, my dear boy, you have much to learn!" Geppetto sighed as he dried off Figaro. "Okay, you can be a helpful boy by helping me to pick up the house a bit before you leave for school."

"All right, Father!" said Pinocchio, and he raced out of the front door.

"Where in the world is he going?" Geppetto wondered aloud, as he followed Pinocchio outside.

Pinocchio was crouching at the base of the house, trying with all his might to lift it.

"What are you doing, son?" asked Geppetto with a twinkle in his eye.

"Trying to pick up the house, Father," said Pinocchio, his voice straining with effort.

Geppetto chuckled and gently guided Pinocchio back inside. "My boy, the sooner you go to school and learn about the world, the better for us both," he said. He collected Pinocchio's hat, his schoolbook and an apple for the teacher, and sent him on his way.

As Geppetto watched his new son walk off to school, he shook his head worriedly. "I hope he manages to stay out of trouble today," he said to himself. "My little boy has much to learn about the world."

Spaceship Emergency

Buzz, Jessie and some of the other toys sat in Bonnie's home-made spaceship. It was actually a shoebox with some paper plate wings stuck on, but with a bit of imagination it made a fantastic rocket!

"To infinity and beyond!" Buzz cried. Behind him, the other toys cheered.

"Hey, wait up!" yelled Rex, racing towards them. "I wanna play, too!"

The clumsy dinosaur grabbed hold of a wing, only for it to tear off in his hand! "Uh-oh!" Rex whimpered.

"Look what you've done," scolded Mr Pricklepants. Rex felt terrible, but Buzz did his best to come to the rescue.

"Don't panic," he said. "I'll have that wing fixed in a flash!"

Or ... maybe not. No matter how hard he tried, Buzz couldn't get the wing to stick back in place. The toys started to worry. Bonnie would be back soon, and she'd be really upset to see her spaceship damaged.

"What'll we do?" Rex worried.

"Take it easy," said Buttercup the unicorn. "There's a roll of tape in the kitchen. We'll get it and use it to attach the wing."

"Great!" said Jessie. She caught Buttercup by the ear and pulled him along. "Let's go, pal!"

In the kitchen, Buttercup soon spotted the tape, but it was too high for the toys to reach.

Jessie had an idea. Grabbing a feather duster, she stretched up and tried to knock the tape off the table. A cloud of smelly dust rained down on Buttercup. The little unicorn coughed and spluttered, then let out a yelp of pain as the roll of tape fell from the table and bumped him on the head.

"Well, at least we got the tape," Jessie said.

Sneezing with the dust, Buttercup followed Jessie back to Bonnie's room. Buzz worked quickly to repair the damaged wing, and soon it was as good as new.

"All aboard, Space Command," he cheered.

"All right!" replied Rex, excited to be joining the adventure. In fact, he was so excited he didn't notice his tail snagging on the spaceship's cardboard engines. With a rip, one of the engines tore free.

"Looks like we'll need some glue," said Dolly, examining the damage.

"No problem!" said Buttercup helpfully. "I saw some in the living room."

Jessie's face lit up. She caught Buttercup by the ear and tugged him again. "We're in for another adventure, pal!"

Buttercup groaned. The last adventure had been very messy and painful. In future, he decided, he really should learn to keep his mouth shut!

Fear of Flying

Skipper and Dusty rolled out of the hangar, chatting excitedly. "Well?" asked Skip. "What do you think?"

"Awesome!" cheered Dusty. "I can't wait to try it!"

Chug rolled over. He tried to peer into the hangar just as Skipper nudged the doors closed. "What's in there?" Chug asked.

"Nothing special, nosy parker!" laughed Skipper. "Just a little something an old pal from the squad lent me. We'll show you it later – if it works."

Chug rocked from side to side on his wheels. "I wanna see it now!" he protested. "There shouldn't be any secrets among friends."

Dusty laughed and explained that it was up to Skipper, and that Chug would find out soon. He just had to be patient.

But Chug didn't like the sound of that. As soon as Dusty and Skipper had lifted off, he wedged open the hangar doors and creeped inside.

Standing in the middle of the hangar was ... actually, Chug had no idea what it was. It was a large metal box, that much was obvious. But what did it do?

After checking no one was coming, he rolled slowly into the box to try to figure out what it was. The door slammed closed behind him, making Chug jump in fright.

Searching around for a way to open the door, the little fuel truck found a big red button. "Maybe this will open it," he said, rolling a wheel over the button. Almost at once, the walls seemed to melt away, and Chug found himself outside. "Argh! It opened too much!" he yelped.

And it got worse! Chug began to race forwards, getting faster and faster as he sped towards the end of the runway. Before he knew what was happening, his wheels lifted off the tarmac and he rose quickly up towards the sky.

What was going on? Chug had no idea, but one thing he did know – he wanted to get down! He screwed his eyes shut, then screamed as he plunged into a sudden dive. "Not so quick!" he howled, then he sobbed as he went into a spin and the whole world flipped around and around.

Then, out of nowhere, Dusty appeared right in front of him. "Come on out of there, Chug," Dusty said. Chug trundled out of the box, feeling queasy. His wheels were shaking, but at least he was back on solid ground.

"What's that c-crazy machine?" he asked.

"It's a flight simulator!" Dusty said.

Chug spluttered. A simulator? Well, if that was what fake flying was like, he was glad he'd never have to do it for real!

Disney MICKEY & FRIENDS
Goofy at Bat

One sunny day, Goofy was walking past the sports stadium when he heard a baseball recruiter calling to passers-by. "Come, one and all, put your skills to the test. Try out today! Our new team needs the best!"

Goofy decided to sign up. He knew his friends would teach him to play!

After signing his name, Goofy gathered Mickey, Minnie, Donald, Daisy and Pluto. They went to the park to practise, but Donald wasn't happy about having to spend the day teaching Goofy to bat.

"Donald, please help," Goofy said. "You're the best player I know!"

Donald agreed and walked Goofy to the centre of the field. First, Donald demonstrated how to hold the bat.

After a few practice swings, Mickey threw the ball. It curved in the air, swinging and swooping. Goofy tried to follow the ball's path, but ended up in a big Goofy-knot!

After his friends untangled him, Goofy was ready to try again.

"Goofy, try to hit this one far," Donald said. But it took Mickey so long to get ready to pitch that Goofy fell fast asleep and the ball ended up hitting Donald on the head!

"Gawrsh, I'm sorry, Donald," Goofy said, sheepishly shuffling his feet.

Next, Mickey threw a fastball. Goofy stood still, determined not to let the ball pass him. The ball got closer and closer. Goofy swung hard and the ball rebounded fast and low.

Coach Donald called, "Hurry up, run, go!"

Goofy was so excited that he ran straight to the last base by mistake!

"No! Run to third base!" Donald cried out.

Goofy felt confused – his feet went one way, while his body tried to head in the opposite direction, and he fell flat on his face.

"Okay, why don't we try catching?" Donald suggested.

Minnie stepped up to bat. Goofy picked up his mitt and waited for the pitch. Mickey threw the ball and Minnie struck it straight towards Goofy. He ran backwards, fast, hoping he'd be better at catching than he was at batting.

The ball started to fall. Goofy raised his gloved hand ... and caught the ball right in the middle of his mitt! All his friends cheered.

"That was great, Goofy!" said Donald. "Now, try it again."

Mickey threw, Minnie hit and Goofy caught the ball again! And again. And again!

"Goofy, you're going to go far. This is clearly your game," Donald said.

"I couldn't have done it without your help," Goofy told him. "Thanks, buddy."

The Good Thing About Rain

"Rise and shine!" cried Pongo. One by one, he nudged each of his 15 Dalmatian puppies with his nose.

The puppies yawned and stretched.

But Rolly just rolled over and slept on.

"Aw, come on, Rolly," Pongo whispered in the pup's ear. "It's morning! Don't you want to go out?"

At the mention of the word 'out', Rolly was instantly wide awake!

And Rolly was not alone. As if by magic, the sleepy group had become a pack of jumping, barking puppies.

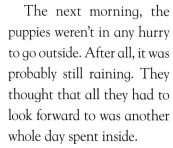

They raced together through the kitchen to the back door, where they jumped up and down excitedly, waiting for Nanny to let them out into the garden.

"Okay, here I come," said Nanny, as she made her way across the kitchen. Then she flung the door open wide and stepped out of the way to let the puppies race past.

But they didn't move. It was raining!

"Oh, go on," said Perdita, trying to nudge the pups out of the door. "It's only a little water."

But they wouldn't budge.

The next morning, Patch awoke with a start. With a few sharp barks, he helped Pongo wake the other puppies. Within seconds, all 15 were crowding around the back door.

Nanny rushed to open the door again.

And once again, the puppies were very disappointed to see raindrops falling.

"Well," said Pongo with a sigh, "April showers bring May flowers!"

The next morning, the puppies weren't in any hurry to go outside. After all, it was probably still raining. They thought that all they had to look forward to was another whole day spent inside.

So, when Nanny opened the door on a sunny morning, the puppies were so surprised that they didn't know what to do.

Then, springing into action, they tumbled over one another in their rush to get out of the door. They raced off in different directions, ready to sniff, dig, roll and explore.

But then, almost at once, all 15 puppies froze in their tracks. They looked around at each other, then down at themselves. What was this stuff getting all over their spotted white coats? It was brown. It was wet. It was squishy.... It was mud! And it was fun!

From the doorway, Pongo and Perdita looked out at their muddy puppies and laughed.

"You know what this means, don't you?" Pongo asked Perdita.

Perdy nodded. "Baths."

Pongo smiled, watching the frolicking puppies. "Let's not tell them – just yet," he said.

Abracadabra!

Manny was not at his best. Gypsy could tell. Already that day, he had lost two magic wands and stepped on his turban.

And with the matinee show at P.T. Flea's World's Greatest Circus about to begin, Gypsy knew she had to be on her toes. Manny was going to debut his new trick – the Levitating, Flaming and Disappearing Water Torture Chamber of Death.

"Ladies and gentlemen," Manny declared, "prepare to be stunned and amazed by the Levitating, Flaming and Disappearing Water Torture Chamber of Death. You will watch as my lovely and talented assistant, Gypsy, climbs inside this chamber" – Manny motioned towards the empty sardine can at his side – "where I will bind her hands and feet. Then I will fill the chamber with water, seal it, levitate it five inches off the ground and set it ablaze. And, finally, you will watch in awe as the chamber disappears before your very eyes!"

Manny and Gypsy had rehearsed the act thoroughly. Everything was planned down to the last detail. But, if one little thing went wrong with the trick, Gypsy could be in big trouble.

As it turned out, one little thing didn't go wrong – three big things went wrong!

Manny made his first mistake when he tied Gypsy's hands and feet together. He was supposed to leave the strings loose so Gypsy could wriggle out of them once she was inside. But Manny accidentally tied them too tight!

Then Manny filled the chamber too high with water. In rehearsals, he had left a bit of space at the top so that Gypsy had some air inside. But, this time, he forgot!

Manny's third mistake was locking the trapdoor. Together, he and Gypsy had rigged an escape hatch in the back side of the sardine can. Once Manny sealed her inside, Gypsy wriggled out of her bonds, opened the trapdoor and, unseen by the audience, escaped from the chamber before Manny levitated it, set it on fire and made it disappear. But, this time, Manny accidentally nudged the latch that secured the trapdoor from the outside. Gypsy was locked inside.

Luckily, Gypsy hadn't left anything to chance. She had stowed a sharp shard of glass inside the sardine can. She had learned to hold her breath for 10 minutes. And she had put a release latch on the inside of the trapdoor.

She was safely out of the chamber in one minute flat.

At the end of the trick, Manny called Gypsy in front of the audience. "How did you do it, my dear?" he asked dramatically.

"It was magic!" she replied, with a smile.

A Very Good Idea

Buzz, Woody and Rex strode through the streets of an old west town. "I sure like the easy life here in Bonnieville," said Buzz.

Woody nodded. "You can say that again."

But the friends had spoken too soon. A flying saucer swooshed by above their heads. "It's evil Dr Porkchop and the aliens," Woody warned, just as the spaceship began to fire laser blasts in their direction.

Panicking, Rex turned and ran. "Ahhh! Every toy for himself!"

"Wait, Rex!" cried Buzz. "Don't go that way. That leads to the dark, endless gorge!"

Bonnie dropped Rex in a toy box and slammed the lid shut. "Oh no! How are we going to rescue Rex, Buzz?" she gasped, moving Woody so it looked like he was the one asking the question.

Before Bonnie could start the rescue, her mum told her it was time for bed. The game – and Rex – would have to wait until tomorrow.

That night, as Bonnie slept, Woody and Buzz made plans on how they would rescue Rex. Little did they know, the toy dinosaur had clambered free on his own. But then they saw him, sighing sadly as he approached them.

"What's wrong, Rex?" asked Woody. "Aren't you happy with this adventure?"

Rex shrugged. "Yeah, but I always get the part of the scaredy-cat. At least once I'd like to be the brave hero! But I guess that's not the way things work for a dino in the Wild West."

Woody and Buzz watched their friend walk off to bed.

"You thinking what I'm thinking?" Woody wondered. Buzz nodded in agreement.

Working quickly, the friends used some of Bonnie's craft materials to build something very special.

"Are you sure this is a good idea?" asked Buzz.

"Trust me, Buzz," Woody assured him. "When Bonnie sees our creation, Rex will be the star of this adventure!"

When Bonnie woke up the next morning, she cheered with excitement. Sitting on her floor was a home-made dinosaur island! "Thanks, Mum!" she cried. "This is the greatest island ever, and the great Rex can be its ruler!"

Bonnie grabbed her toys and began to play. Soon, her imagination was working at top speed as she created a new adventure.

"Rex! Buzz and Woody are in trouble," said Hamm.

Dressed as a brave adventurer, Rex pushed back his hat. "Don't worry, I'll handle this one!"

Woody and Buzz had helped their friend be the hero he'd always wanted to be, but as they dangled above the island's volcano they wondered if they had made a very big mistake!

DUMBO

You're Gonna Be Huge!

Dumbo sat in the corner with a big frown on his face.

"What's the matter, kid?" Timothy asked.

Dumbo just shook his head.

"You've got nothing to be sad about," Timothy continued. Dumbo didn't say anything.

"Well, if you're not going to tell me what's bugging ya, I guess I'll just have to figure it out for myself," Timothy said. "I know!" he exclaimed. "You're hungry?"

Dumbo shook his head.

"Thirsty?" Timothy asked his friend.

Dumbo shook his head again.

"Concerned about the June bug population in Saskatchewan?" Timothy suggested.

Dumbo shook his head doubly hard.

"Well, then," Timothy concluded. "It can only be one thing. It pains me to say it, but I think you have a case of 'feeling sorry for myself-itis'."

Dumbo's large ears pricked up.

"Yes," Timothy continued. "It's a dangerous disease that has affected many of us. Even the strongest cannot avoid it."

Dumbo looked to his left and to his right, then pointed to himself.

"Yes, that's right – you!" Timothy said. "I bet I know what's got you down – your above-average ear size."

Dumbo nodded.

"And the fact that people make fun of you," Timothy continued.

Dumbo nodded even more.

"And, on top of all that," Timothy said, "you've been separated from your mother."

A tear started to form in Dumbo's eye.

"Don't feel sorry for yourself!" Timothy ordered. Dumbo looked up, surprised.

"You know why?" Timothy asked. "Because one day you're gonna be huge!"

Dumbo blinked at him in disbelief.

"We're talking autographs, your name in lights. They're gonna eat their hats for the way they treated you," Timothy predicted.

Dumbo looked nervous.

"I don't mean eat their hats for real," Timothy explained. "It's just a figure of speech. Not that some of them wouldn't deserve it if they had to eat their hats. But that's not what we're talking about. What I mean is, they're gonna be really sorry they treated you so bad, do you understand?"

Dumbo nodded his head.

"All right then," Timothy said cheerfully. "Feeling better?"

And Dumbo nodded doubly hard as visions of success, happiness – and being with his mother again – filled his head.

Disney
HERCULES

Destructo-boy

"Hercules!" Amphitryon called. "This haystack is about to fall over. Could you hold it up while I go to get the cart?"

"Sure, Pop!" Hercules told his father.

Hercules was the strongest boy in his village. He could easily hold up the enormous stack of hay bales with one hand.

Soon, another farmer approached, struggling to hold on to a team of six disobedient mules.

"Do you need any help?" Hercules asked.

"Yes!" the farmer gasped. "If you'll hold these mules, I can fetch my sons to help me get them home."

"Be glad to!" Hercules took the mules' leads with his free hand.

Just then, a woman came by dragging a cart filled with pottery. She was panting.

"Good day, ma'am," Hercules said politely. "Could I give you a hand with that?"

"Why, thank you," the woman replied. "But it looks like you have your hands full!"

"Oh, I'll be finished here in a second," Hercules said. "Then I can...."

His voice trailed off. He'd just noticed some children his own age running down the road, laughing and shouting as they tossed a discus.

Hercules gazed at them longingly. For some reason, he'd never seemed to fit in with the other village children. Perhaps it was because they didn't understand him. Or perhaps it was because Hercules once challenged them to a 45 metre dash – and beaten them all by 44 metres.

"Hey, guys!" he called as the discus sailed towards him. "I've got it!"

He lunged towards the discus. The mules' leads went flying. The haystack teetered.

"Uh-oh," Hercules said.

He tried to grab the hay and the mules at the same time, but he accidentally tripped one of the mules, which crashed into the haystack, which fell right onto the woman's cart, and all over the boys.

Hercules winced at the sounds of breaking pottery and shouting boys. The mules were already running off towards the horizon.

"My pottery!" the woman wailed.

"What's the big idea?" one of the other children demanded, standing and brushing himself off.

"Yeah." Another boy grabbed the discus from Hercules. "Stay out of our way from now on ... Destructo-boy!"

Hercules' shoulders slumped. Why did this sort of thing always happen to him? Whenever he tried to help, he only made things worse. But he knew that, one day, his strength would help him be a hero. He just hoped that day would come soon. There was only so much unbroken pottery left in Greece!

A Change of Scenery

D r Sherman had left for the day when Gill called everyone together for a Tank Gang meeting.

"We need to make some changes around here," Gill began. "We've all been living in this glass box for how long now? And every day we stare at the same scenery – the same volcano, the same sunken ship, the same treasure chest and tiki hut. Well, seeing as how we can't change what's in our tank, I propose we rearrange things a little. Who's with me?"

"Great idea!" cried Peach the starfish.

"I'm with you," said Deb. "And Flo is too," she added, pointing at her reflection.

Everyone agreed. "We can completely transform the place," said Bloat.

"All right!" said Gill. "Then how about we start with the tiki hut? Bloat, you hoist it up. Gurgle and I will help you move it. The rest of you guys tell us where you think it should go."

Gill, Bloat and Gurgle swam over to the tiki hut. Bloat wriggled his body underneath it and blew himself up, hoisting the hut a few inches off the gravel. Meanwhile, Gill and Gurgle stationed themselves on either side of the hut and prepared to push.

"Let's try it over there," said Peach, pointing to a far corner of the tank.

With blown-up Bloat acting as a cart underneath the hut, Gill and Gurgle pushed the tiki hut into the corner.

"Oh, no," said Deb, "that's all wrong. Can we see what it looks like over there?" She pointed to the opposite corner of the tank.

So Gill, Gurgle and Bloat worked together to move the tiki hut again.

"That's a disaster!" said Jacques, in disgust.

"Yeah, Jacques' right," Nemo agreed.

Gill, Gurgle and Bloat were getting worn out by all the moving. "Can we all just agree on where it should go?" said Gill. "And quickly?"

"Ooh! I know!" said Deb. "Bring it over this way." She led Gill, Gurgle and Bloat over to a shady spot next to some plastic plants. "Put it down here," she said. So they did.

"I like it!" exclaimed Peach.

"The perfect spot," said Jacques.

"Mmm-hmm," said Bubbles.

Gill stepped back and looked around. "Guys, this is where it was in the first place!"

"Is it?" asked Peach.

Deb giggled. "Well, no wonder it just seems to fit here!"

The other fish nodded – except for Gill, who sighed in frustration. And that was the end of the tank redecoration for the evening.

Pictures in the Stars

Ever since Mufasa had died and Simba had left the Pride Lands, Timon and Pumbaa had been Simba's only friends – but what fun the three of them had together. One of their favourite things to do after their evening meal was to lie on their backs in the tall grass and gaze up at the night sky, looking for shapes in the stars.

"Okay, okay, I got one," said Pumbaa, lifting a foreleg to point to one area of the sky. "See, over there, that long, thin, curving outline? It's a big, juicy, delicious slug!" Pumbaa licked and smacked his lips, imagining the taste of a slug snack. "Mmm-mmm!"

Simba chuckled. "Pumbaa, how can you still be hungry? We just ate!"

Pumbaa shrugged. "It's a gift," he said.

Timon cleared his throat. "I hate to disagree with you, Pumbaa, my friend, but that's no slug you see up there. That's an elephant's trunk. If you follow that curving line of stars, you see it connects with the elephant's head at one end. And there are the ears," Timon said, tracing it out with his finger, "and there are the tusks."

Simba chuckled again. "Somebody still has his mind on that elephant stampede we almost got flattened by this afternoon," he said.

"Hey...." Timon said defensively. "What's that supposed to mean?"

"Oh, no offence, Timon," Simba replied. "I just think it's funny that the things you and Pumbaa see in the stars just happen to be the same things that are on your mind at the time."

"Ooh! Ooh! I've got another one!" Pumbaa interrupted. "A big bunch of tasty berries right over there," he said, pointing at a grouping of stars. "Don't they look good?"

"See what I mean?" Simba said to Timon.

"All right, all right, Mr Smarty-Pants," Timon replied. "So what do you see in the stars?"

"Well, now, let's see," said Simba, gazing intently at the tons of tiny lights twinkling down at them. There were so many that you could see practically any shape in them that you wanted to. It all depended on how you looked at them. But just to annoy Timon, Simba wanted to find something really bright and clear. Something Timon couldn't deny that he saw too.

Just at that moment, a shooting star flew across the entire length of the night sky.

"I see a bright streak of light rocketing across the sky!" exclaimed Simba.

"Ooh! Me, too!" said Pumbaa. "Timon, do you see it?"

Timon had to admit that he did. "Yeah, I see it," he muttered. "Ha-ha. Very funny, Simba."

Drastic Cure

At Sunnyside Daycare Centre, the rock monster, Chunk, was having a bad day.

"What's the matter, Chunk?" asked Twitch, the bug-like action figure.

"Why do you look so angry?" wondered Ken.

Chunk shrugged his stony shoulders. "I'm not angry, my friends. I just look angry," he explained. "The button that changes my face from happy to angry is stuck on angry."

Ken leaped forwards. "Here, let me help," he said, tickling Chunk. The rock creature scowled. Tickling wasn't going to fix his button.

High up on his shelf, Bookworm checked Chunk's manual, but there was nothing in there about how to unstick a stuck button. "A whack on the head might help," he suggested.

Chunk braced himself as Twitch swung with his fighting staff. He hit Chunk on the head, but the rock figure remained stony-faced. Twitch wasn't strong enough.

"I have an idea," said Ken, steering Chunk towards the door. "This way."

"OK, but no more tickling," Chunk warned. "And no jokes."

Ken smiled warmly. "No, we just want to take you ... in here."

With a shove, Ken pushed Chunk through into the Caterpillar Room, where the daycare centre's youngest children played. They had no idea how to take care of toys, and no toy wanted to be stuck in there if they could help it. It was too dangerous.

But Chunk had no choice. As Ken closed the door the children came racing in from break. They spotted Chunk at once and gathered round him.

"It looks like a stone," said one toddler.

"We can hit things with it!" cheered another.

On the other side of the door, Ken and the others toys listened as Chunk was banged and thumped against every surface. "What have we done?" Ken gasped.

"It's too late to help," said Chatter the telephone. The toys could only wait until the bell had rung and the children had gone back outside to play.

Racing into the Caterpillar Room, they found Chunk upside-down in the corner. To their amazement, he was smiling!

"It worked!" cried Twitch. "He isn't stuck on angry any more."

Chunk got to his feet and staggered past his friends, dazed and confused.

"Are you angry with us, Chunk?" Twitch asked shyly.

"No, I can't be angry," said Chunk, shaking his head. "Because now ... I'm stuck on happy!"

The Old Recipe

Remy came running into the restaurant kitchen one morning, clutching an old sheet of yellowing paper. He looked very excited as he scurried up the table leg and stopped beside his brother, Emile.

"I've got it!" he cheered. "I found an old copy of the Yummy Cake recipe!"

Emile looked up from the carrot he was munching on. "What's that?" he asked, between chews.

"It's the tastiest, most delicious recipe of all time!" Remy explained. "It was lost, but I've finally been able to get my hands on it!"

Emile swallowed his carrot and licked his lips. If the Yummy Cake recipe was as delicious as Remy said, he couldn't wait to have a taste!

Remy told him it was more delicious than he could even imagine, and Emile began to bounce up and down in excitement.

Before he could make the cake, Remy had to gather up all the ingredients. After studying the list of things he needed, he scampered off to the far corners of the kitchen and quickly began to collect everything.

"I need a large pot, flour, butter, apricots...." he began, darting this way and that across the kitchen floor.

Remy had spent months searching for the recipe, and he could hardly believe he was finally going to be the first person in years to bake the Yummy Cake.

Next, Remy collected raisins, apples, sugar and cinnamon.

He checked the apples one at a time to make sure he took the freshest and tastiest. The Yummy Cake deserved only the very best and finest ingredients, and bruised apples would not do.

Balancing everything on his shoulders, Remy clambered back up onto the table and placed all the ingredients in a big pile. He knew there were still a few things missing, though, so raced over to where he'd left the recipe.

When he got there, though, the recipe was nowhere to be seen. Frantically, Remy searched around. "Eek!" he squeaked. "Where is it?"

Emile finished chewing and swallowed noisily. "In my stomach," he said, and Remy almost fainted. "You kept going on about how delicious it was, but I don't think so," Emile said. He shrugged. "It just tastes like paper to me."

Remy sobbed. He'd done such a good job of making the cake sound delicious, his brother had eaten the recipe!

The secrets of the Yummy Cake were lost forever – but at least Emile's tummy ache would stop him eating anything else for a while.

Disney
THE **Rescuers**

Albatross Taxi Service

Orville the albatross was feeling low. His maintenance job at the Central Park Zoo (hours: 9–3; duties: eating all the popcorn, pretzels and half-finished hot dogs that the little children dropped) had just ended for the season. What would he do next?

Orville sighed and leaned against a lamp post at the busy junction of 45th and Broadway. He liked to watch the cars zoom back and forth. Just then there was a tap on his wing. He looked down to see an elderly mouse couple. "Excuse me, sonny," said the grandfather mouse. "Would it be possible for you to help us cross this busy street?"

Orville looked confused. "You want me to go into the middle of the street and stop traffic?"

"Perhaps you could give us a lift ... *over* the traffic," the grandmother mouse suggested. "We'll buy you a hot dog as payment."

Mmm! Orville couldn't say no to the promise of a tasty hot dog with mustard and sauerkraut, so he readily agreed. Besides, it was the right thing to do, lending another animal a helping wing. "It's a deal!" he said.

Just then, the grandmother mouse whistled to a group of mice standing nearby. "Harvey, Mildred, Polly, Carl – let's go. We have a ride!"

"Wait!" Orville said. "I can't give *all* of you a ride. Just how strong do you think I am?"

"Think about it this way," said the grandfather mouse. "More mice, more hot dogs."

Well, that was certainly true. With this in mind, Orville agreed to help all the mice across the road. It took three trips. The mice held on just a bit too tightly to his feathers, and Orville's landings left something to be desired, that was certain, but soon everyone was across the road, safe and sound.

"Here are your hot dogs!" the mice said. Orville was disappointed to see that they were offering him hot dogs from the mouse hot dog stand, which were considerably smaller than the human kind. Still, a deal was a deal, and Orville was not one to look a gift horse – or mouse – in the mouth.

Orville then found a discarded sardine tin, which he used for seats, and thus began the Albatross Taxi Service for Mice. Word spread, and soon Orville couldn't keep up with the demand! He was a very successful businessbird.

Then one day it hit him – he was selling himself short! Forget about Albatross Taxi Service – it was time to think bigger. He'd get himself a scarf and goggles and start Albatross Airlines! He sold his taxi business to an entrepreneurial pigeon and set up shop at the airport.

Now, if he could only learn how to land, everything would be perfect!

Monster in the Drawer

Rex was passing Andy's dressing table when he heard a strange buzzing noise coming from one of the drawers. The more the nervous dinosaur listened, the more frightened he became. Maybe there was a monster in there!

"Help! There's a monster in the drawer!" he cried. Hamm sighed.

"Uh-oh! Here comes Mr Fraidy-saurus!" he said.

Woody tried to calm his friend down. "There's no such thing as monsters."

"Then check this out!" Rex said, showing them the dressing table. Sure enough, they all heard the buzzing sound coming from the drawer.

"Sounds like a buzzing monster," said Buzz.

Rex yelped in panic and tried to hide behind the space ranger. "How can you tell?"

"Take it easy," Buzz smiled. "I was joking."

There was definitely something strange going on in the drawer, though, even if it probably wasn't a monster. Woody and Buzz decided to investigate.

Clambering up a stack of building blocks, they peered into the dark drawer. "I can't see a thing," Woody complained.

"Hold on, I'll activate my space laser," said Buzz. He shone the blinking red light into the drawer, then he and Woody both cried out in fright as the buzzing sound came again.

There was definitely something in there. The friends could see it lurking under one of Andy's socks. Could it really be a monster?

"This calls for a group meeting," whispered Woody, as he and Buzz climbed back down.

"No!" said Buzz. "It'll cause a panic. We'll have to defeat it by ourselves."

Rex trembled. "D-do we have to?"

Woody and Rex armed themselves while Buzz climbed back up to the drawer. Heaving, he pulled it all the way open. "C'mon out, buzzing monster!"

A voice crackled from inside the drawer. "Do you want whiter teeth?"

Buzz frowned. What an unusual thing for a monster to ask.

"Extra-fresh is the toothpaste for you!" the voice continued.

Woody rubbed his chin. There was something very suspicious about all this. He climbed up next to Buzz, and the two of them jumped into the drawer to find out what was going on.

As they lifted the socks, they realized it wasn't a monster making the noises, it was Andy's MP3 player. He'd left it on by mistake! "Here's your monster, Rex," Woody laughed.

Buzz smiled. "I have to admit, I was almost scared," he whispered.

"Shh," said Woody. "Don't say a word!"

DISNEY·PIXAR
MONSTERS, INC.

Celia's Bad Hair Day

"Some encrusted evening," Mike sang to himself as he danced around the bathroom getting ready for his date. He could not wait to see his girlfriend, Celia. The round green monster was in the mood for love.

Pulling his car into the restaurant car park, Mike hopped out and hurried inside. "Here I come, my little Schmoopsie-Poo," he murmured.

When Mike caught sight of his snake-haired sweetie, his heart skipped a beat. The stunning cyclops was sitting alone at a table for two. Her green scales glowed in the candlelight. She was monstrously beautiful.

But, as Celia turned towards Mike, he noticed something. Rather than rustling happily, her hair-snakes were writhing angrily!

"How's my little Schmoopsie-Woopsie?" Mike decided to ignore the grumpy-looking snakes. He leaned in to kiss Celia on the cheek, but the closest snake lashed out at him.

"Yowch!" Mike exclaimed, jumping back. "Bad hair day, Snookums?"

"Oh, Googly Bear." Celia sighed, running her hand through her serpentine tresses. "It's just awful. I'm out of conditioner, my shower went cold on me, and I've been in an awful tangle ever since. Are they terrible?"

Choosing a seat far enough away from his love to avoid being bitten, Mike looked closer. Celia's snakes glared at him, their fangs bared. Mike tried not to flinch when they hissed at him. But, he had to admit, they were a little knotted, and they did not have their usual body or lustre.

"They're not so bad," Mike fibbed. He blew Celia a kiss from across the table and tried to smile. This was not the romantic evening with his sweetie that he'd been looking forward to.

At the next table a pair of many-armed monsters held hands and hands and hands. They rubbed their warty noses together and whispered sweet nothings into each other's many ears. Mike sighed. They looked so cosy. Then he had an idea.

"Excuse me, my sweet." Mike stood up and approached the couple. When he came back to the table, he was holding a large purple hat. "Amelia, Ophelia, Octelia, Bobelia and Madge," Mike addressed Celia's snakes. "How would you like to cosy up in this until we can get you untangled?" Celia's snakes cooed in delight.

"Oh, Googly Bear!" Celia cried. She wound her hair-snakes and stuffed them into the hat. "You even know how to fix a bad hair day!"

With her hair contained, Celia gave Mike a big hug and a well-deserved smooch.

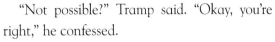

Tony and the Tramp

Tramp licked the last of the tomato sauce from his chin. "So, what do you think, Pidge?" he asked Lady.

"That was the most wonderful meal I've ever had," Lady gushed.

"What did I tell ya?" Tramp boasted. "There's no one in the world who can cook up a meal like Tony!"

"I couldn't agree with you more," Lady said. "Can I ask you a question?"

"Sure thing," Tramp said. "Ask away!"

"I was just wondering," Lady began, "how you and Tony met."

"How I met Tony?" Tramp laughed. "Now that's a story!"

"I bet!" Lady said.

"Well, see, it goes like this," Tramp began. "It was a cold and snowy night. I don't think it had ever been that cold before, and I know it hasn't been since. I had been walking uphill for miles. Icicles were hanging from the tip of my nose."

"Wait a minute!" Lady interrupted. "You were walking for miles – uphill? In this town?"

"That's right!" Tramp said. "You've never seen the likes of it."

"Exactly!" Lady told him. "You know why?"

Tramp shook his head.

"Because it isn't possible! There are no big hills around here!" Lady said.

"Not possible?" Tramp said. "Okay, you're right," he confessed.

"So, then, what's the truth?" Lady asked.

"The truth is," Tramp began, "I wasn't always the slick, handsome devil you see before you."

"Is that right?" Lady was amused.

"And this one afternoon I was being harassed by a group of mangy mutts who outnumbered me ten to one. So, I took off as fast as my paws could carry me. And as they were chasing me, along came this dogcatcher!"

"Oh, no!" Lady cried.

"Exactly!" Tramp continued. "The mutts scattered out of sight, so I didn't have *them* to worry about any more. But now the dogcatcher was closing in! I thought I was a goner!"

"What happened?" Lady asked.

"Then Tony came running out with a bowl of steaming hot pasta," Tramp explained. "He told the dogcatcher I was his dog. The dogcatcher didn't believe him. But, when Tony put the bowl of pasta down in front of me, the dogcatcher had no choice. Let me tell you, I thought I'd died and gone to heaven."

"I can relate to that," Lady said, recalling the meal.

"And the rest," Tramp said, "as they say, is history!"

"And a tasty one at that!" Lady concluded.

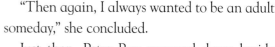

Should I Stay or Should I Go?

Wendy sat watching Michael and John play with Peter Pan and the rest of the Lost Boys.

"John and Michael seem so happy," Wendy said to herself. "And why wouldn't they? Never Land is such a beautiful place, and the flying is just so much fun!

"Still," she had to admit, "it is also dangerous. Who knows what sort of trouble we could get into, especially with Captain Hook running around the place?

"And," Wendy went on, "I don't think that Tinker Bell likes me very much."

Wendy considered this, then burst out, "What am I talking about? I'm making it sound like it's an awful place, but, the truth is, Never Land is the most wonderful place on earth!

"Perhaps that explains it!" Wendy suddenly realized. "Maybe I really want to stay in Never Land, but in my heart of hearts I know I shouldn't. After all, Mother and Father must miss us terribly. And we miss them too! Oh, and what about Nana?" Wendy began to fret. "She must worry about us endlessly!

"That settles it!" Wendy stood up abruptly. "We must leave for home immediately.

"But if I stay –" Wendy stopped herself. "I'll never have to grow up!

"Then again, I always wanted to be an adult someday," she concluded.

Just then, Peter Pan swooped down beside her. "What are you doing, Wendy?" Peter asked.

"Oh, nothing," Wendy told him.

"Then why don't you come join us?" he suggested.

"I will," Wendy told him. "In a minute."

"All right! But last one there is a rotten...." Peter took off before he could finish his sentence.

"How can I ever leave Peter and the Lost Boys?" Wendy wondered. "They need me so much.

"But so do our parents," she quickly reminded herself. "Should I stay?" she wondered aloud. "Or should I go?"

Wendy's eyes fell upon a daisy. She bent over and pulled it out of the ground. "Should I stay?" she asked as she pulled a petal from the daisy. "Or should I go?" she asked as she pulled a second petal from the daisy.

Wendy did this over and over again until there was only one petal remaining on the daisy.

"Well," she said, "this flower says we should go back home. And I suppose it's right. We'll go back ... but maybe not just this minute."

Wendy stood up. "Hey, Peter, wait up!"

And with that, she flew off after Peter, her mind finally at ease.

Let's Go to the Movies

Andy was in his bedroom, playing with his toys while he watched an exciting western on his TV. On screen, the brave sheriff was racing on horseback to save a beautiful cowgirl from bandits.

"Ye-haa!" Andy cheered, waving Woody around. "Ride, cowboy!"

Just as the film was about to reach its exciting conclusion, Andy's mum called him for dinner. Andy raced downstairs, but not before turning off the television.

The moment Andy was out of the room, the toys sat up. "That was really some movie!" said Buzz.

"I wonder how it ends," said Jessie.

Woody pushed a button on the remote control. "Let's turn it back on!"

The screen lit up just in time for the toys to see the film's end credits. "Oh no, we've missed it," groaned Hamm.

Woody leaped to his feet. "Don't worry! I know how it ends – I've seen it before!"

The toys asked Woody to tell them how the film ended, but the sheriff had a better idea – he'd show them by acting the ending out for them. It would be just like watching the movie!

Hopping onto Bullseye's back, Woody pretended to be the hero of the film. "This is what happens next, guys," he said, grinning. "Now watch carefully!"

At first, things went well. Woody hurtled across the floor on Bullseye's back, just like the cowboy on the screen had done.

"Great acting, Woody," Jessie said.

"It's just like watching TV," agreed Buzz.

But then – oh no! Bullseye tripped on a pencil, and Woody was launched off the little horse's back at high speed. He thumped, face first, into Andy's dressing table, then slid to the floor.

"Is that what happens in the film?" Jessie asked.

A dazed Woody got shakily to his feet. "Er ... sure," he said, taking Jessie's hand. "And after that, the brave cowboy frees the beautiful girl, and they ride off into the sunset!"

They both swung up onto Bullseye's back. Woody heaved on the reins, rearing the toy horse up onto his hind legs and striking a dramatic pose.

It was the perfect ending to the story ... until the saddle slipped off and Woody and Jessie landed in a heap on the floor.

"Er, that wasn't quite what happened in the film," Woody said, helping Jessie up. "But it gives you an idea of how the story ends."

The other toys gathered around them. "I thought it was a western, not a comedy," said Hamm, and all the friends – including Woody – laughed until their sides ached.

Say Cheese!

Dusty was spending some time with Skipper, his flight school teacher, admiring the collection of military equipment he'd built up over the years.

"What are these gizmos?" Dusty asked, stopping at a row of metal and glass boxes.

"Old cameras!" Skipper laughed. "I used them when I trained the Jolly Wrenches."

Skipper explained that during combat training, they would replace their guns with cameras. If a plane was able to take a picture of their opponent in mid-air, that counted as a hit.

"That's a great idea," said Dusty. "Can I try one?"

Skipper agreed, and after fixing a camera to his nose, Dusty flew off in search of some subjects to photograph. He spotted a bridge, and snapped off a few pictures. Then he spied an interesting row of trees, and spent a few seconds capturing those.

For a while, Dusty was happy taking photographs of the scenery, but soon he became bored. "This is too easy. If I'm going to be involved in an air duel, I need a moving target to practise on."

Spotting Leadbottom dusting the fields, Dusty banked upwards, then swooped low. "I bet old Leadbottom isn't expecting an attack from above," he laughed, firing the camera. "Say cheese!" he shouted, and Leadbottom yelped in fright.

Dusty flew off again, and soon Leadbottom touched down on the runway. He told Dottie and Chug about Dusty's new photography hobby. The trucks were both very excited. They loved getting their photographs taken.

"Let's spread the word!" said Chug, and they sped off to round up the others.

That evening, there was a lot of excitement on the airfield. Sparky the forklift was asking Skipper what was going on when a fire engine sped by.

"Are you guys coming to Dusty's photo exhibition?" the fire engine asked.

"He asked us to stop by and invite you," added Chug, speeding past. "You can't miss it!"

Skipper rolled along to join the others at one of the larger hangars. Inside, huge photographs of Dottie, Chug, Leadbottom and other familiar faces lined the walls. They were all smiling broadly and posing happily for the camera.

"So, Skip," said Dusty, "was I as good as the Jolly Wrenches?"

"Even better!" said Skipper, laughing. "Although for them it was harder."

"Yeah," added Sparky, chuckling. "Because their targets were a little more camera-shy!"

Flo's Tailgate Party

Doc and Flo couldn't believe their wing mirrors as they gazed upon the crowds of tourists before them. There were cars everywhere, all slurping away on tasty treats from Flo's café. She could barely keep up with the orders as the thirsty tourists rapidly came and went.

"Flo! Look at all these tourists!" exclaimed Doc. "Radiator Springs has come back to life!"

"Everyone's here for tonight's big race!" she said, placing a trophy of her infamous 'Piston Cup' bubbly beverage in front of a waiting customer.

"Your business must be doing great at the moment," Doc said, marvelling at the crowds.

"Yes, but I'll have to close soon," Flo replied.

The tourists couldn't help but overhear. They surrounded Flo in panic.

"But why?" asked a green car.

"We love your specials!" cried a blue van.

"I'm sorry," said Flo. "My supplies are low and I'm running out of room to serve customers!"

"That's a shame," said the green car. "This is a great place to hang out."

Flo looked at the faces before her, all filling with disappointment. "Hey!" she shouted. "Wait here while I call a few friends."

Later that day, the tourists found Flo on the outskirts of town, in a yard of sun umbrellas, supported by podiums of tyres all balanced on top of each other. It was like a make-shift diner with a perfect view of Radiator Springs.

"Here we are!" announced Flo. "A new location where good times are guaranteed!"

Sarge pulled back the flap of a brown tent, revealing boxes of tasty treats to the thirsty crowd.

"Sarge will take care of the food!" Flo said, "And Fillmore will be serving up his special bio-fuel."

Fillmore waved his wipers in greeting.

"My fantastic friend Red will be entertaining you!" she said, as Red sent jets of water into the air that formed magnificent spirals and swirls.

"Last but not least," Flo cried, "here's our special guest!"

The crowds gasped in anticipation.

"Lightning McQueen!" they roared when he appeared.

Lightning McQueen spun his wheels this way and that, changing direction in the blink of an eye, so the crowd could applaud his speed and agility.

"Welcome to Radiator Spring's tailgate party!" Flo cheered.

The tourists settled in at last and all agreed it was the most fantastic party that they had ever been to.

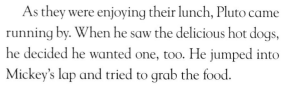

A Good Day for a Sail

One lovely summer day, Mickey Mouse asked Minnie if she'd like to go for a boat ride.

"I would love to," Minnie said with a smile.

Mickey and Minnie were preparing to set sail when Goofy came running by on the shore.

"Hiya," he said. "What a great day for sailing!"

Distracted, Goofy didn't see a squirrel in front of him and he accidentally stepped on its tail. The squirrel squealed, then leaped up and landed in the boat! Mickey and Minnie were so startled that they jumped, making the boat rock.

Mickey tried to stop the rocking, but the boat tipped over, and Minnie shrieked as she and Mickey fell into the water.

Donald Duck came up in his speedboat and helped Mickey and Minnie into his boat. "Why don't you ride with me?" he suggested.

Relieved, Mickey and Minnie sat back and started to relax. But moments later, the boat's engine suddenly stopped.

"What do we do now?" Minnie asked.

"I have an idea," Donald said. He took off his hat and started to paddle with it. Mickey and Minnie did the same. Huffing and puffing, they made their way back to shore.

"How about some lunch while we dry off?" said Mickey. So they sat in the sun, eating hot dogs.

As they were enjoying their lunch, Pluto came running by. When he saw the delicious hot dogs, he decided he wanted one, too. He jumped into Mickey's lap and tried to grab the food.

"No, boy!" cried Mickey.

But it was too late. Pluto knocked Mickey and Minnie into the water again!

Mickey and Minnie swam to shore and climbed out of the lake. Coughing and spluttering and really fed up, they settled on the grass to dry off yet again.

Not long after, Huey, Dewey and Louie came by in their sailing boat.

"Would you like to borrow our boat?" called Dewey. "There's a good wind today."

"Yes, please!" said Mickey. He and Minnie hopped into the triplets' sailing boat and took off.

"Aah, this is the life," Mickey said.

Just then, the wind stopped blowing.

"Oh, no!" Mickey groaned. "Not again!"

Mickey and Minnie tried to paddle with their hands, but it was no use. The boat just kept going round in circles. As they huffed and puffed, Mickey saw Goofy and Donald coming towards them in rowing boats.

"We thought you might need some help," said Donald.

As Donald and Goofy towed the sailing boat, Mickey and Minnie sat back and relaxed. They had finally got their nice, easy boat ride!

Disney · PIXAR

TOY STORY 3

Bath Time

Bonnie loved creating exciting new adventures in the garden with her toys, but as a dark cloud passed overhead her mum appeared from inside the house.

It was going to rain, so Bonnie grabbed Hamm while her mum gathered up all the other toys.

Or so she thought! As Woody was carried inside, he realized Dolly had been left out on the grass!

Up in Bonnie's bedroom, the toys made a plan. "If it rains, Dolly will get soaked," said Woody.

"We've got to rescue her," gasped Buttercup, the unicorn.

Luckily, Woody and Buzz had lots of experience of leading rescue missions. Together, they lowered Slinky Dog out of the window, just as the rain began to fall.

Slinky's spring stretched all the way to the ground. The brave little pup caught hold of a clump of grass to stop himself springing back up and called over to Dolly.

"Great! I knew you wouldn't leave me outside in the rain," Dolly cheered.

"Quick, take my paw," Slinky began, but just as Dolly took hold, the grass Slinky was holding broke.

Slinky sprang upwards, dragging poor Dolly across the ground and through a bush, before catapulting her into Bonnie's bedroom.

Dolly flew through the air, then landed in a messy heap on Bonnie's favourite chair.

"Nice to have you back, Dolly," said Woody, tipping his hat. Dolly flipped herself the right way up and smiled. It was nice to be back.

Suddenly, the toys heard the sound of footsteps outside the bedroom door. "Quick, someone's coming!" yelled Jessie and the toys dropped just as Bonnie's mum walked in.

"Oh no, look, Bonnie," said Mum, stooping to pick up the messy-looking doll. "I hadn't realized how dirty Dolly got outside."

Mum shrugged as she took Dolly out of the room. "No big deal. We'll give her a bath!"

"Poor Dolly," whispered Buzz.

Woody nodded. "Uh-oh! She's gonna be soaked after all!"

Sure enough, just a few minutes later, Mum and Bonnie returned, carrying a dripping-wet Dolly. They made a little washing line from string and clipped the doll to it, then went downstairs for dinner.

Dolly looked at her friends and folded her arms, crossly. "As you can see, guys, I avoided the shower," she said. "But not the bath!"

Try as they might, the other toys couldn't help but laugh. Maybe a little bit of rainwater wasn't so bad, after all!

Disney
Bambi

First Impressions

Bambi was just discovering the wonders of the forest. His mother had brought him to a little clearing in the woods. The sudden sunshine and bright green grass surprised and pleased him, and he bounded around on his still-wobbly legs, feeling the warm sun on his back and the soft grass under his hooves. While his mother grazed nearby, Bambi began to explore.

He found a patch of green grass and clover, and he bent down to eat. This was not an easy feat, as his long legs made it difficult for his little neck to reach the ground. When his nose was just a few centimetres from the tips of the grass, he suddenly leaped backwards in alarm. A leaf had just sprung up from the patch of grass and had landed a few metres away. *A hopping leaf?* he wondered. He followed it and, as soon as he drew close, the leaf hopped away from him again!

Bambi looked around at where his mother stood, still grazing. She seemed to think they were in no great danger. So, he followed the leaf all the way to the edge of the clearing, where a wide brook babbled over craggy rocks.

Bambi's fascination with the hopping leaf faded as he approached the brook. Water cascaded over the rocks, bubbling and frothing in shallow pools. He took a step closer and felt his foot touch a rock at the edge of the water.

Suddenly, the rock moved! It shuffled towards the water and then – *PLOP!* – jumped right in and swam away.

Bambi was dumbfounded as he watched it dive beneath the surface and vanish. He stared at the spot where the rock had been for a moment, and then stooped down to have a drink, widening his stance in order to do so.

Suddenly, he jumped back in alarm. There in the water, staring right back up at him, was a little deer! Cautiously he approached again, and there it was!

Bambi turned and bounded back across the clearing to his mother.

"Mama! Mama!" he cried breathlessly. "You will never guess what I have seen!"

His mother lifted her head and gazed at him with her clear, bright eyes.

"First," he said, "first I saw a jumping leaf. Then, I saw a rock with legs that walked right into the water and swam away! And then," he he continued in amazement, "and then I saw a little deer who lives right in the water! He's right over there, Mama!"

His mother nuzzled her son, thinking over what he had said. Then she laughed gently.

"Darling," she said, "I think you have just seen your first grasshopper, your first turtle and your very own reflection!"

DISNEY·PIXAR
MONSTERS, INC.

Crash Course

A big award ceremony was taking place at Monsters, Inc., and Sulley had just been revealed as Monster of the Year. As Mr Waternoose presented Sulley with his trophy, he asked a favour. The son of one of the company's investors had been given a job at Monsters, Inc., and he needed help to turn him into an effective scarer.

Sulley was happy to take on the challenge. He soon changed his mind, though, when he saw his new apprentice.

Edwin was short and skinny, with thick glasses and two buck teeth. He looked awkward and unsure, and Sulley realized he really had his work cut out for him.

Sure enough, when Sulley tried to teach Edwin how to roar, the skinny monster ran and hid under the table. "You aren't the one who should be scared," Sulley pointed out, but Edwin admitted he was afraid of everything!

Mike encouraged him to give roaring a try. Edwin took a deep breath, opened his mouth and ... wheezed. He coughed and spluttered, gasping for breath.

"Black Widow-flavoured liquorice?" asked Mike, holding open a bag of sweets. All monsters loved them, and they were great for soothing the nerves.

Edwin jumped back in fright. He was terribly allergic to the sweets, and didn't even want to be near them in case they brought on a reaction.

Sulley and Mike worked hard to turn Edwin into a scarer, but no matter what they tried, the boy just didn't get any more frightening.

In workouts, he managed just three push-ups and collapsed after running ten metres. When they tried the scare simulator he had a friendly conversation with the robot kid, rather than trying to be scary. It was no use, Edwin would never be a real scarer.

But Mr Waternoose was demanding results. He arranged to come and see Edwin in action. Mike and Sulley groaned. Sulley's Monster of the Year title would almost certainly be taken away when Mr Waternoose saw how hopeless Edwin was.

As Sulley headed off to fetch Mr Waternoose, Mike made a plan to talk their boss to sleep before he saw Edwin in action. To prepare himself, Mike ate a Black Widow liquorice, and tossed one to Edwin. Without thinking, Edwin swallowed it whole.

When Sulley returned with Mr Waternoose, they couldn't believe their eyes. Edwin was in the scare simulator, bouncing and roaring and sending the scare meter off the scale. Edwin's allergy had sent him crazy, but Mike decided to keep that as his little secret.

Massage in a Bobble

On the edge of the reef, with its beautiful plant life of every colour imaginable, Nemo and his friends waited to ride to school on the back of their favourite teacher, Mr Ray. In the distance, they could just make out Mr Ray's long barbed tail trailing behind him as he swooped through the water.

Dory had come to visit the night before and was keeping the children company as they prepared to board.

"See you later, Fido, Earl, Chad and Milton. Have fun at school!" she said with a wave of her yellow and blue fins.

"It's Nemo, Pearl, Tad and Sheldon," Nemo corrected his forgetful friend, "but thanks!"

Mr Ray ushered the children onto his back. "Come on, kids, this way to knowledge."

Dory overheard the word 'knowledge' and was intrigued. "That sounds like fun," she said. "I bet if I swim around long enough, I just might learn a thing or two as well."

She wandered through the seaweed and coral formations, casting her eyes down for something interesting. "Hey, what's that?" She paused in front of her discovery. "Oh, I know what that is! It's a message in a bottle!"

How exciting! The message could hold the secrets to the ocean. Or be a long-lost love letter!

"I know something," Dory realized. "Now I have to remember I found this message in a bottle so I can tell Remo later."

She thought hard, trying to lock it into her memory. "What helped me remember before?" she asked herself. "A song! No, no, that never works." She thought harder. "Aha! I know. A song! I'll sing a song!"

Dory headed back home, humming and warbling and singing to her heart's content. "I found a message in a bottle ... a massage in a bobble ... messy eggs and nooooodles! Bottom oodle poodle...."

Later that day, Dory caught up with the children. "Nemo, Pearl, Tad, Sheldon!" she called.

"Hey, you remembered our names!" squeaked Pearl in surprise.

"Yes! And I know this too," Dory insisted. "I found a massage in a bobble. No, wait, an egg in a poodle. Wait ... a giraffe and a beetle! No, no ... a message in a bottle!"

"Wow!" said Nemo. "What did it say?"

Dory's smile melted and her face formed a bewildered expression. "Err ... I don't know," she admitted. "I forgot to read it!"

The children laughed together. They may not know the secret of the message, but it was certainly a victory for Dory ... she'd actually remembered she'd found it in the first place!

DISNEY·PIXAR
MONSTERS, INC.

A Mother's Touch

Work was piling up in the offices of Monsters, Inc. Celia was off with the flu, and there was no one to cover for her.

Sulley, the president of Monsters, Inc., knew he had to act fast. "Who can we get to fill in?" he asked.

"I'll call my mum," replied Mike. "She'd love to help."

And so, later that day, in walked Mrs Wazowski. Sulley and Mike went off to discuss some new plans for the laugh factory, while Mrs W. made herself at home – *very* at home. When Sulley and Mike returned at lunchtime, they scarcely recognized the reception area. Mike's mum had hung ruffled curtains and scattered fluffy rugs everywhere. Mike gave Sulley a weak smile.

"We'll change it back when she leaves," he whispered.

Later that day, Mike rehearsed some new comedy routines. "What do monsters eat for breakfast?" asked Mike. "Anything they want!" Sulley and Mike laughed until their sides hurt.

"I couldn't help but overhear," said Mike's mum. "It might be funnier if you wore a silly hat."

Sulley shot Mike a look. "Thanks, Mum," said Mike. "That's a very helpful suggestion. Say – isn't that the phone I hear ringing?"

A little while later, Sulley and Mike called her over the intercom and summoned her to the Laugh Floor. "Um, Mum, do you know anything about this?" Mike asked nervously. He pointed to the card keys, which were now filed by colour, making it impossible for anyone to know which card belonged to which door.

"I certainly do!" Mrs W. replied proudly. "I have an 'eye' for organization, if I do say so myself."

Sulley turned and spoke to Mike through gritted teeth. "She's *your* mother. Do something!"

Just before the day was over, Mike went to the front desk, sat down and took his mother's hand. He'd never fired his mother before. This wasn't going to be easy! "Mum, you know I love you. And you make a terrific receptionist, but –"

Just then, Celia walked through the front door. "Schmoopsie-Poo!" called Mike.

"Googly Bear!" Celia cried.

"What are you doing here?" Mike asked. "You're supposed to be home in bed."

"I couldn't stand being away from you one day longer," Celia gushed.

Mrs Wazowski beamed. "He *is* irresistible – isn't he? That's because he takes after my side of the family. Well, I guess my work here is done!" she said, gathering up her things.

Suddenly, Mrs W. stopped. "Oh, Mikey, what were you about to tell me?"

"Not a thing, Mum," said Mike as he gave her a kiss. "Not a thing!"

King of the Rodeo

Jessie bounced on Bullseye's back, holding his reins with one hand and waving her hat with the other. "Yippeeee!" she cheered, giggling as Bullseye bucked and kicked.

"What are you doing?" asked Dolly.

"It's a rodeo," Woody explained. "Jessie has to ride Bullseye for as long as she can, while Bullseye tries to throw her off."

Dolly's eyes went wide. "Looks like fun!" she said. "Can I try?"

Mr Potato Head and Mr Pricklepants ran up behind her. They wanted to join in with the rodeo, too.

"It's not as easy as it looks," Woody warned.

"We know all about rodeos, Sheriff," Mr Potato Head said.

"I can play this part to perfection," Mr Pricklepants insisted.

Mr Potato Head pointed an accusing finger at Woody. "Maybe you're afraid we'll ride better than you!"

Woody shrugged. Oh well, they'd asked for it!

A few moments later, Dolly gasped as she shot off Bullseye's back and thumped against the wall. Mr Pricklepants was hobbling away, while Mr Potato Head hunted around for his missing nose and eye. Woody was right – the rodeo really wasn't as easy as it looked!

"Not everybody's cut out to be a cowboy," said Jessie, helping Dolly up.

It looked like the rodeo adventures were over for the day, until a voice rang out behind Woody. "Can I try, too?"

Woody turned to find Slinky Dog looking up at him. "Dachshunds can't ride horses!" Woody said, but Slinky shook his head.

"That's not quite what I had in mind," the springy pup said. "I want to take Bullseye's place!"

Woody wasn't sure. He'd never tried rodeo with a dog before! Still, he climbed onto Slinky's spring and held on. "Climb on, Jessie," Slinky said. "There's room for both of you!" Jessie hopped on behind Woody.

"Ready?" asked Slinky. The Roundup toys nodded. "Here we go!"

BOING! Slinky kicked, stretching his spring out. Woody and Jessie yelled in fright as they were shot upwards into the air at incredible speed.

Woody and Jessie crashed down on the floor just as the other toys started laughing. "See? Now who's king of the rodeo?" Slinky said, smiling proudly.

Jessie took off her hat and gave it to Slinky. She and Woody both giggled. When it came to being a rodeo star, no one could compete with their stretchy pup pal!

Potion Commotion

Emperor Kuzco's royal adviser, Yzma, was down in her secret laboratory, mixing potions. She had enlisted her enthusiastic but dim-witted right-hand man, Kronk, to help her in her work.

"Kronk, I need spider legs, one eye of newt and elderberry juice ... and quickly!" Yzma directed.

"Legs, eye, juice," Kronk repeated. "Right." He hurried across the laboratory to the cupboard that contained all of Yzma's potion ingredients. Inside were hundreds of glass jars, some filled with coloured liquids and powders, others holding creepy-looking body parts of various insects and lizards.

"Let's see," Kronk said to himself as he pored over the containers. "Legs, eye, juice. Legs, eye, juice." He found the 'legs' section. "Newt legs! Check!" Kronk said to himself, confusing Yzma's instructions.

Then he found the 'eye' section. "Spider eyes! Got it!" he said, grabbing the jar. He hurried back to Yzma with the two containers.

"Kronk!" shouted Yzma. "I said spider legs and newt eye! Not newt legs and spider eye! And where's the elderberry juice? Hurry, hurry!"

Kronk hurried back to the cupboard. "Spider legs ... newt eye ... spider legs ... newt eye," he recited as he went. This time, he managed to remember them and took down the right containers from the cupboard. But what was that third ingredient? "Juice!" Kronk cried. "Berry juice." He found a small vial of blueberry juice and took everything to Yzma.

"Not blueberry juice, you numbskull!" screamed Yzma. "ELDERBERRY!"

"Right," Kronk said.

He hurried back across the laboratory and quickly located the 'juice' section. "Boysenberry ... cranberry...." he read, moving alphabetically through the containers.

"ELDERBERRY!" Yzma shouted at him. "Get it over here! *And step on it!*"

Kronk finally located the right bottle. "Got it!" He rushed it across the laboratory. Yzma reached out to take the bottle from him.

But Kronk didn't hand it to her. Instead, he gently placed the bottle on the floor.

Then he lifted his right foot and stomped on it – hard – shattering the bottle and splattering juice everywhere.

"KRONK!" Yzma screamed in surprise. "What are you doing?"

Kronk was confused. "I did just what you said," he explained. "I got the elderberry juice. And I stepped on it."

Yzma let loose a hair-raising scream of frustration and collapsed in a heap on the laboratory floor.

Snake Eyes

"**I**'m ssstarved," hissed Kaa the python as he slithered across the jungle treetops. "I need a sssnack...."

Suddenly, Kaa noticed a small figure relaxing on the ground below. It was Mowgli. Kaa slithered over to him.

"Are you feeling sssleepy?" hissed Kaa. "You look sssleeeepy; jussst look into my eyesss...."

Mowgli tried not to look into the snake's eyes, but it wasn't easy. When he turned one way, Kaa was there. When he turned another, Kaa was there too!

"Sssslip into ssssilent ssslumber," Kaa hissed. "And sssleep ... sssleeep ... sssleep...."

Before Mowgli knew it, his body went completely limp. Kaa had hypnotized him!

Thank goodness Mowgli's friends walked by at that very moment.

"Look!" cried Bagheera the panther. "Kaa's after Mowgli again."

"Get over there and do something," Baloo told Bagheera.

"The last time I interfered with Kaa, he hypnotized *me*," said Bagheera. "*You* do something."

Kaa's fangs watered as he coiled his long body around Mowgli. Then Kaa opened his giant python mouth above Mowgli's head and – hey! Someone had jammed a stick into his jaws!

"Hello there, Kaa," said Baloo, leaning one big paw against the tree.

The python's powerful jaws snapped the stick. "You sssshould not inssssert yoursssself between a sssnake and his sssnack," he hissed.

"Oh! Sorry!" said Baloo. "I was just admiring how very talented you are."

"Talented?" Kaa said.

"Sure!" said Baloo. "I'm very impressed how you hypnotized Mowgli there. I bet you could hypnotize almost anything in the jungle. Almost...."

"What do you mean *almost?*" said Kaa.

Baloo coolly polished his claws against his fur. "Well, let's see," he said. "I bet you can't hypnotize ... a fish." Baloo pointed to the pond.

"Jusssst you watch me," Kaa told Baloo as he slithered towards the pond.

Hanging his head over the water, Kaa hissed, "Jussst look into my eyesss. You feel sssssleeepy ... sssssleeepy ... sssssleeepy...."

Suddenly, Kaa stopped hissing. Or moving. He just stared into the water.

Bagheera stepped up to Baloo and whispered, "What's the matter with him?"

Baloo just laughed. "Kaa was so determined to prove me wrong, he didn't even notice the water was reflecting back his image. That crazy snake hypnotized himself!"

Disney
MICKEY
& FRIENDS

Donald Takes Flight

"Daisy, I have a surprise for you," said Donald Duck one clear spring day. "I've been taking flying lessons."

Donald took Daisy to a nearby airport. On the runway sat an old-fashioned plane with open-air seats. Together they climbed into the small plane. Then Donald started the engine.

"Up, up and away!" he cried as they took off.

"Can you do any tricks?" shouted Daisy.

"Sure!" called Donald. He steered the plane into a loop-the-loop.

"You're a very good pilot, Donald!" Daisy cried, clapping her hands.

Donald was so proud of himself he told Daisy he would fly wherever she wanted to go.

Daisy thought it over. "Let's go to Paris, France!" she said. Donald was so eager to impress Daisy that he didn't think twice. "Paris, here we come!" he cried. Before long, however, the plane's engine began to cough and choke.

"Uh-oh," Donald said to himself as the plane began to drift towards the water.

"Is anything wrong?" asked Daisy.

Donald knew they were running out of fuel. But he didn't want Daisy to find out.

"Don't worry. Everything is fine, Daisy," Donald said nervously.

Just then, he saw something floating below them. It looked like an airport runway. But what would a runway be doing in the middle of the ocean?

As the plane drifted closer to the water, Donald realized he had no other choice. He'd have to land his plane on the floating runway.

Just before he landed, Donald's eyes nearly popped out of his head. It wasn't a runway at all. It was the top deck of a huge ocean liner!

"Duck!" yelled one of the ship's passengers, and a dozen people scattered.

Donald zoomed over their heads and landed the plane on the long, wide deck.

"Hey, it really *is* a duck!" cried one of the passengers, with a chuckle.

Just then an announcement came over the ship's speakers. "Good evening, ladies and gentlemen. Dinner is served!"

Donald helped Daisy out of the plane. He was sure she would be upset. But she wasn't. "Dinner on a cruise ship!" she cried. "Donald, you're just full of surprises, aren't you?"

"Yes, indeed," said Donald with a huge sigh of relief. "And here's one more surprise – I think this ship's on its way to France!"

"Oh, Donald, you're the best," said Daisy.

No, I'm not, thought Donald. *What I really am is one lucky duck!*

Disney
Pinocchio

Look Sharp, Jiminy!

"Gosh." Jiminy Cricket scratched his head between his antennae and yawned a big yawn. Climbing into his tiny matchbox bed, he gazed again at the wooden boy, who was fast asleep.

Jiminy still could not believe his eyes – or his luck. It had been a miraculous night. Not every cricket got to witness a wish granted by the Blue Fairy and see a puppet come to life. And not every cricket was chosen to be somebody's conscience!

Jiminy hopped out of bed. It was pointless to try to sleep. He already felt like he was dreaming. Being a conscience was a big job, but he was just the bug to do it. "Right and wrong." Jiminy looked from one of his hands to the other. "Sure, I know the difference. All I have to do is tell Pinoke. It'll be a snap." Jiminy snapped his fingers. "And I'll even look good doing it."

Jiminy ran his hands down the new jacket hanging by his bed. He picked up the hat and twirled it. "My, my," he said, shaking his head. Then he could not resist any longer. He put on his new shirt, coat, hat and shoes. Then he hopped over to Cleo's fishbowl to see his reflection.

Jiminy whistled low. "Don't you look smart," he told his reflection. "Smart enough to help that wooden boy. Except for that smudge." Jiminy leaned down to inspect a dull spot on his shoe.

He breathed on it and rubbed it with his sleeve. Soon it was shining like new. He looked like a million dollars!

Suddenly Geppetto snored loudly. Jiminy jumped and looked up. Outside the sky was starting to lighten.

"Well, would you look at that?" Jiminy knew he had to get to bed. A conscience needed to be alert! He hurried out of his new clothes, hung them up carefully, and tucked himself back in bed. "Big day tomorrow." He yawned. "Very big day." A moment later the little cricket was chirping in his sleep.

Jiminy woke to the sound of hundreds of cuckoo clocks. He sat up and rubbed his eyes. He barely remembered where he was. Then the events of the evening before flooded back. Why, he had work to do!

"Get up, Pinoke!" Jiminy called towards the big bed. But Pinocchio was already gone. The bed was made and Geppetto and Figaro were gone too!

Cleo swished nervously in her bowl and pointed towards the door.

"I must have overslept!" Jiminy pulled his new clothes on quickly. "I can't let Pinoke start school without me. You don't have to be a conscience to know that's wrong!" And, quick as a flash, Jiminy hopped out of the door.

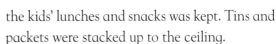

A Day of Rest

At Sunnyside Daycare, Woody and the other toys were exhausted. They loved being played with, but with so many kids to please, it was a lot of hard work.

"I'm a wreck," Woody sighed, slumping down on the floor after another long day of fun.

"You said it," agreed Slinky, collapsing in a tired heap beside him. "We could use some rest."

Stretch the octopus told them that the toys in the centre used to get lots of rest, once upon a time.

"The secret to peace and quiet for us toys can be found in that old album," she said, pointing to a book of photos.

Woody and Slinky rushed to get the book from the shelves, suddenly full of energy again at the prospect of getting some rest! They flipped open the pages, revealing black-and-white photographs of smiling children mixing up home-made dough and making origami hats.

"There weren't many of us back then, so the kids played with water and flour and newspapers," Stretch explained.

Woody turned a page. A little girl looked very happy as she made herself a necklace out of pasta. "Looks like fun," said Slinky.

That gave Woody a great idea. He and Slinky hopped aboard a toy truck and trundled through to the Sunnyside's storeroom, where the food for the kids' lunches and snacks was kept. Tins and packets were stacked up to the ceiling.

"Everything we need is right here," said Woody, smiling.

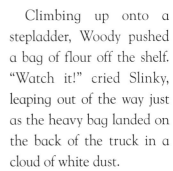

Climbing up onto a stepladder, Woody pushed a bag of flour off the shelf. "Watch it!" cried Slinky, leaping out of the way just as the heavy bag landed on the back of the truck in a cloud of white dust.

Next it was Slinky's turn. He sprang up as fast as he could. "Flying pasta!" he shouted, knocking a box of dried macaroni off the shelf.

After collecting everything they needed, Woody carefully set it all out on the table, along with the photo album. Once that was done, all they could do was wait and see if the plan worked!

Next morning, the teachers and children all filed in from outside. Woody and the other toys held their breath as the teacher flipped through the photo album, then looked down at the flour, pasta and newspapers. A smile spread across her face.

"Kids, today we're going to play a new game," she said.

Woody almost cheered. The kids would have a day filled with fun, which meant he and his friends could finally have a well-deserved day of rest!

The Hospitality of Champions

"I've got to find a solution," said Sally, as she wandered along the main street of Radiator Springs, feeling a little sad.

"Hey, Sally!" came a voice behind her.

Sally turned, surprised. "Hi, Clink! Hi, Clank!"

"My brother and I have just rolled into town for a few days," Clink said. "You don't happen to know where we could...."

"Oh no!" Sally cried. "You're not looking for a place to stay as well?"

Clink and Clank exchanged confused looks.

"Well, yes," Clank said.

Sally groaned. "Sorry guys, I didn't mean to be rude," she apologized. "It's just, since tourists and travellers got wind of our town, finding accommodation for everybody has become a real problem!"

Clink and Clank felt sorry for poor Sally, who looked so worried.

"Doc asked me to handle it," Sally added with a deep grumble. "But there's not a vacancy in the whole town."

"Sally!" yelled Flo, racing up the road. "At last, I've caught up with you!" Flo panted breathlessly. "An entire club of racing fans is on its way! The club president called to book!"

Clink and Clank looked at Flo and an increasingly miserable Sally.

"I'll do my best," Sally sighed.

"Don't worry about us," insisted Clank. "We'll stay in the Rust-Eze team's mobile garage."

It was as if a lightbulb had switched on in Sally's engine. "Say, guys, have you brought your racing equipment?"

"It's on its way now," Clink told her.

"But the garage isn't big enough for an entire club, Sally," reminded Clank.

"I'm not thinking about the mobile garage...." Sally murmured thoughtfully.

When the club members rolled into town in a wild, excitable pack, Sally was there to greet them all with a broad grin. "Welcome, everyone!" she called.

"Miss Sally?" asked a colourful car. "We're from the Lightning McQueen fan club!"

Sally led the way proudly. "Here we have it, guys. Special accommodation just for you!"

The fan club gasped in appreciation of a massive tent, built to perfection. "A real race car paddock!" they marvelled in unison.

"Come inside," Sally said. "It's all set up." Posters and bunting covered the inner walls. But that wasn't the best part....

"It has all the modern comforts!" Sally said.

"Including a refrigerator," a red car pointed out happily.

"Courtesy of our sponsor...." Sally smirked.

And as the refrigerator door swung open, they cheered, "Stocked full of Rust-Eze!"

101 DALMATIANS

Patch and the Panther

One dark night, 15 Dalmatian puppies sat huddled around a black-and-white TV set. They watched as Thunderbolt, the canine hero, creeped through a deep, dark jungle.

Thunderbolt suddenly pricked up his ears. The puppies held their breath. Two yellow eyes peered out of the bushes beside him. It was a panther!

"Thunderbolt, look out!" Penny barked.

"How will Thunderbolt escape the panther?" the TV announcer asked. "Don't miss next week's exciting episode!"

"Aww!" the puppies groaned, disappointed that their favourite show was over.

"I'll bet Thunderbolt tears that ol' panther to pieces," said Patch.

"I'd be scared to fight a panther," said his brother Lucky.

"Not me!" cried Patch.

"All right, kids. Time for bed," Pongo said, shutting off the television with his nose. He watched as the puppies padded upstairs and settled down in their baskets.

"Goodnight, pups," Pongo said.

"Goodnight, Dad," the puppies replied.

Pongo switched off the light. Moments later, the sound of soft snores filled the room. The puppies were fast asleep.

All except for one. Patch was wide awake. He was still thinking about Thunderbolt and the panther.

"I wish a panther would come around here," Patch said to himself. "I'd teach him a thing or two."

Just then a floorboard creaked. Patch pricked up his ears. Then he crawled out of his basket to investigate.

The floorboard creaked again. *What if it's a panther?* Patch thought with a shiver. *But I'm not scared of any ol' panther*, he told himself.

Suddenly Patch saw a shadow flicker across the doorway. The shadow had a long tail. Panthers have long tails. Just then two yellow eyes peered out of the darkness.

"Aroooo!" Patch yelped. He turned to run, but he tripped on the rug. In a flash, the panther was on top of him. Patch could feel its hot breath on his neck. He shut his eyes....

"Patch, what are you doing out of bed?" the panther asked.

Patch opened his eyes. It was Pongo!

"I was just keeping an eye out for panthers," Patch explained.

Pongo smiled. "Why don't you get some sleep now?" he suggested. "I can keep an eye out for panthers for a while."

"Okay, Dad," Patch said with a yawn.

Pongo carried Patch back to his basket. And in no time at all, the puppy was fast asleep.

DISNEY · PIXAR

WALL·E

The Perfect Place

WALL·E had a surprise planned for EVE. He was taking her to a special place she'd never been to before – an old funfair he'd discovered back when he was all alone on Earth.

Together, they sped down a mountain of junk and began to explore the funfair. Most of the rides and games were still intact, and they were soon having fun using fishing rods to hook little plastic goldfish from a pretend pond.

Next, WALL·E found some balloons and a canister of lighter-than-air helium gas. After filling the balloons, he began to float up and up until he was flying alongside EVE.

There was lots to see and do at the funfair, but there was one place in particular WALL·E wanted to show EVE – the Tunnel of Love.

But EVE seemed to have no interest in following WALL·E into the tunnel. Instead, she used her blaster arm to destroy a row of targets at a sideshow stall. She turned proudly to show off her handiwork, but WALL·E was cowering nervously, scared one of the laser blasts might hit him by mistake!

WALL·E soon became even more nervous when EVE dragged him onto the funfair's rickety roller coaster. The little car climbed higher and higher, until WALL·E felt like he was looking out over the whole world, then....

"Waaaaah!" WALL·E screamed as the car hurtled down a steep drop, then looped and spun around the rest of the twisty-turny track.

With his wheels wobbling, WALL·E rolled off the roller coaster and onto solid ground. There was no time to recover, though, as EVE pulled him onto a merry-go-round.

The ride's gentle spinning was much more relaxing than the roller coaster, and WALL·E soon started to enjoy himself. EVE wasn't enjoying it at all, though – the ride was far too slow.

Taking hold of one of the poles, EVE began to push. The ride rocketed round and round, spinning faster and faster until – whoosh! – WALL·E shot off and landed in a tangled heap.

Poor WALL·E struggled to get himself upright. He clicked one of his arms back into place and straightened his bent eyebrow. He'd been so excited about the funfair, but it wasn't nearly as much fun as he'd hoped.

Just then, EVE tapped him lightly on the shoulder. WALL·E turned slowly, expecting her to drag him onto another high-speed ride. Instead, she took him by the hand, and WALL·E gasped happily as she led him towards the Tunnel of Love.

WALL·E loved the funfair, but he still loved EVE best of all.

The Lost Button

Bonnie was off to the daycare centre, leaving the toys to have fun on her own.

"Good morning, Woody," said Dolly, hopping down from her spot on the bed.

Woody pointed to Dolly's dress. "Hey! You're missing a button," he said.

Dolly looked down. "Oh no! You're right," she gasped. "Where could it be? My dress isn't the same without it!"

Woody rested a hand on her shoulder. "I can help you look for it," he said.

That cheered Dolly up. She knew with Woody on the case her button wouldn't stay lost for long.

"OK, let's start looking!" she smiled, grabbing him by the hand and pulling him out of the room.

They raced downstairs and out to the garden. "Yesterday, Bonnie took me to play outside," Dolly said. "My button could be somewhere out here. You have to find it."

Woody looked at the jungle of tall grass and sighed. "Me? I knew it."

The sheriff wrestled his way through the jungle. There was no button to be found – but there was an angry bee which chased him all the way round the garden!

The nimble Woody managed to escape the insect, but not before falling and landing in a puddle of thick, gloopy mud!

"Did you find it?" asked Dolly, when he finally returned.

"No," Woody wheezed. "I sure could use a nice warm bath, though."

Dolly's eyes widened. "Good idea! Let's head straight for the bathroom."

Woody was suspicious. Dolly seemed oddly excited.

In the bathroom, Dolly pointed to a basket of brushes, bows and other hair products. "Yesterday, we played with these," Dolly said. "Look in there."

Woody groaned. "I wish I would learn to keep my big mouth shut."

In the basket, Woody was jabbed by combs, pricked by hair clips and caught in a hair net. There was no sign of the button anywhere.

"Wait, I remember!" said Dolly. "My button's in Bonnie's room."

Woody untangled himself from the net. A spotty red bow was hooked on his hat. "What?" he spluttered.

Sure enough, they found the button on Bonnie's pillow. "It fell off and Bonnie put it here so she wouldn't lose it," Dolly remembered. She smiled. "You know, it was actually fun looking for this button, wasn't it, Woody?"

Woody looked at the new bow on his hat and sighed. Dolly was a good friend, but her idea of fun and his were sometimes very different!

DISNEP

DUMBO

The Best Gift Ever

Apart from Dumbo's mother, Mrs Jumbo, all the elephants at the circus made Dumbo feel like a nobody. They laughed at his large ears and said that he would never amount to anything.

But Timothy Q. Mouse was different. Since the day he and Dumbo had met, Timothy had encouraged Dumbo. Dumbo was so happy to have a friend like Timothy. He wanted to do something nice for him.

So, one afternoon, Dumbo decided to give Timothy a gift. At feeding time, Dumbo put aside a bale of hay. Then he lugged the hay behind the big top and looked around for Timothy. Dumbo found him lounging in the shadow of the lion cage and plopped the hay bale down.

"Hiya, Dumbo!" said Timothy. "What's with the hay?"

Using his trunk, Dumbo nudged the hay bale closer to Timothy.

"For me?" Timothy said. "Wow. Uh ... thanks. I, uh, wonder what I'll do with it all."

Dumbo's heart sank as he realized that mice didn't eat hay. And he wanted to give Timothy something he'd really like.

The next day, Dumbo came upon a patch of flowers growing just outside the elephants' tent. He picked a nice big bouquet and took it behind the big top to Timothy.

"Shucks, Dumbo," said Timothy. "You shouldn't have." Tiny Timothy took the flowers from Dumbo's outstretched trunk and promptly fell over, dropping the flowers everywhere. "Oh dear, look what I did," said Timothy.

But Dumbo thought *he* was the one who should feel bad. The bouquet was too heavy for Timothy to enjoy.

The next day, under the big top, Dumbo spotted a bunch of balloons tied to a seat, left behind by one of the children. *Balloons!* thought Dumbo. *Why, those wouldn't be too heavy for Timothy. They stay up all by themselves.* So Dumbo untied them and brought them to Timothy.

But, when Timothy took hold of the balloon strings, the helium-filled balloons lifted him right off the ground! Quickly, Dumbo reached out with his trunk, grasped Timothy around his waist and placed him gently on the ground.

Then, with a disappointed sigh, Dumbo took the balloons back. *Will I ever find a good gift for Timothy?* he wondered.

"Dumbo," Timothy said, "I wanted to thank you for giving me the best gift ever."

Dumbo's eyes widened in surprise. What could Timothy mean? Every gift he had tried to give him had been all wrong.

"You're my best friend," Timothy said. "And that's the best gift I could ever ask for."

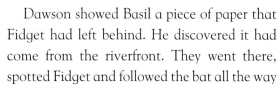

Basil Saves the Day

It was Olivia Flaversham's birthday, and she was celebrating with her father. Suddenly, there was a knock on the door. It was late, and Mr Flaversham felt uneasy. He told Olivia to stay in a cabinet. Olivia peeked out and saw a scary bat. Soon she heard a commotion and ran out. But Olivia's father had been kidnapped!

Olivia knew that only Basil the Great Mouse Detective would be able to save her father so she set off across London to find him.

Meanwhile, Dr David Q. Dawson had just travelled to London. He heard someone weeping.

"Are you all right, my dear?" asked Dawson.

Olivia explained she was looking for Basil.

"Come with me," said Dawson. "We'll find him together." The two mice soon found Basil and explained Olivia's situation to him. He knew that the bat, named Fidget, was employed by his arch-enemy, Professor Ratigan!

Just then, Olivia screamed! Fidget had appeared in the window. Basil, Olivia and Dawson raced outside and followed him to a toyshop. Basil noticed that mechanical parts were missing from many of the toys. Olivia wandered over to a pretty doll cradle. Curious, she peeked inside. Suddenly, Fidget jumped out and stuffed her into a bag and flew away! Now they had to save Olivia and her father!

Dawson showed Basil a piece of paper that Fidget had left behind. He discovered it had come from the riverfront. They went there, spotted Fidget and followed the bat all the way to Ratigan's secret lair.

But Basil had walked right into a trap! Ratigan tied Basil and Dawson to a mousetrap and then left. He was sure the mice wouldn't escape.

Basil thought hard and came up with a brilliant idea that would save them. He calculated the timing of the trap and stopped it just before the mousetrap went off. They escaped!

Basil and Dawson found Olivia and raced to Buckingham Palace. There they discovered what Ratigan was up to – he had forced Olivia's father to build a robot replica of the queen. Then Ratigan had replaced Queen Moustoria with the robot.

A huge crowd was listening to the robot queen. It was announcing that Professor Ratigan was her new royal consort! The crowd gasped in horror.

Offstage, Basil and Dawson finally took control of the robot queen. Ratigan's plan was foiled!

Basil rushed onstage and yelled, "Arrest that fiend!" Ratigan was defeated. Best of all, Olivia and her father were reunited.

A Sandy Adventure

The Sunnyside Daycare kids had gone home for the day, and the toys were getting ready to relax. Suddenly, Jessie realized something terrible.

"Bullseye has been left in the playground all by himself!" she announced.

Buzz flexed his muscles. "Don't panic. Buzz Lightyear will save him!"

Stretch the octopus volunteered to join him. She'd been at the centre longer than most of the other toys, and knew her way around the place better than anyone.

Leading Jessie and Buzz through the dusty air ducts, Stretch swung open a vent which led to the outside. Buzz and Jessie fell out, getting themselves tangled in the octopus's long rubbery arms on the way to the ground.

"Wasn't there an easier route out?" Jessie panted.

"Or one with no tentacles in the way?" grumbled Buzz.

The toys looked around the playground, but there was no sign of Bullseye. Then, from over by the sandpit, Jessie heard the thunder of tiny hooves. "He must be inside," she said. "Let's go!"

The friends rushed to the sandpit. Sure enough, Bullseye was racing around inside it. He was trying to climb out, but the sides of the pit were too steep.

"He can't get out," Jessie realized.

"Don't worry! I have a plan," said Buzz. He pointed at Jessie. "We'll make a chain."

Stretch tried to interrupt, but Jessie and Buzz sprang into action. Taking one of Jessie's hands, Buzz lowered the cowgirl into the pit. She stretched out, trying to reach for Bullseye. "Just a little more...."

"I can't hold on!" Buzz yelled. His fingers slipped and Jessie tumbled down into the pit beside Bullseye.

Stretch tried to make a suggestion, but Buzz was deep in thought.

"We need a new supergalactic plan," Buzz said. He clicked his fingers. "That's it! I'll get a rope, lower myself inside the sandpit and ... are you getting all this, Stretch?"

Buzz looked at the octopus in time to see her reaching two long tentacles down into the pit and lifting Jessie and Bullseye to safety with ease.

"We're almost there, guys," Stretch said. Jessie laughed and Bullseye whinnied loudly with relief.

In no time, the toys were safely out of the sandpit. Stretch used her long arms to dust them down. "Great job, Stretch!" Jessie said.

Buzz agreed. He had to admit, Stretch had been the one to save the day. Maybe all those tentacles weren't so bad, after all.

How to Build a Fire

Carl and Russell were making their way through the depths of the Tepui jungle, pulling Carl's house behind them. Most of the balloons had blown away, and the house was barely floating above the trees.

The sun was going down, and soon it would be dark. Carl said they should stop and build a fire, and Russell jumped up and down with excitement.

"Me! Oh, please let me do it, Mr Fredricksen! I have my campfire badge," he cheered.

"Are you sure you know what you're doing, Russell?" asked Carl. Russell insisted he knew exactly what to do, and after a quick check of his guidebook, he jumped into action.

As Russell worked, he explained every step. First, he had to clean the area where the fire was going to go, being careful to remove any stray pieces of debris that might cause problems.

Next, he had to build a ring of rocks to stop the fire spreading. He explained at great length the best types of rock to use, then spent a long time searching the jungle to find some that were just right.

Once the fire ring was built, it was time to gather the materials for the fire. Carl yawned as he watched Russell start collecting pieces of wood from the rainforest floor.

"Did you know there are three types of materials, Mr Fredricksen?" Russell asked.

Carl sat on a rock and listened as Russell launched into a detailed explanation of all the different types and sizes of wood needed to build a proper campfire.

Small pieces of kindling were used to start the fire, larger sticks were needed to keep it going, then finally the biggest pieces could be added to help the blaze grow.

Russell gathered up a large pile, but when he reached to pick up a stick and realized it was actually a snake, he dropped the whole lot and had to start all over again.

When he had collected enough wood, Russell took great care building it into a perfect pile. Just throwing it in a heap wasn't good enough, and it seemed to take forever for him to get the pile the way he wanted it.

But then, it was finally time to light the fire. Proudly, Russell held up his fire-lighting kit. He was about to create the first spark, when Carl stood up.

"Well done, Russell. Now let's go," Carl said, pointing to the sky. Russell had taken so long to build the fire, the sun had already risen.

Russell's shoulders slumped sadly as he put his fire-lighting kit back in his pocket. "Happens every time," he sighed.

Disney · PIXAR
FINDING
NEMO

Finding Ne-who?

"The coral reef is falling down, falling down, falling down."

Nemo was home, brushing up against the anemone, when the most awful singing he ever heard in his life made him cringe. He swam deeper into the anemone, but it didn't help. The song went on.

"My fair octopus."

And there was something familiar about it.... Still cringing, Nemo poked his head out of the golden tentacles to see who was making the awful racket.

"Dory!" Nemo should have known. How could he have forgotten that voice? Nemo swam as fast as he could towards the regal blue tang fish. "Dory! Where have you been?" It seemed like a whale's age since Nemo had seen the fish that helped his dad rescue him from the dentist's fish tank. And he couldn't wait to give her a big hug!

When Nemo got closer Dory stopped singing. That was good. But when she looked at him her face was blank. That wasn't so good.

"Did you say something, kid?" she asked.

"Dory, it's me. Nemo," he replied.

"Ne-who?" She looked at Nemo blankly. "Sorry, kid, don't know you. I was just swimming by, minding my own business, singing a song. Hey, why was I singing? Am I famous? Maybe that's how you know me."

"Dory! We're friends, remember?" Nemo had been missing Dory a lot. She just *had* to remember who he was.

"Friends? I just made friends with a hermit crab ... I think." Dory swam in a circle looking for the crab, but got distracted and started chasing her tail.

"Please try to remember, Dory," Nemo asked again. "You helped save me. You helped me find my dad. You know my dad. Big orange guy? Three white stripes? Looks kind of like me?"

"My dad? Looks like you? Sorry, kid, you don't look anything like my dad." Dory looked at Nemo like he was crazy and began to swim away.

Nemo swam after her. "Just think about it for a second," he pleaded. She *had* to remember something. "I'm Nemo!"

Dory did not turn around but she slowed down. Swimming in a wide circle, she came back. She looked at Nemo sideways, and then started laughing so hard bubbles came out of her nose.

"Had you going, huh?" Dory gave Nemo a big hug and smiled at him slyly. "That was just my little joke. You know I could never forget you!"

Nemo giggled and swam circles around his friend. "Good one, Dory!" He grinned.

Dory smiled back. "Good one, *who*?"

Nemo groaned. That Dory!

THE LION KING

Simba's Thank-you Present

Simba lounged in the jungle, feeling happier than he'd felt in ages. After the terrible stampede near Pride Rock, he didn't think he'd ever be happy again. But his new friends Timon and Pumbaa had helped him feel better.

"I should do something to thank them," Simba told himself as he watched his friends in the river nearby. "Something really special!"

He decided to make them a present. When he saw a piece of bark lying on the ground, he had an idea.

"Ta-da!" he exclaimed a while later, leading his friends to the gift.

Pumbaa blinked. "Thanks," he said. "Er, what is it?"

"A scratching spot," Simba said, flexing his claws. He'd used vines to attach it to a thick tree trunk at shoulder height.

"Gee," Timon said. "Nice thought and all, Simba. But it's a little high for me." He stretched to his full height but could barely reach it.

Pumbaa nodded. "And I don't scratch." He held up one foot. "Hooves, you know."

"Oh." Simba hadn't thought of that.

"Thanks anyway, kid," Pumbaa said.

Simba decided to try again by building them a nice, soft bed to sleep in. He dug a cosy hole in the ground, then filled it with soft things like feathers, sand and bits of fur.

"Ta-da!" he cried when he showed his friends.

Timon sighed. "What are you trying to do, kill us? Prey animals here, remember? If we sleep on the ground, we become somebody's midnight snack!"

Simba sighed as they left again. Why couldn't he think of a present they'd like?

"I would've loved that scratching spot," he mumbled. "The bed, too."

Suddenly he sat up straight, realizing what he'd just said. All this time he'd been thinking of presents *he* would like – but the presents weren't for him.

"I've got to think like they think," he said. Slowly, a smile spread across his face....

A little while later he called them over. "I've got something for you." He pointed to a pile of palm fronds. "I think you're really going to like it. Ta-da!"

He pulled back the leaves. Underneath was a mass of wriggling, squirming, creeping, crawling creatures – bugs and grubs and worms of every shape and size ... and flavour.

Timon and Pumbaa gasped with delight. "Simba!" Timon cried. "You're a prince! It's just what we always wanted!"

"Yeah, thanks," Pumbaa mumbled through a mouthful of grubs. "You're a real pal!"

Simba smiled. "No," he said, "thank *you.* Both of you. *Hakuna matata!*"

Dressed to Thrill

It was Sunday, and Ken had spent most of the weekend preparing for a party he was throwing. He had hung up decorations and the Sunnyside Daycare centre looked amazing!

"Really cool, Ken," said Jessie as she and Woody admired the place.

"Please save your compliments for tonight," Ken said. He handed them two love-heart-shaped cards. "Here are your magical invitations."

Woody read his invitation. "What does 'dress to thrill' mean?" Ken looked Jessie and Woody up and down. "It means you can't come to the party wearing your old cowboy outfits," he said. Turning to the aliens, he added, "And those spacesuits are definitely out of style."

Buzz puffed out his chest. "Of course, my space ranger uniform will be fine for your party, right, pal?"

Ken raised his perfect eyebrows. "It's not exactly in keeping with the party's theme, Buzz. You've got to be elegant, stylish and chic," Ken said. "In short, you've got to dress like me!"

As Ken hurried off to continue the preparations, the other toys discussed their problem. None of them had any other clothes they could wear.

Luckily, Woody had an idea. He knew just where to find lots of different outfits. "We'll find everything we need right here in Ken's Dream House!" he said.

Jessie's eyes widened as she studied the rows and rows of outfits. "Wow! Look at all these clothes!" she gasped.

Buzz picked up a shirt. It was covered in pink flowers. He quickly put it back down again. "Are you sure Ken won't get mad?"

Woody pulled on a cap. "Well, he's the one who asked us to change."

Buzz grinned. "Then he's in for a surprise all right!"

That evening, as he welcomed guests to the party, Ken couldn't believe his eyes. Jessie, Buzz, Woody and the aliens were wearing a mishmash of some very familiar clothes.

"Hey! Those are my precious outfits you're wearing!" he spluttered.

"Right you are!" beamed Jessie, twirling to show off her new hat, and the pink poncho she had turned into a skirt.

Buzz tugged on the lapels of his suit jacket. "You said you wanted us to dress like you!"

Woody tightened his colourful tie. "And we've done just that."

Ken couldn't really argue. The toys had certainly dressed to thrill, but as he watched them stretching his valuable outfits out of shape, he decided that at his next party he'd let guests wear whatever they liked!

DISNEP
THE ARISTOCATS

Street Cats

"Oh, Mama!" said Marie dreamily. "Paris is so pretty in the morning! May we please go and explore just a bit?"

The kittens and their mother had spent the previous night in Mr O'Malley's swinging bachelor flat, and were now making their way through the streets of Paris back to Madame's house.

"All right, darlings," their mother replied sweetly. "But just for a few minutes. Madame must be missing us terribly. Be sure to stick together!"

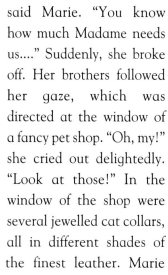

They passed a doorway to a jazz hall, where the previous night's party appeared to be still in full swing. "Oh yeah!" said Toulouse as he danced in the doorway to the swinging beat.

"Come on, Toulouse," said Berlioz crossly. "I'm hungry!"

A few steps down the block, a fishmonger was just setting out his wares in the window of his shop. The three kittens put their paws on the windowsill, licking their lips as they watched him lay out the gleaming fish. The fishmonger smiled at them through the window, then came out of his shop and tossed them each a sardine. "Here you are, my pretty cats!" he said to them.

Yum! Sardines! The three miaowed back a thank you and gobbled up the tasty treat.

"The streets of Paris are the coolest place on Earth!" said Berlioz as they continued walking. "I don't want to go back to Madame's house!"

"Berlioz! You mustn't speak like that!" said Marie. "You know how much Madame needs us...." Suddenly, she broke off. Her brothers followed her gaze, which was directed at the window of a fancy pet shop. "Oh, my!" she cried out delightedly. "Look at those!" In the window of the shop were several jewelled cat collars, all in different shades of the finest leather. Marie thought they were simply beautiful – especially the pink one. "I must say, the streets of Paris are a wonderful place!" Marie said dreamily.

Just then, they heard a loud barking. A moment later, a huge dog came bounding around the corner. The kittens froze in fear. Then all three of them turned and scampered back down the street in the direction of their mother and Mr O'Malley, with the dog hot on their heels.

"Paris is a fine city," said Berlioz, panting, as he raced down an alleyway. Darting behind some rubbish bins, the kittens were able to lose the snarling dog.

"Yes," replied Marie. "But I'm not sure how I feel about the Parisians – particularly the canine kind!"

Disney·PIXAR

MONSTERS, INC.

Monster Daycare

Mike always arrived at Monsters, Inc. at half past eight, put his lunch box in his locker and promptly reported to his station on the Laugh Floor. But one morning, as he came out of the locker room, Celia was waiting for him. "We have a little problem, Mike," she said. "The daycare teacher is sick today, so we need a sub. And seeing as how you've already met your laugh quota for the month, I thought maybe you –"

"Daycare?" cried Mike. "Wait a –"

Just then Sulley stepped in. "Happy to do it, Celia," he said. "Daycare, here we come."

"Are you crazy?" Mike grumbled.

"What's the big deal?" Sulley shrugged. "We handled Boo, didn't we? What's a few more kids? We'll eat some snacks. Watch a few videos. Play a little peekaboo. It's like having a paid holiday, Mike, my man!"

But the minute they opened the daycare room door, they both knew Sulley was wrong....

There were monster children everywhere! Swinging from the ceiling. Slithering up the walls. Bouncing from corner to corner. Mike's and Sulley's jaws dropped open. What were they going to do?

Sulley took a deep breath. "We just have to let them know who's in charge, is all," he told Mike.

"Okay, kids!" he announced. "Uncles Sulley and Mike are here. It's time to settle down."

But, instead of settling down, the little monsters dived on them, yelling, "Horsey rides! Yeah!" and "Play ball!"

"I think they know who's in charge ... *help!*" Mike shouted as an oversized, six-handed monster child scooped him up and tossed him to his twin.

Sulley quickly intercepted Mike and set him back down on his feet.

"'Paid holiday', my eye," muttered Mike.

"All we need to do," said Sulley calmly, "is get their attention. Let's see ... a video?" But the TV was too covered with monster slime and finger paint for anyone to watch it.

A snack? No. Every cracker and fright roll-up had been gobbled up long before.

A story? Of course! Except a four-eyed toddler seemed to be happily tearing the pages out of each and every book.

"How about a song?" said Mike finally.

"Great idea!" said Sulley. And do you know what? It was! They sang "The Huge Gigantic Spider" and "The Wheels on the Monster Bus". Before long, even Mike was having fun.

"What did I say, Sulley? I said it'd be like a paid holiday and it is! I don't understand why you were so reluctant," Mike said.

Sulley rolled his eyes. "Whatever you say...."

HERCULES
Disney

Bring a Friend

Hercules was training to be a hero, and it was a lot of work. One day, Phil, his coach, set up a practice course for Hercules and then tied his student's hands behind his back. Herc had to run the course with no hands!

Phil had put a doll at the end of the course. He said it was a "practice damsel in distress" and Hercules was supposed to rescue it. So the hero-in-training rushed into the first section of the course – a darkened cave. Herc plunged into darkness and fell headlong into stagnant water.

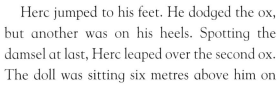

"Yuck!" Hercules spat out the putrid water and scowled. He wanted to be a hero more than anything. But sometimes Phil made things a little more difficult than necessary.

Feeling his way cautiously in the darkness using his feet, Herc suddenly felt something slithering around his ankles. Snakes!

Herc shook several of the water snakes out of his sandals. He hurried towards the other end of the cave and dived into the daylight, shaking the last snake off his feet. Panting, Herc lay down on the grass to rest for a moment.

"Rest later!" Phil shouted.

Herc rolled over slowly. The doll had to be around here somewhere. Behind him Hercules heard stamping hooves and turned around. A huge ox was thundering towards him!

Herc jumped to his feet. He dodged the ox, but another was on his heels. Spotting the damsel at last, Herc leaped over the second ox. The doll was sitting six metres above him on the edge of a steep cliff.

At least Phil had left him a rope. In fact, it looked as though Phil had left two. Gripping the first rope in his jaws, Herc creeped steadily upward. He was about halfway up when Phil lit the end of the second rope, which was soaked with oil! The fire raced up the rope towards a stack of dry wood under Herc's damsel.

Hercules threw himself the last few metres. He tackled the damsel, rolling away from the stack of wood, which was now blazing merrily away.

Breathing hard, Hercules finally relaxed.

"And another thing...." Phil's gruff voice echoed up to him from the base of the cliff. Hercules held his breath, but not because he was waiting for Phil's next words. Herc was holding his breath because he had spotted a scorpion next to his foot. The insect was poised to sting!

CRUNCH. Hercules' winged horse Pegasus used his hoof to flatten the creature.

Hercules smiled at Pegasus as Phil's final words of advice reached his ears. It was the best tip yet – "Always bring a friend!"

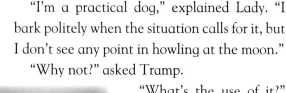

Howling at the Moon

Lady had been having a really bad day. First, she'd had a run-in with two nasty cats. Then, she'd been put in a horrible muzzle. But, because of Tramp, everything had changed.

"It's amazing how a day can start off terribly but end wonderfully," Lady told Tramp as they trotted through the moonlit park. "Thank you for helping me escape that terrible muzzle and for dinner at Tony's."

"Aww, shucks, don't mention it!" said Tramp. "Hey, you wanna have some real fun?"

"I don't know," Lady said cautiously.

While she was fond of Tramp, she also knew they were very different dogs. Tramp was used to life on the streets. So his idea of 'fun' might be very different from hers.

"Don't worry," Tramp teased. "This is something I think you'll enjoy."

"What is it?" asked Lady.

"Well, for starters, you have to look up," said Tramp.

Lady did. The sky was filled with stars and a big, bright moon.

"What am I looking for?" she asked.

"The moon, of course!" cried Tramp. "Haven't you ever howled at the moon?"

Lady laughed at Tramp's suggestion.

"What's so funny?" asked Tramp.

"I'm a practical dog," explained Lady. "I bark politely when the situation calls for it, but I don't see any point in howling at the moon."

"Why not?" asked Tramp.

"What's the use of it?" asked Lady.

"You know, Lady," said Tramp, "a thing doesn't have to be useful to be fun. You like to chase a ball, right?"

"Right," said Lady.

"So, there you go," said Tramp. "Sometimes it's good to chase a ball. And sometimes it's good to just let go and howl at the moon, even for no reason."

Lady thought it over. "Okay," she said. "What do I do?"

"First, sit up real straight," said Tramp. "Then, look up at the moon, take a deep breath, and just let all the troubles of your day disappear in one gigantic howl!" He demonstrated. "*Ow-Ow-OWWWWW!*"

Lady joined Tramp and howled as loudly as she could.

"You're right!" she cried. "It does feel good to howl at the moon!"

"Stick with me, kid," said Tramp. "I know what's what."

Lady suspected Tramp did know what was what, but there was an even better reason for her to stick with him. He'd become the very best friend she'd ever had.

Disney
Peter Pan

The Lost Boys Get Lost

The Lost Boys were walking single file through the woods of Never Land, on their way home after an afternoon of adventure-seeking, when Slightly, who led the way, stopped in his tracks on the bank of Mermaid Lagoon.

The others – Rabbit, the Raccoon Twins, Cubby and Tootles – came to an abrupt halt behind him.

"Wait a minute," said Slightly. "We already passed Mermaid Lagoon. What are we doing here again?"

Behind a bush, Tinker Bell giggled as she watched the Lost Boys looking around in confusion.

Tink had spotted them on their march and had not been able to resist playing a joke. So, she had flown ahead of them and used her fairy magic to enchant various landmarks on their route home. She had made Bald Rock look like Spiky Rock, causing the Lost Boys to make a right turn where they should have turned left. Then she had enlisted the help of the sparrows, convincing them to move from their usual perch in the Sparrow Bird Grove to another group of trees, thus tricking the Lost Boys into making another right turn too soon. And finally, she had enchanted the Towering Elm Tree to look exactly like the Weeping Willow, and the Lost Boys had made yet another wrong turn, thinking they were nearly home.

But now, here they were, walking past Mermaid Lagoon, when Slightly remembered passing the same spot a good while back.

"I think we're walking in circles!" Slightly proclaimed. "Lost Boys, I think we're ... lost!"

Tinker Bell overheard and tried desperately to stifle her laughter. But, before she could contain it, one giggle exploded into a fully fledged laugh and –

"Hey!" said Cubby. "Did you hear that?"

He darted over to a bush growing alongside the path and moved a branch to one side. There was Tinker Bell, hovering in mid-air, holding her stomach and shaking with laughter.

"Tinker Bell!" cried Tootles.

It didn't take them long to work out that Tinker Bell was laughing at *them* – and that she was the cause of their confusion.

Still laughing, Tinker Bell flitted away, taking her normal route home to the fairy glade – left at the Weeping Willow Tree, right just before Sparrow Bird Grove, right again at Spiky Rock, and on towards the Sparkling Stream, which led to Moon Falls and the fairy glade entrance.

But – wait a minute! After turning right at Spiky Rock, Tinker Bell saw no sign of the Sparkling Stream anywhere. Where was she? She had got completely lost.

Do you know how?

Rescue Mission

Up in her bedroom, Bonnie was playing with the toys. They were having an outer space adventure, and Bonnie laughed as she swooshed and looped Buzz around and around.

When Bonnie was called downstairs, she placed Buzz on the windowsill, next to Woody – and right beside the open window! A gust of wind pushed the spaceman backwards, knocking him out of the window!

As the other toys raced up onto the windowsill, Woody leaned out and looked down. "Don't worry. He's holding on to the house," Woody said. He reached a hand down to his pal, who was clinging tightly to a plank of wood. "I've almost ... got him!" Woody said, but then he lost his grip and he tumbled out of the window, too!

Buzz and Woody grabbed hands, and both fell towards the hard stone path far below!

"There's a snake in my boot," said Woody's voice feature as the string on his back caught on a nail sticking out of the house, stopping their fall.

"Pull us up!" Woody shouted, as he and Buzz dangled helplessly in mid-air.

But before the other toys could organize a rescue mission, they heard Bonnie coming back.

The toys ducked for cover as Bonnie raced into the room. When she saw that Woody and Buzz were missing, she realized what must have happened. She flew down the stairs calling for her mum, then they both ran outside.

"Are you sure they fell out the window?" Bonnie's mum asked, searching the flower beds.

"Yes, I left them on the windowsill. The wind must have knocked them out," Bonnie insisted. "I hope they're not broken!"

Bonnie's mum stood up and looked around. "Where are they? I don't see them."

High overhead, Woody was starting to worry. All those batteries meant that Buzz was a heavy toy and Woody wouldn't be able to hold him forever. "She'll never find us up here," he groaned.

"We've got to get her attention," said Buzz.

"How?" asked Woody. "We can't just say 'Hey, we're up here!'"

Buzz shook his head. "No, but there's something else we can say." He cupped a hand to his mouth took a deep breath and shouted, "There's a snake in my boot!"

That did the trick! Buzz sounded almost exactly like Woody. Bonnie and her mum looked up. Bonnie cheered as she realized her toys were safe and sound.

As Bonnie's mum went to get the ladder, Woody winked at Buzz. "Good job, pal," he whispered. "I loved that imitation!"

THE JUNGLE Book

Baloo's Secret Weapon

Mowgli and his pal Baloo were taking a lazy afternoon stroll through the jungle. Suddenly, Mowgli stopped in his tracks. "Did you hear that?" he asked.

"Hear what, little buddy?" Baloo asked.

"It sounded like twigs snapping," Mowgli said. "I think somebody might be following us!"

"That was just your old Papa Bear's stomach growling," Baloo told him. "It's time for some lunch."

"And I know just where to get it!" cheered Mowgli. He shimmied up a tree, plucked a bunch of bananas and tossed them down to the bear.

"That's my boy!" Baloo cried proudly.

But, as he was scrambling back down, Mowgli spotted a flash of orange and black.

"Shere Khan!" Mowgli whispered to Baloo. "We've got to get out of here!" The tiger had been after Mowgli ever since the boy had first set foot in the jungle.

The two friends didn't know which way to turn. Now that Shere Khan had their scent, it would be hard to lose him. Then they both heard a drum beat echoing through the jungle.

"Oh no," said Mowgli. "King Louie and his crazy band of monkeys. That's all we need!"

Baloo's eyes suddenly lit up. "That's *exactly* what we need, Little Britches!" he cried.

Still clutching the bananas, Baloo and Mowgli ran towards King Louie's compound. When they arrived, Baloo disguised himself as a monkey. The monkeys were so busy dancing and singing they didn't notice his disguise. Then the bear quickly found a huge empty barrel and filled it with the bananas.

"Look!" cried Baloo, peering into the barrel. "Lunch!" The monkeys ran over and jumped right into the barrel! They greedily ate the feast, tossing out peels as they made their way through the bunch.

Baloo signalled to Mowgli, who came out of hiding. "Come and get me, Shere Khan!" the Man-cub taunted.

Within seconds, the tiger appeared in the clearing, a fierce gleam in his eye. "Hello, Stripes," Baloo greeted him cheerfully. Then the bear picked up the barrel, heaved it and sent King Louie's troop flying at Shere Khan. The monkeys landed on the tiger's back, where they frantically jumped up and down, pulling on his tail and ears. Mowgli and Baloo watched as Shere Khan raced back into the jungle, trying to free himself from his shrieking passengers.

"Like I always say," Baloo declared as he grinned at Mowgli, "there's nothing more fun than a barrel of monkeys!"

Monster Truck Mater

One day, outside Flo's V8 Café, Lightning McQueen pointed out a monster truck that was driving by.

"I used to wrestle trucks bigger than that," Mater said. He began to tell Lightning about the time he was a wrestler called The Tormentor. His first match was in an arena filled with cheering fans. Mater wore a blue-and-red mask.

An ice-cream van with monster wheels rolled into the ring. The Tormentor wasn't sure how to wrestle such a big van. So he put on a cap, hoping to trick his opponent instead. "Can I have one double-dip sundae, please?" he said.

"Huh?" said the I-Screamer. "Oh, sure." When the ice-cream van reached for a sundae, The Tormentor grabbed his bumper with his tow hook and flipped him. The referee announced that The Tormentor had won.

After his first win, The Tormentor just couldn't stop winning, and soon he made it all the way to the World Championship! He was feeling confident until he saw ... Dr Frankenwagon's Monster! Just one of the Monster's tyres was bigger than The Tormentor. He had a giant scoop on one side and a claw on the other. The wrecking ball on his back could crush a truck with one direct hit.

Back in Radiator Springs, Lightning interrupted the story. "Whoa!" he cried. "What did you do?"

Mater looked over at his friend. "Don't you remember nothin'? We was a tag team."

Mater continued his story, except this time, Lightning was also in the ring.

"Tag, you're it!" said Mater, touching Lightning with his tyre. The Monster lunged for the race car, ignoring the tow truck.

Lightning saw their opponent coming straight at him. Lightning raced around the ring to avoid the Monster's wrecking ball. When The Tormentor heard Lightning call for help he ducked back into the ring. Luckily, The Tormentor had a plan.

While the Monster's wrecking ball was on the ground, The Tormentor quickly snagged it with his tow hook. Then he zipped under one side of the ring and out the other. With a wink at his fans, the Tormentor yanked his tow rope. He flipped the entire ring – trapping the Monster underneath!

"The winners!" the referee announced. "The Tormentor and...." He turned to Lightning. "What's your name?"

"Lightning McQueen," he replied.

The referee frowned. "And Frightening McMean!" he announced.

Disney
THE
HUNCHBACK
of NOTRE DAME

Funny Faces

Hugo, Victor and Laverne were gargoyles at the great Cathedral of Notre Dame. Most of the time they were stone, but they came to life in the presence of Quasimodo, the bell ringer at Notre Dame. Although they were all good friends, Hugo and Victor were always finding something to bicker over, and today was no exception.

"That's ridiculous!" Hugo snapped at Victor.

"No, *you're* ridiculous!" Victor shot back.

Victor had suggested that Quasimodo should tell Frollo, the Minister of Justice and Quasi's master, that he wanted to take some time off. Hugo had pointed out that Frollo would sooner become a gypsy than give Quasimodo a holiday. Then the argument had really started.

"Well, you started it," Hugo told him.

"I started it?" Victor asked.

"That's right, Stone Face!" Hugo shouted.

"Who do you think you're calling Stone Face? Blockhead!" Victor fought back.

Suddenly, a loud whistle interrupted them.

"May I have your attention, please?" Laverne said. "I would like to propose a way for you to settle this dispute like gentlemen."

Victor and Hugo looked intrigued.

"What is it?" Quasimodo asked.

"A face-making contest," Laverne said.

"Here are the rules – you two take turns making faces at each other, and the first one to make the other laugh wins!"

"I'm going first!" declared Hugo, sticking his tongue out at Victor.

"Child's play," said Victor scornfully. He crossed his eyes at Hugo.

"Try resisting *this* then!" Hugo replied. He crossed his eyes, flared his nostrils, and stuck his lower jaw out, baring a crooked row of teeth in a hideous grimace.

Victor managed to keep a straight face at this, but Quasimodo couldn't help but laugh out loud.

"Shh!" Laverne said. "Frollo's coming!"

"Frollo?" Hugo and Victor grew pale and quickly turned back to stone.

Just then, Frollo marched in. "What's going on up here?" he asked Quasimodo.

"Nothing, sir," Quasi said, trying not to laugh. He was having a hard time keeping a straight face because, behind Frollo, Victor and Hugo were still busy making faces at each other.

"Hmm," said Frollo suspiciously. As he turned to go, Victor and Hugo stopped making faces at each other, and began making funny faces at Frollo's back. When he was out of sight, all four friends collapsed with laughter.

"You know what," Quasi told them. "I have so much fun with you, it beats going on holiday!"

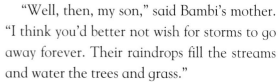

Rain, Rain, Go Away

RRRUMBLE, RRRUMBLE, BOOM! The loud clap of thunder startled Bambi and his friends.

"I hate thunderstorms!" cried Thumper, looking a little scared.

"I don't like them either!" exclaimed Flower.

"Bambi!" called his mother as the clouds grew dark and the rain began to fall. Bambi followed his mother out of the open meadow and into the sheltered woods. From their warm, dry thicket, Bambi watched sheets of rain pour down through the trees.

"I hate thunderstorms," he told his mother, echoing Thumper's words. "I wish the storm would go away and never come back again."

"Oh, my," said his mother. "Do you mean you never again want to drink the cool, fresh water from the forest stream?"

"Well, no," said Bambi.

"Then, do you want the big trees to go thirsty? Their leaves to wither and branches to become brittle?" asked his mother.

"No! Of course not!" cried Bambi. "The trees give us shelter and their branches give the birds a place to make their nests."

"Then, do you want the sweet grass to turn brown?" asked his mother.

"No," said Bambi. "We eat the grass. We'd go hungry if that happened!"

"Well, then, my son," said Bambi's mother. "I think you'd better not wish for storms to go away forever. Their raindrops fill the streams and water the trees and grass."

"But storms are so scary," Bambi said.

Just then, the rain began to let up, and Bambi's friends scampered through the underbrush and into Bambi's thicket.

"Look at the pond!" cried Flower.

Bambi peered through the thicket. The pond was alive with activity. The frogs were leaping and playing. And a family of ducks was shaking their feathers and waddling into the water.

"Uh-oh," said Thumper. "That old bullfrog's gonna get a surprise."

Bambi watched the lily pad with a big bullfrog on it drift closer and closer to the line of ducklings. The last duckling wasn't paying attention. The sudden collision sent the frog toppling off its lily pad with a startled *croak!* and surprised the duckling so much it did an underwater somersault!

Bambi, Thumper and Flower laughed.

"I guess I like thunderstorms after all," Bambi told his mother.

"You didn't like thunderstorms?" said Thumper. "That's silly! Why would you ever say a thing like that?"

Disney·PIXAR

MONSTERS, INC.

The Spooky Sleepover

It was a quiet morning at Monsters, Inc. Sulley had arrived early to catch up on paperwork when he got a phone call from Dispatch. "Annual slumber party at Shannon Brown's house. Waxford is out sick. We need a replacement."

"I'll get right on it," replied Sulley. He knew there would be a lot of kids at the party, and he wanted to make sure he had a monster there to tell jokes and capture laughs. Who better for the job than his one-eyed pal, Mike?

Mike was in the locker room getting ready for work when Sulley entered and explained the situation.

"Piece of cake," Mike said as a door slid into his station on the Laugh Floor. Then Mike walked through the wardrobe in Shannon Brown's room. It was empty. "Uh ... hello?" Mike called. Just as Mike started to leave, he heard the sound of laughter.

Then thunder cracked across the sky. Mike ran to the wardrobe door to return to the factory. He jiggled the doorknob, but it just opened into the wardrobe, not the Laugh Floor at Monsters, Inc.!

Mike soon realized that lightning must have struck the door and broken it. He took a deep breath and headed into the hallway.

Meanwhile, back at Monsters, Inc., Sulley was working on the Laugh Floor. The floor manager came running over. "Sulley!" he shouted. "Mike hasn't returned from the slumber party. He's never been gone this long!"

When Sulley went to check on the door, he saw it was broken and brought someone in to fix it. After a few hours, the door was working! Now it would open into a different room at Shannon's house.

Back at Shannon's, Mike had heard laughing down the hall. When he'd found the right room and went in, it was quiet.

Slowly, Mike entered the dark, silent room. All of a sudden, a light went on! Mike jumped. Shannon Brown and all her friends started roaring with laughter! They thought Mike looked funny sneaking into the room. Mike screamed in fright.

At that exact moment, the wardrobe door opened and Sulley burst into the room. Sulley was so surprised to find Mike screaming that all he could do was scream too! Then he and Mike huddled in fright. Shannon and her friends laughed even harder.

"Looks as if our work here is done," Sulley said to Mike.

"I was never scared for a second," said Mike.

"Me neither, buddy," Sulley replied, his fingers crossed behind his back. "Me neither."

Flik Wings It

Flik knew that Hopper and his gang of hungry grasshoppers would soon come to steal all the food from the peaceful ants of Ant Island. So Flik headed off to the big city to find warrior bugs to help fight the grasshoppers.

On his way, Flik saw a shiny dragonfly flutter across the sky.

"Wow, I wish I could fly like that!" he exclaimed.

Suddenly, Flik had an idea. "I built a harvester that harvests pretty well. I wonder if I could invent a flying machine?"

When he returned from the city, Flik got to work. He gathered sticks, vines and leaves. He found a mushroom cap to use for a seat, and a long red feather for a tail.

When he had gathered all the parts, Flik began to strap the pieces together.

After lots of hard work, Flik took a step back and studied his invention.

"Well, it certainly *looks* like it could fly," Flik said finally. "It has wings that flap and a long red tail."

The frame of Flik's flier was made of twigs and the wings were made of leaves. The whole machine was tied together with strong vines.

"Time for a test flight," Flik decided.

He climbed onto the mushroom cap seat and used a vine as a safety belt. Then he put his feet on the little pedals and started to pump. The green wings began to flap. Soon, Flik's flier began to rock; then it leaped into the sky!

With the air racing between his antennae, Flik watched the world flash under his feet. He saw all the other creatures that ate ants.

"Flying is so much safer than walking," said Flik.

But he spoke too soon, for high in the sky above Flik a mother bird was teaching her three little hatchlings how to fly. She spied Flik's strange-looking contraption and thought one thing – dinner!

Flik looked up and saw the mother bird and her babies coming down on him like dive-bombers!

"Test flight over!" Flik cried.

Pedalling faster, Flik steered his flier through the branches of a tall tree. The mother bird and two of her babies were blocked by the branches. But the third baby bird raced between the leaves and caught up with Flik.

Pecking wildly, the little bird ripped a wing from Flik's flier. Spinning out of control, the machine crashed to the ground.

Luckily for Flik, he had also invented a parachute made from a spider's web, and he made a soft landing in the middle of a daisy.

"Another failed invention," Flik said with a sigh. "Maybe someday I'll have a chance to make a flying machine that really works!"

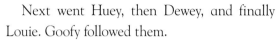

An Ice Skating Game

Mickey woke up and looked outside. It had snowed last night! "It's a perfect day for ice skating!" he cried. "I'll invite all my friends to come."

On the way, Mickey picked up Goofy, Donald, Daisy, Huey, Dewey, Louie and Minnie. When they got to the pond, everyone laced up their skates and made their way to the ice. It was as smooth as glass. The friends began skating around and around.

"Hey, I have an idea!" shouted Mickey. "Let's play crack the whip!"

Nobody else knew how to play, so Mickey explained the game. "I'll start out as the leader," he said. "We all join hands and form a line. Then we all skate around and around in a big circle. Once we get going, the skater at the end of the line lets go!"

"That sounds like fun!" said Goofy.

"Cool!" cried Huey, Dewey and Louie.

They all joined hands and began skating in a circle. Around and around and around they went. Donald was at the end of the line.

"Okay, Donald, let go!" shouted Mickey. Donald let go and went sailing away.

Around and around and around the rest of the gang went.

"Now, you go, Daisy!" cried Mickey. Daisy let go and went flying away across the ice.

Next went Huey, then Dewey, and finally Louie. Goofy followed them.

Now just Mickey and Minnie were left. Around and around they skated. Then Mickey shouted, "Let go, Minnie!"

Minnie let go and zoomed off with a squeal.

Mickey was having a fine time. Now all alone, he began to spin around and around and around. When he finally came to a stop, it took quite some time for his head to stop spinning. "Wasn't that fun, guys?" he said. "Want to do it again? Guys? Where is everyone?"

Mickey looked around. Where had everyone gone? And then he saw them. Seven pairs of ice skates at the ends of seven pairs of legs were sticking out of seven different snowbanks, kicking away.

"Uh-oh," said Mickey. He dashed over to the side of the pond and, one by one, he pulled all of his friends out of the snow.

"Gee, sorry about that," said Mickey.

Goofy shook his head, and snow flew everywhere. "That was fun!" he said cheerfully. "But I sure could use a cup of –"

"Yoo-hoo!" came a cheerful cry. It was Grandma Duck, standing at the edge of the pond. She was carrying a flask filled with hot chocolate!

"Hooray!" cried all the friends.

DISNEY·PIXAR
MONSTERS, INC.

Tough Audience

The sticker on the door read: 'Enter At Your Own Risk'. But Mike wasn't scared. He always collected the most laughs on the floor and he had never met a child he couldn't crack up. Tossing his microphone from one hand to the other, Mike sauntered through the wardrobe door to face his audience.

"Hey, how ya doin' tonight?" Mike greeted the child. The boy in the racing-car pyjamas just glared. "Did you hear the one about the monster who made it in show business? He really clawed his way to the top." Mike paused for a laugh, but the boy was silent. "Talk about making a killing!" Mike added. Still he got nothing.

"All right. I can see you're a tough audience. Enough of the B material." Mike pulled out the stops. He told his best jokes. He worked the room. He was on the stool, off the stool, hanging on the curtains, standing on the bedstead. But the child didn't even crack a smile.

Mike prepared to let the one about the seven-legged sea monster fly when he heard tapping on the wardrobe door.

"You know you really ought to get that checked," Mike said, pointing to the wardrobe. "You could have skeletons in there." The child didn't blink.

Mike pulled the door open a crack. "I'm working here," he whispered.

Sulley poked his head in. "Mikey, you're dying," he said. "You've been on for 20 minutes and you're getting nothing. There are plenty of other kids to make laugh tonight. You can come back to this one later."

"No way," Mike hissed. "When he laughs he's going to laugh big. I can feel it." A teddy bear sailed through the air and hit Mike in the eye. "See, Sulley? He's throwing me presents."

"Cut your losses, Mikey. Let this one go," Sulley pleaded.

"I'm telling you, I've almost got him," Mike spoke through clenched teeth, barely flinching when the unamused boy tossed a banana peel at him.

"And I'm telling you to give ... it ... up." Sulley pulled harder on Mike. Mike grabbed the door frame and braced himself. Suddenly Sulley lost his grip, and Mike flew backwards, skidding on the banana peel and falling flat on his face.

"Why, I oughta...." Mike leaped to his feet ready to charge Sulley but was interrupted by the sound of laughing. In fact, the child was laughing so hard tears streamed down his face. Mike high-fived Sulley. "You know, some kids just go for the physical comedy," he said with a shrug.

Games Old and New

It was a cold, rainy day and Bonnie was away for the weekend with her parents. Dolly and Mr Pricklepants sat by the window, feeling bored.

"Let's play draughts or bingo," Woody suggested. "I'm the champion!"

Trixie the triceratops snorted. "Please, Woody. Those old games are no fun," she said. "There are lots of great modern games on the computer!"

"Yeah!" Dolly cheered. "We'll see who's got the fastest joystick!"

Reluctantly, Woody joined the others at the computer. "Now all we have to do is decide which game to play," said Trixie. "I vote for Dinorace!"

Dolly shook her head. "No! Dress the Doll is much better."

"What are you talking about?" said Mr Pricklepants. "I say the Tyrolean Dances."

Then it was Woody's turn to give his opinion. "No way! We're playing Western Duels," he said, tapping the monitor.

"Hey, don't touch the screen – you'll leave fingerprints," snapped Trixie.

All four toys began to talk at once, as they argued over which game they should play. Even when Trixie pointed out they could play all four games, they couldn't agree on which one to start with.

The argument was really heating up when the computer's screen suddenly went dark. The storm outside had caused a power cut!

"The computer doesn't work without electricity," Trixie sobbed. Dolly and Mr Pricklepants sighed. It looked like they'd have a boring afternoon, after all.

But Woody had other ideas. After taking his friends back up to the bedroom, he explained the rules of bingo and set up the game.

Soon, every toy in the house was gathered around a bingo card. They whooped and cheered as Woody called out the numbers, and hurried to be the first to cross them off their card.

"Well, I have to admit that this is fun, Woody," said Trixie.

"The old games aren't so bad after all," Woody laughed. "And unlike your video games, they're blackout-proof!"

Trixie and Woody looked across the table, to where Dolly was giving Buzz a telling-off for cheating. Buzz was insisting he'd done nothing of the sort, and very quickly their voices began to get louder and louder.

"It looks like arguments are blackout-proof, too," giggled Trixie.

Woody laughed. "Yep!" he agreed. "They sure are!"

149

Disney
THE **RESCUERS**

Miss Bianca's First Rescue

The headquarters of the Rescue Aid Society was buzzing with activity. Mice from all over the world had gathered together for an emergency meeting. The Chairman of the Society had to shout to be heard over the noise.

"Attention, delegates!" he cried. "I have called this meeting because a canine urgently needs our help." He clapped his hands. "Mice scouts, bring in the distressed doggie!"

Two mice workers ran into the room leading a small dog with a long body and short little legs. His head was stuck inside a dog food tin.

"*Mama mia!*" cried the mouse from Italy.

"Arooooo!" howled the dog.

The mouse from Yemen suggested pulling the can off the dog. Four muscular mice set to work, pulling and tugging. But it held fast.

The mice finally decided that the can would have to be removed by mechanical means. The Zambian delegate suggested they could use a tin opener.

Suddenly the door to the meeting room flew open. In the entrance stood a pretty little mouse. She wore a fashionable coat and expensive perfume.

"Oh, excuse me," she said, "I seem to be in the wrong place. I'm looking for Micey's Department Store?

"Dear me," she continued, noticing the delegate with the tin opener. "What are you doing to that poor dog?"

"The dog is quite stuck, I'm afraid," the Chairman told her. "But the situation is under control."

The glamorous mouse pushed up her sleeves and marched over to the dog.

She kicked the top of the tin three times. Then she gave it a swift twist to the left. And the tin popped off!

"Hooray!" the mice all cheered happily.

The little mouse smiled. "That's how I open pickle jars at home," she explained. "Well, I'd best be on my way."

"Ah, Mr Chairman?" a voice piped up from the corner of the room. It was the Zambian delegate.

"Yes?" said the Chairman.

"I'd like to nominate Miss ... uh, Miss...." The delegate looked at the pretty mouse.

"Miss Bianca," she told him.

"I'd like to nominate Miss Bianca to become a member in the Rescue Aid Society," he said.

The Chairman turned to the rest of the mice delegates. "All in favour say, 'Aye!'"

"Aye!" all the mice cried.

"Woof!" the dog barked happily.

Miss Bianca smiled. "Well," she said, "I suppose Micey's can wait for another day."

THE JUNGLE BOOK

A Bear-y Tale

It was time for Mowgli, Bagheera and Baloo to go to bed.

"Goodnight, Man-cub," purred Bagheera.

"But I'm not sleepy yet," protested Mowgli. "I need a bedtime story."

"Bedtime story?" said Bagheera. "At this hour?"

Mowgli turned to the big bear. "Please, Baloo?"

"A bedtime story, huh...?" said Baloo. "Now, how do those things begin?"

"Once upon a time...." purred Bagheera.

"Oh, right.... Once upon a time ... in a house not far from this very jungle, there lived a clan of men," Baloo began.

"Real men?" asked Mowgli.

"Yep," said Baloo. "A father and a mother, and a little cub, just like you. Well, now, this clan, they cooked their food, and one day, don't you know, they made a mighty tasty stew ... only thing was, when they sat down to eat, it was just too hot. So the mother got an idea. They'd go for a walk in the jungle and, by the time they got back, their stew would be nice and cool. But do you know what happened next?"

"No," Mowgli said.

"Well, that family had barely been gone a minute, when an old bear came wandering up, and stuck his nose into the Man-house."

"He did?" gasped Mowgli.

"Well, now, can you blame him? That stew just smelled so awfully good. And the next thing you know, he was tastin' it – startin' with the biggest bowl, but that was still too hot. So next he tried the middle bowl, but that was too cold. So – he tried the littlest bowl, and, don't you know, it was just right! That old bear didn't mean to, but he ate the whole thing right up!"

"What happened next?" said Mowgli.

"Oh, well, after that, this bear, he started to get tired. Real tired. And, don't you know, Little Britches, that right there in that house, looking so soft and comfortable, were three cushy-lookin' pads ... I think men call them 'beds'. Anyway, that bear, he had to try them, too. Naturally, he laid down on the biggest one first. But it was too hard. So he tried the middle one, but that was much, much too soft. So, he tried the littlest one, and, son, let me tell you, that thing was so comfortable he fell asleep right then and there! And he would have slept clear through the next full moon ... if only that family hadn't returned and –"

"And what?" Mowgli asked breathlessly.

"And startled that bear so much he ran back into the jungle ... full belly and all."

Mowgli smiled and tried to cover a big yawn. "Is that a true story, Baloo?"

The bear grinned. "Would I ever tell you a tall tale, Little Britches?"

A Rash Judgement

Chick Hicks rocketed along the open racetrack. "There's only one winner in tomorrow's race," he shouted. "Chick Hicks!"

His engine roared as he began the final lap, but then it started to splutter. Rubber screeched and the next thing he knew, he was heading face first into a pile of tyres.

"Oh no! I've ruined my sponsor's sticker," he cried in disappointment.

Chick Hicks drove off to find his manager, who didn't seem impressed by the damage.

"It'll be two days before your new sticker gets here," his manager said.

Chick Hicks grumbled. He was devastated.

"Hey, Chick! What's up?" asked Lightning McQueen, who couldn't help overhearing.

"Outta my way," Chick Hicks grunted. "This ain't my day."

"Hang in there. We'll find a way," Lightning McQueen assured him. "In Radiator Springs!"

In Radiator Springs, the townsfolk were out and about as usual. Outside the famous tyre shop, Luigi and Guido were arranging their prized wheels.

"What are those jalopies up to? Nothin' pretty!" Chick Hicks chuckled meanly.

"Chick," said Lightning McQueen. "Don't you think you've made a rash judgement?"

Chick Hicks ignored him.

At last they came to Ramone's body-art shop. Chick Hicks remained unimpressed.

"This is my friend, Chick! He's scratched his sticker," Lightning McQueen explained. "Can you help him?"

Ramone looked at Chick Hick's paintwork. "Of course! It won't take long."

In the rev of an engine, Ramone had finished.

"There you are, pal! Do you like the new sticker?"

Lightning McQueen was impressed with the vibrant Dinoco logo, but Chick Hick's glowered at it. "Barely good enough," he spat. "I'm outta here. So long, jalopies!" He sped off, leaving the others with gaping jaws, but as he raced away he felt his tyres slipping and sliding over puddles in the road.

"Not again!" Chick Hicks yelped.

BANG!

The others heard and gathered quickly, finding Chick Hicks in a complete mess of scratches, bumps and smoke.

"It'll be a while before you're back on track, Chick!" Guido giggled.

"Really! You've got a long list of repairs...." Ramone added.

"And a long list of apologies!" Lightning McQueen laughed.

Chick nodded sulkily. They were right. And he had better start apologizing quickly!

DISNEY·PIXAR
TOY STORY 3

A Big Suprise

The toys were having an emergency meeting in Bonnie's room. "Buttercup and Bullseye have been missing since yesterday," Woody announced. "And the Potato Heads have been gone since this morning. We have to find out where they are before Bonnie gets home."

The other toys agreed. Splitting into three groups, they set off to explore the house. Each group had a walkie-talkie so they could keep in touch with the others as they searched for their missing friends.

In the hall, Woody, Buzz and Jessie couldn't see any sign of the missing toys.

Team Two – made up of Rex, Hamm and Trixie – had nothing to report in the kitchen, either, but there was something going on right next door.

"This is Team Three," Dolly whispered into the walkie-talkie. "Something's moving in the living room. We're checking it out."

Out in the hall, Buzz gasped as Dolly's voice went silent. There was a crackle over the radio, as if someone was struggling. "Team Three, what's going on?" Buzz barked. "Dolly?"

Suddenly, Rex's voice crackled out of the walkie-talkie. "It's Bonnie's mother," he whispered. "She's come to take us away!"

Before Buzz could answer, Rex's voice became a hiss of static. "Rex?" Buzz said, turning the dial. It was no use. The other two teams were no longer answering.

"Why would she be toynapping us?" Woody wondered.

"Maybe she wants to throw us away," said Jessie.

The hall door creaked open and Bonnie's mum stepped into the room.

The terrified toys dropped and kept very still as Bonnie's mum picked them up and stuffed them into a dark bag.

When the lights came back on, Woody recognized a friendly face. "Bullseye! Glad to see you, buddy," he said, studying their odd surroundings. "Even if I don't know where we are."

All the toys huddled together. "Are they really throwing us away?" Jessie wondered.

Just then, they all heard Bonnie's voice getting closer. Part of the wall peeled away, letting in the light.

"Surprise, dear!" said Bonnie's mum. Bonnie looked down at her toys and jumped for joy.

"Wow! A bouncy castle!" she cheered, admiring her amazing new gift. "Full of all my favourite toys!"

Bonnie's mum hadn't been throwing the toys away, she'd been gathering them up as a surprise. Little did she realize, she gave the toys a pretty big surprise, too!

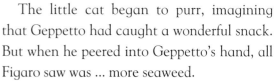

Fish Food

Figaro the cat was scared. He was also hungry. But he knew there wouldn't be any dinner. Figaro, Geppetto and Cleo the goldfish had just been swallowed by a whale – and now they were in its stomach!

"Don't worry, Figaro," Geppetto said, seeing the cat's worried look. "We'll get out of here somehow – and when we do, we'll keep searching for Pinocchio."

That Pinocchio! Figaro growled. After all that Geppetto and the Blue Fairy had done for Pinocchio, he had run away from home without a care in the world. That was how they had ended up inside the whale! Now what would become of them?

Figaro decided then and there that if they ever found Pinocchio, he was going to use both of the wooden boy's legs as scratching posts. It would serve him right.

Meanwhile, Geppetto was peering into the puddle of water at the bottom of the whale's stomach. Figaro watched curiously.

"Let's see," Geppetto murmured, bending over and poking at the water. "There must be something in here ... Aha!" Geppetto cried happily. He was clutching a small, soggy clump of seaweed.

Figaro blinked. Seaweed?

A moment later, Geppetto bent down again. "Aha!" he cried once more.

The little cat began to purr, imagining that Geppetto had caught a wonderful snack. But when he peered into Geppetto's hand, all Figaro saw was ... more seaweed.

Seaweed is fish food, Figaro thought with a scowl. Surely Geppetto didn't expect him to eat that for dinner?

But, as he watched, Geppetto carefully divided the seaweed into three portions. He placed one portion in Cleo's bowl. He set one portion in front of Figaro. The third he kept for himself.

"Let's eat!" Geppetto said, smiling bravely.

Figaro sniffed his seaweed. He stirred it around with his paw. But he just couldn't eat the seaweed. With a twitch of his tail, Figaro turned away.

Geppetto watched the little cat with sad eyes. Figaro sighed. He couldn't help but feel ungrateful.

Reluctantly, Figaro turned back to his dinner. He nibbled at the seaweed. It was cold. It was slimy. But it tasted like – fish!

Figaro gobbled down the rest of his meal. With his belly full, the little cat felt better. He decided that if they found Pinocchio, he would only use one of the puppet-boy's legs to sharpen his claws on.

Probably.

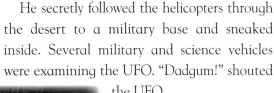

Unidentified Flying Mater

In Radiator Springs, a hubcap flew past Mater and Lightning McQueen. "Hey, look – a UFO!" Mater shouted. "And I know, 'cause I seen one once."

Mater began to tell his friend a tale about the time he saw a spaceship. He had pulled up to a level crossing in the desert when suddenly he saw a UFO floating right in front of him! "Well, hey there," he said. "My name is Mater."

"My name is Mator," the UFO replied.

That sounded a lot like his own name, the tow truck thought. "Should I take you to my litre?"

"Your leader," the UFO echoed. Mater led the UFO to the spot where he kept his oil cans. "Here are all my litres," he said.

The UFO looked excited. Mater grabbed a can and drank the oil through a straw. When he glanced over, the UFO was slurping from a large oil drum. Later, Mater showed his new friend around. They did all of Mater's favourite things, including tractor tipping. Then his new friend taught Mater how to fly! "We're going to be best friends forever!" Mater exclaimed.

Suddenly, a giant magnet dropped from the sky. ZING! It grabbed the UFO and pulled him upwards. Three military helicopters were hovering overhead.

"Mator! I'll save you!" Mater yelled.

He secretly followed the helicopters through the desert to a military base and sneaked inside. Several military and science vehicles were examining the UFO. "Dadgum!" shouted the UFO.

"I think he's trying to communicate!" one of the scientists said. "Where is Dr Abschleppwagen?"

Mater quickly put on a scientist disguise. "Here I am!" he announced.

"What does 'dadgum' mean?" asked one scientist.

"It means...." Mater began. Then he flicked a switch, turning off the magnet! Mater and Mator flew away at top speed. Everyone from the military base chased after them....

In Radiator Springs, Lightning interrupted. "Do you expect me to believe that?"

"You should," Mater said. "You was there, too!" Then he continued his story. Except this time, Mater described how Lightning was zooming across the desert too. Suddenly, an enormous mother ship appeared. It pulled Mater, Mator and Lightning aboard in a beam of light. Then the ship blasted into space. After a quick ride through space, it was time for Mater and Lightning to get back.

"Thank you!" Mater called when they were safely home. He would miss his new friend, Mator, but he was glad the little UFO was safe.

Disney
The Fox and the Hound

A Party of Three

The Widow Tweed hummed cheerfully as she decorated her cottage. Tod, the little fox she had adopted not long ago, watched with excitement. This was his first birthday in his new home!

"Now, Tod," said the widow, "who shall we invite to your party?"

Tod jumped on the windowsill and looked over at Amos Slade's farm. The Widow Tweed knew what that meant – Tod wanted his friend Copper the hound dog to share in the celebration. "I know Copper is your friend," she said, "but what if Amos catches him over here? There's no telling what that old coot might do!"

Tod jumped on the kind woman's lap and gazed up at her with big, sad eyes. "Oh, Tod! Stop looking at me like that. Well – all right! You can ask Copper over just this once!"

"I'm not supposed to leave the yard," Copper explained when Tod invited him. "I'll get in trouble with my master."

"Don't worry," Tod said. "I've got it all figured out." He lifted up one of the hound dog's floppy ears and whispered his plan.

Soon Tod showed up in Amos Slade's chicken yard. He ran among the birds, causing them to flap their wings and cluck in panic. That was Copper's signal to bark as loudly as he could. Slade burst out of the cabin just in time to see Copper chasing Tod into the woods.

"Follow me!" yelled Tod to Copper. He led his friend through a series of hollow logs, and then through a long, underground burrow. When the two pals emerged above ground, they were right outside Tod's back door. The Widow Tweed was waiting.

"Quick!" she said, shooing the two into the cottage.

While Slade wandered around the woods trying to find Tod and Copper, the party festivities at the Widow Tweed's were just beginning. The three played hide-and-seek, pin-the-tail-on-the-donkey and drop-the-clothes-peg-in-the-jug. Tod won every game. Finally, it was time to cut the cake. After everyone had seconds, the widow spied Slade coming out of the woods. She let Copper out through the back door, where he stood barking ferociously.

"Good tracking, Copper!" Slade cried. "Did you chase that no-good fox all the way through the woods?" Copper looked up at his master and wagged his tail. "Copper," Slade said, "what's that on your face?" The hound turned his head and quickly licked the cake crumbs off his muzzle. "Hmmm," said Slade. "Must be seeing things. Let's go home then."

Inside the cosy cottage, Tod smiled. It had been a wonderful birthday – and sharing it with his best friend had been the icing on the cake!

A Smile for Chuckles

Chuckles the clown gazed glumly out of Bonnie's bedroom window. *Poor Chuckles,* thought Jessie. *He always looks so sad.*

The clown's big frown gave Jessie an idea. "We'll each try to get him to smile," she said, rounding up her friends. "The first to succeed will be crowned 'The Funniest Toy'!"

After taking some time to prepare, the toys began their acts. Buttercup the unicorn was up first. "Look, pal!" he cried, standing on one leg as he balanced a spinning ball on his horn. "I'm a juggling unicorn!"

Chuckles frowned. "Um ... right," he said.

Buttercup trudged back to the others, disappointed. "I thought a clown would enjoy a good circus number," he said.

Jessie hopped onto Bullseye's back. "Maybe he prefers the rodeo!" she suggested.

She twirled her lasso as Bullseye hopped and bucked around the room. It was quite a show, but Chuckles didn't look impressed.

Next it was the turn of Mr and Mrs Potato Head. They were barely recognizable as they stumbled out from below the bed. Their arms were where their eyes should be, their mouths were poking out of their earholes and their noses were on top of their heads!

"Oops, I feel a little mixed-up!" giggled Mrs Potato Head.

They really were a funny sight, but not funny enough to amuse Chuckles.

Jessie gathered her friends beside the house of cards Bonnie had built that morning, out of sight of Chuckles. "It sure is tough to get a smile out of him," Jessie said.

Suddenly, there was a loud *BOING!* and something whizzed over Jessie's head. "Run for cover!" she cried, as three little green balls bounced into the house of cards, knocking it flat.

"Comin' through!" the little green balls giggled.

The cards toppled down on Jessie and her friends, sending them sprawling onto the floor.

"What was that?" asked Buttercup.

"Maybe an earthquake," said Mrs Potato Head, looking worried.

Mr Potato Head knew better, though. The mess had been caused by the Peas-in-a-Pod toys, who loved bouncing around Bonnie's room. Mr Potato Head was about to give them a telling-off, when he heard a sound he'd never heard before.

Chuckles was laughing! "You peas are really funny," he chuckled.

Jessie was happy. The funniest toys had been found – but tidying up the mess they had made before Bonnie got home was going to be no laughing matter!

101 DALMATIANS

Lucky's Last Laugh

It was getting quite late at Pongo and Perdita's house, but their darling little puppies were still not asleep. It wasn't that they didn't want to go to sleep. At least most of them. No, the problem was that one of them wouldn't let them go to sleep – and that puppy was Lucky!

"And then, don't you remember, you guys, the part at the very beginning, when Thunderbolt jumped across that canyon? *Whoosh!* Like a rocket! Clear to the other side!" Lucky said.

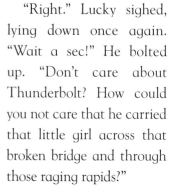

"Yes, we remember, Lucky," his sister Penny said with a groan. "How could we forget? You've reminded us 101 times!"

Lucky just smiled. "It was so great! And there was that part when –"

"Lucky!" wailed Rolly. "We all watched the same episode of *Thunderbolt* tonight. You don't have to tell us about it."

"Yeah, I know, but I just wanted to tell you about the part when Thunderbolt found the little girl, then ran back to tell the sheriff –"

"Lucky! It's late! We want to go to sleep!" barked Patch.

Lucky laid his head on his paws. "Okay," he said. "I'll be quiet."

All the puppies closed their eyes.

"Oh! But what about the part when the sheriff told Thunderbolt to climb up that cliff, and he got to the top, and he grabbed that rope with his teeth, and he pulled up the little girl –"

"Lucky!" yelped Pepper. "We don't care about Thunderbolt. We want to go to bed!"

"Right." Lucky sighed, lying down once again. "Wait a sec!" He bolted up. "Don't care about Thunderbolt? How could you not care that he carried that little girl across that broken bridge and through those raging rapids?"

"We mean," said Freckles, "we want you to be quiet so we can go to sleep!"

"You mean," said Lucky, "you don't want me to tell you about the last part where Thunderbolt ran back to the mountains and into that cave and found that amazing thing?"

"Yes!" Lucky's siblings shouted together.

"Why didn't you say so?" replied Lucky, closing his eyes. "Goodnight."

For a minute, everyone enjoyed the silence. Then Penny sat up.

"Hey, wait a minute," she said. "What thing did he find?"

"Yeah," said Patch. "I missed that part."

"Me, too," said Rolly. "What was it exactly that he found, Lucky? Tell us."

But there was no answer. Lucky was fast asleep. And now the *other* Dalmatian puppies were wide awake!

Disney · PIXAR

MONSTERS, INC.

Bedtime for Billy

Mike and his friend, Sulley, were excited about their evening. They were monster-sitting for Mike's nephew, Billy. Billy's mother told her son to be good, and he said that he would.

"Everything will be fine, sis," said Mike. "Sulley and I will take good care of the little guy. You don't have to worry."

Billy's parents kissed him goodbye and hopped in the car. The three monsters went inside and ate pizza and popcorn while they watched classic movies like *Gross Encounters of the Kid Kind*. After the movies were over, the three monsters listened to music, sang and danced. Billy and Mike even had a video game contest! The night flew by and soon it was bedtime.

"It's time for some shut-eye, buddy," said Mike with a yawn. But putting Billy to bed wasn't going to be that easy. There was one very important detail that Billy's mother had forgotten to tell her monster-sitters. He was scared of the dark!

"Aaaaahhh!" screamed Billy.

"Wh-wh-what is it?" shouted Mike as he and Sulley ran back into the bedroom.

"There's a kid hiding in the c-closet...." stammered Billy. "It wants to g-get me!"

Mike and Sulley searched for human children. They checked the whole room, once with the lights on and twice with the lights off.

"There aren't any kids in the closet," said Mike.

"All clear under the bed," announced Sulley.

"See, there's nothing to worry about," Mike said. "You can go to sleep now."

But Billy was still frightened. Mike and Sulley quickly realized they had to come up with another plan. How could they show Billy that children weren't scary?

"I've got it!" exclaimed Mike. "The scrapbook!"

"You're a genius, Mikey!" declared Sulley.

The three monsters looked through the scrapbook. It was filled with photographs of monsters with children, newspaper clippings of them together and laugh reports.

"See, Billy," said Mike. "Human kids are not dangerous, and they love to have fun just like you."

"And they help us!" added Sulley. "Their laughter powers our city!"

"You know, Billy, sometimes human kids get scared of us," said Mike. "But once they see that we're funny and friendly, they realize there's no reason to be scared of monsters."

Billy soon fell fast asleep as Mike and Sulley watched from the doorway. "Another job well done, Mike," said Sulley.

A Dream Come True

Dusty was lost in a daydream. He imagined himself painted in the colours of the Jolly Wrenches, getting ready to go out on patrol with the greatest fighter jets, Echo and Bravo.

"We fly a lot faster than you," Echo warned. "We've got a huge area to cover."

Dusty sighed sadly. "I was hoping to make myself useful," he said.

Bravo smiled. "Well, if you've got your heart set on it.... After all, you are an honorary Jolly Wrench!"

Cheering with delight, Dusty took off behind the jets. They screamed through the air ahead of him, leaving him trailing in their wake.

Spinning his propeller at top speed, he hurried on. "I caught up with you," he panted, as he drew level with them over the ocean.

"Actually, we slowed down to wait for you," said Bravo. The jets explained that they usually flew much higher to avoid air resistance, but that it was too dangerous for Dusty to go that high.

"Does that mean I can't do anything to help you?" Dusty asked.

Echo rolled his eyes. "You're a rally champ, not a navy jet!"

Dusty's wings slumped. Echo was right. He was just a glorified crop duster. How could he compete with the navy's finest fighter jets?

Suddenly, a distress call crackled over the radio – "Control tower to Echo and Bravo. We've got a Mayday. A commercial aircraft has made an emergency water landing. It should be due west of your present location."

The jets' rockets fired, shooting them across the ocean at blistering speeds. The only problem was, they were going the wrong way!

"Hey, where are you guys going?" Dusty cried.

The jets explained that at their speeds they needed lots of room to turn. Before heading west, they had to fly south far enough so they could change direction and search for the downed plane.

Dusty didn't share the same problem. He banked to the west immediately and descended over the water. Almost at once, he spotted something large bobbing up and down in the middle of the sea.

"I found it!" he said, swooping down low. The plane was sinking fast, so Dusty radioed back to base and gave the the plane's location.

In no time, a helicopter rescue team arrived and began the job of saving the plane. At the same time, Echo and Bravo arrived, out of breath. "Good job, Dusty," they said. "You beat us here."

Dusty smiled. It seemed you didn't have to be super-fast to be useful, after all.

DUMBO

Ears a Job for You, Dumbo!

It had been a hard day for little Dumbo. It was bad enough that everyone made fun of his ears except his mother, but then they had put his mother in a cage, so Dumbo couldn't even be with the one person who loved him and treated him kindly.

What made things even worse was that Dumbo didn't have anything to do. It seemed that he was the only creature in the circus who didn't have a job. Everyone had a purpose except Dumbo. All he could do was feel sad and be laughed at.

Dumbo heaved a sigh and went for a walk through the circus tents. Soon, he found himself among the refreshment stalls. Everyone here had a job, too. Some were squeezing lemons to make lemonade. Others were popping popcorn or roasting peanuts. Wonderful smells filled the air.

Finally, Dumbo came to a little candyfloss wagon. The puffy cloud of sugar looked tempting, and Dumbo wanted a taste, but there were so many customers he couldn't get close enough.

Suddenly Dumbo heard a loud buzzing. Then all the customers waved their hands over their heads and ran away.

The smell of sugar had attracted a swarm of nasty flies!

"Scat!" cried the candyfloss man. "Go away before you scare off my customers."

Dumbo reached out his trunk to smell the delicious candyfloss.

"Not you, Dumbo!" the candyfloss man cried. "It's bad enough chasing flies. Do I have to chase elephants, too?"

Poor Dumbo was startled. With a snort, he sucked candyfloss right up his nose. *AH-CHOO!* When he sneezed, Dumbo's ears flapped and something amazing happened.

"Remarkable!" cried the candyfloss man. "All the flies are gone. They think your ears are giant fly swatters!"

The candyfloss man patted Dumbo's head. "How would you like a job?"

Dumbo nodded enthusiastically and set to work waving his ears. Soon, the candyfloss stall was the most popular refreshment stall in the circus – and had the least flies. But, best of all, Dumbo now had something to do to take his mind off his troubles. He was still sad, but things didn't seem quite so bad. And, who knew, perhaps soon he would have his mother back.

"I wonder what other amazing things those big ears can do?" said the candyfloss man, giving Dumbo a friendly smile. "I'll bet they carry you far...."

Disney · PIXAR
FINDING
NEMO

Hide, Dude!

"Come on, Squirt!" Nemo cried happily. "Race you to the coral shelf!"

Nemo took off, pumping his mismatched fins as hard as he could. His young sea turtle friend laughed and swam after him.

Squirt was visiting Nemo at his home on the reef. "This way, dude!" Squirt yelled. "I'm catching some rad current over here!"

Nemo hesitated for just a second, watching as his friend tumbled along past some stinging coral. Squirt was so brave! Even after all that Nemo had been through – being captured by a scuba diver, then escaping from a tank to find his way home again – he still got scared sometimes.

With a deep breath, he threw himself into the current. He tumbled after Squirt, fins flying as the water carried him along. Finally, he came out the other end of the current, landing in the still ocean beside Squirt.

He giggled. "Hey, that was fun!" he cried. "Let's do it again! Squirt? Squirt, what's wrong?"

The sea turtle was staring into the distance, his eyes wide. "Hide, dude!" Squirt cried.

Before Nemo could respond, Squirt's head and legs popped into his shell and he landed on the sea floor with a flop.

Nemo started trembling. What had scared Squirt so much?

Nemo looked around, expecting to see a shark. But all he could see nearby were a few pieces of coral with a lone Spanish dancer floating along above them. He swam down and tapped on Squirt's shell. "Hey," he said. "What is it? There's nothing scary here."

"Whew!" Squirt's head popped out. He looked around, then gasped and hid again. When he spoke, his voice was muffled. "It's totally still there!"

Nemo blinked and looked around again. Again, all he saw were the coral and the Spanish dancer.

"Hey, wait a minute," he said, suddenly realizing something. "Haven't you ever seen a Spanish dancer before?"

"A – a Spanish wha-huh?" Squirt asked, still muffled.

Nemo knocked on his friend's shell again. "It's a kind of sea slug," he explained. "Don't worry, Spanish dancers are nice – you don't have to be scared. I promise."

Finally Squirt's head popped out again. He smiled sheepishly at Nemo.

"Sorry, dude," he said. "I never saw one of those before. It totally freaked me out."

"It's okay." Nemo smiled back. He already knew that new things could be scary – and now he knew he wasn't the only one who thought so. "Come on, let's go and play," he said.

DISNEP
THE
LION KING

The Best Fisherman of All

Simba and his friends Timon and Pumbaa were hungry. They wandered through the forest until they came to an old, rotten tree. Timon knocked on the trunk.

"What's it sound like, Timon?" Pumbaa asked.

"Like our breakfast!" Timon replied.

He yanked at the bark and hundreds of grubs slithered out.

Timon handed Simba a fat grub.

"No, thanks." Simba sighed. "I'm tired of grubs."

"Well, the ants are tasty," said Timon. "They come in two flavours. Red and black."

Simba shook his head. "Don't you eat anything but bugs?"

"Fish!" Pumbaa declared.

"I love fish!" Simba exclaimed.

"Why didn't you say so?" said Timon. "There's a pond at the end of this trail." The three friends started off down the trail.

"What now?" asked Simba when they arrived at the pond.

"That's the problem!" said Timon. "We're not the best fishermen in the world."

"I'll teach you!" Simba said.

The lion climbed up a tree and crawled onto a branch that hung over the water. Then he snatched a fish out of the water.

"See!" Simba said, jumping to the ground nimbly. "Not a problem. Fishing's easy."

"Not for me!" Timon cried. He dangled from the branch, but his arms weren't long enough to reach the fish.

Simba laughed. "Better let Pumbaa try."

"What a joke!" cried Timon. "Pumbaa can't even climb this tree."

"Want to bet?" asked Pumbaa indignantly.

"Stay there," Timon warned. "I don't think this branch is strong enough for both of us."

With a hop, Pumbaa landed on the branch next to Timon. The limb started to bend.

"Yikes!" Timon cried as he leaped to another tree.

CRACK! The branch broke under Pumbaa. With a squeal, he landed in the pond. The splash was enormous!

Simba, sitting on the bank, was soaked. Timon was nearly blasted from his perch. Pond water fell like rain all around them.

Simba opened his eyes and started to laugh. So did Timon.

Pumbaa was sitting in a pool of mud where the pond had been. He'd splashed so much water out that dozens of fish now squirmed on the ground, just waiting to be gobbled up.

"Wow!" Timon cried. "I think Pumbaa is the very best fisherman of all!"

Rescue Squad Mater

Red the fire engine was watering some flowers in front of the fire station. "I used to be a fire engine," Mater said to him, out of the blue. Then he began to tell the story of Rescue Squad Mater....

Rescue Squad Mater was at the fire station when an emergency call came in. "Fire in progress at 120 Car Michael Way."

Rescue Squad Mater recognized that address. "That's the old gasoline and match factory!" he exclaimed. He zoomed out of the station and roared down the street. Moments later, Rescue Squad Mater sped up to the burning building. Rescue Squad Mater aimed a water hose and started spraying. He bravely battled the flames, ignoring the danger.

"Mater," Lightning said, stopping the story. "I can't believe you were a fire engine."

"You remember, don't you?" Mater replied. "You were there, too!" Then he went on telling his tale. The fire had spread through the entire factory, but Rescue Squad Mater still continued to battle it. Suddenly, a frightened voice called out. "Ahh! Help! Please, help!" Lightning was stuck on the top floor of the burning building!

The rescue truck began to raise his ladder towards the top floor. Soon the ladder was right beneath Lightning. Would there be enough time for Rescue Squad Mater to get him to the ground – before the factory exploded? The crowd watched, waiting on the edges of their tyre treads.

KA-BLAM!

The factory blew up in a huge explosion! Luckily, Lightning was out of the building by then. Mater used his ladder to lift him into an ambulance. Finally, Mater turned towards the crowd and smiled.

When Lightning arrived at the hospital, he was rushed into the operating room. A whole team of nurses was there, too. Lightning looked around. Where was the doctor? Then he heard a nurse's voice over the loudspeaker. "Paging Dr Mater."

Lightning blinked. Had he heard that right? Seconds later, the doctor rolled in. Lightning could hardly believe his eyes. It was Mater! "Mater, you're a doctor, too?"

"That's right, buddy," replied Dr Mater.

Lightning spotted Dr Mater's diplomas on the wall. "Clear!" Dr Mater called out as he swung the arm of a scary-looking medical instrument towards Lightning. Then Mater stopped telling his story.

"What happened?" Lightning asked.

"I saved your life," Mater said.

"Whaaa...?" Lightning was pretty sure he would remember something like that.

Survival of the Smallest

It was the first day of summer, and Dot and the other Blueberries were getting ready for a big adventure. They were heading out for the First Annual Blueberry Wilderness Expedition. Their journey would take them to the thicket of tall grasses next to the ant colony. It was only a few metres from home – but, to a little ant, it seemed like an awfully long way.

As the group prepared to leave, some boy ants arrived to tease them.

"How do you expect to go on an expedition without supplies?" asked Jordy.

Dot put her hands on her hips. "For your information," she said in a superior tone, "the whole point is to survive just using our smarts. Whatever we need, we'll make when we get there."

The Blueberries hiked a few metres from the ant colony, then Dot consulted her survival manual. "Okay," she said, "the first thing we need to do is build a shelter from the sun."

"I know!" Daisy volunteered. "We could make a hut. All we have to do is stick twigs into the dirt side by side to make the walls, then lay leaves over the top for the roof."

The rest of the Blueberries decided this was a great idea. With a lot of teamwork and determination, they completed a shelter to hold the troop comfortably.

When they had finished, Dot looked at the manual again. "Now," said Dot, "it says here we need to protect our campsite."

So the girls dug a narrow trench in front of the hut, just as the manual instructed.

The girls gathered some seeds and went into their home-made hut to have some lunch.

A short while later, the girls heard a scream. When they went to investigate, the girls discovered Reed, Grub and Jordy at the bottom of the trench.

It was clear to the girls that the boys had been up to no good.

"Girls," said Dot, pointing to the boys, "observe one of the Blueberries' most common natural enemies – though certainly not one of the smartest." The other girls broke into fits of giggles.

When it was time for the Blueberries to pack up and hike home, the boys were still stuck in the trench. "Say the magic words and I'll get you out of there," said Dot.

"Okay, okay!" Reed, Grub and Jordy agreed.

"Well?" demanded Dot.

"Blueberries rock," the boys admitted.

Dot lowered down a ladder she had expertly made of sticks. "You bet we do!" she said, smiling. "'Cause if we can survive you, we can survive anything!"

Simply Tentacular

Twitch jumped, throwing his arms to the sky. A Sunnyside child had left Twitch's staff on a stool, and no matter how high he jumped, he just couldn't reach it.

Chunk, his rock-toy friend, came over to lend a hand. "No need for that, pal," said Chunk. "If we build a stairway with blocks, we'll walk right up!"

The friends tried to pull the basket of building blocks out from the shelf, but no matter how hard they tugged they couldn't budge it. "It's too heavy!" Chunk groaned.

"Hey, Stretch," called Twitch. "Can you lend a tentacle?"

The stretchy purple octopus toy gave a nod. "Sure I can!"

Wrapping her long arms around the other toys, who were holding on to the basket, Stretch pulled. The basket slid out easily. "Thanks!" cheered Chunk. "You're really strong!"

Stretch smiled sadly and slunk away across the room. "What's the matter with her?" Chunk wondered. "I paid her a compliment, but she doesn't look happy."

As they built the stairs to get the staff back, Twitch reminded his friend that Stretch was a girl, and sometimes she liked to be treated as one.

"But it's not my fault," said Chunk. "She doesn't look much like a girl!"

That gave Twitch an idea! Chunk was right, Stretch needed some help with her look – and he knew just the person to ask.

"Barbie!" he cried. "Please can I borrow a few items?"

Barbie looked surprised, but she was always happy to help a friend. "No problem! What do you need?"

After borrowing a few things from Barbie, Twitch tracked down Stretch and set to work. In no time, he was finished. He stepped back to admire his handiwork, then called for the others. "Hey, everybody! Gather around."

The other toys came racing over. "Is something the matter?" asked Chunk, getting ready to switch to his angry face if needed.

Twitch laughed. "No, everything's fine!" he said. "I just want to introduce you to Stretch and her new look!"

Everyone gasped as Stretch stepped into view. She wore a different dress on each pair of tentacles, and on her head sat a beautiful hat decorated with colourful flowers.

Stretch smiled happily as she twirled round and spun for her friends, who clapped and cheered her new look. "Sheer elegance, right?" she said.

All her friends agreed. Barbie always looked great in her outfits, but only Stretch could wear four of them at the same time!

THE INCREDIBLES

Diamond Disaster

Mr Incredible, in his secret identify as Bob Parr, was at the museum, where a new diamond exhibition was being held. The museum's owner, Mr Bradbury, wasn't happy to see him.

"I just need to check the system to make sure it complies with Insuricare's standards before we upgrade your policy to cover the diamonds," Bob explained.

Mr Bradbury snorted and began to show off the museum's state-of-the-art security system. He pointed out the hidden cameras watching the visitors' every move. He indicated the futuristic-looking laser cannons, designed to blast anyone who was up to no good.

Finally, Mr Bradbury showed off the most prized part of the whole system – a fleet of robot security guards he insisted were indestructible.

Bob wasn't all that impressed. Back during his Super days, he'd seen – and destroyed – much more impressive security systems while attacking the headquarters of various supervillains. Still, it all seemed up to the job of keeping the diamonds safe.

He and Mr Bradbury stepped outside to arrange the insurance, but they both gasped when the museum's alarm began to ring.

"Someone is stealing the diamonds!" yelped a young security guard, frantically running out of the building.

Bob's hero instincts quickly kicked in. "I can help!" he said, preparing to race back into the museum. Mr Bradbury stopped him.

"Not to worry. My system will stop the thief. It's incredible," said the museum owner. He sat on a bench and started to go over again how impressive his security was. He was just getting to the part about the motion-tracking lasers when the guard interrupted.

"The lasers misfired and the robots are out of control!" the guard cried.

Mr Bradbury's face fell as an explosion rocked the building. He stood up, suddenly panicked. If those diamonds got stolen, he was ruined!

Suddenly, a masked thief raced out through the museum's front door, carrying a bag over his shoulder. The thief was big and strong. He easily shoved Mr Bradbury aside as he raced towards the main road.

At the sound of the museum owner's cry, Bob turned. The robber ran straight into him, thudding his face against Bob's broad chest.

For a moment, the robber staggered, trying to stay upright, then he slumped to the ground, unconscious.

Mr Bradbury cheered with relief and thanked Bob for his help. "That was incredible!" he cried.

Bob shrugged. "I'm just here to save the day," he said. "One policy at a time!"

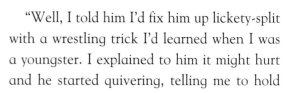

Fabulous Doc

On a quiet day in Radiator Springs, Doc had recruited his two friends Sally and Lightning McQueen to help clean out his garage. It was a mess and needed all wheels on deck if he was going to see it tidy again.

"Look at all the dust, Doc! It's about time this place got a good cleaning," said Sally.

"Hey, what's this?" asked Lightning McQueen.

"Just an old newspaper clipping," said Doc, quickly.

Lightning McQueen read the article closely. He couldn't believe his eyes. "You mean you used to be a wrestler?"

"No," said Doc. "I used wrestling moves to help someone ages ago...."

"Would you tell us about it?" asked Sally.

"It was during a big race," he began. "I was in the final lap with Gorgeous Gus O'Line. Head-to-head. But all of a sudden, the announcer cried out that Gus was in trouble."

"I've heard that before at the races!" laughed Lightning McQueen, who had got into a few tricky situations himself on track.

"I won, of course. But had no idea what had happened," Doc continued. "I found Gus with a busted tyre; dislocated his semi-axle. He was convinced his racing days were over."

"And were they?" asked Sally, on the edge of her bumper.

"Well, I told him I'd fix him up lickety-split with a wrestling trick I'd learned when I was a youngster. I explained to him it might hurt and he started quivering, telling me to hold on ... but I slammed the wheel back into place."

"Ooh, painful," said Lightning McQueen. He'd had few injuries himself in the past.

"Yup! And it worked. The cameras were flashing and Gus felt like new again. He couldn't thank me enough," Doc smiled. "Gus suggested I give up racing and take up medicine ... or wrestling! Both seemed like silly notions!"

"And yet here you are, a doctor to friends," said Sally, grinning.

Lightning McQueen had heard a lot about Doc's racing days, but very little about his medical training. "You did graduate in medicine, didn't you?" he wondered.

Doc ignored the question with a *humph*. "Your semi-axle looks dislocated, Lightning!" He turned to Sally. "Wanna help me put it back into place? It's going to be very painful!"

Lightning McQueen paled as Doc drew nearer. "I'm fine!" he said. "Though I'm sure you're a real pro at it!"

One thing was for sure, Lightning McQueen would never question Doc's medical expertise ever again.

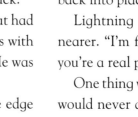

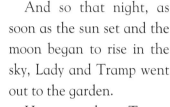

In the Doghouse

"Good morning, Tramp," said Lady, with a yawn and a stretch. She rolled over on her silk cushion. "Wasn't that just the most wonderful night's sleep?"

But Tramp's night's sleep had been far from wonderful. In fact, he hadn't had much sleep at all.

The past night had been Tramp's first sleeping in Lady's house ... or in any house, come to think of it.

"How do you do it?" he grumbled. "That bed is so soft I feel like I'm sinking into a feather pool. And between Jim Dear's snoring and the baby's crying, I could barely hear the crickets chirping."

"Oh dear," Lady said, feeling truly sorry for him. "Well, Jim Dear and Darling love you so – I'm sure they'd let you sleep up on their bed tonight. There's nothing in the world better than that!"

But Tramp shook his head. "I'm afraid it's the outdoors I need," he explained. "I mean, I know you grew up this way and all ... but it's so much fun to sleep under the moon and the stars. There's nothing to howl at in this bedroom."

"You can see the moon out of the window," Lady told him.

"It's not the same," he sighed. Then he had a thought. "You know, we've still got that fine doghouse in the garden. What do you say we go back out there tonight? It'll be like a honeymoon!"

Lady looked at poor Tramp's tired eyes. "Well ... okay."

And so that night, as soon as the sun set and the moon began to rise in the sky, Lady and Tramp went out to the garden.

Happy at last, Tramp turned three times and then plopped down. "Oh, how I love the feel of cool dirt on my belly!" he said with a dreamy smile, while Lady gingerly peeked into the dark kennel. The stars were not even out, and already she missed the comforts of Jim Dear and Darling's room.

Tramp watched as Lady stretched out on the kennel floor, then got up and moved outside, then back in once again. It was plain to see – try as she might, Lady just could not relax on the cold, hard ground.

"Don't worry," Tramp announced, "I have an idea."

And with that, he ran into the house ... and in seconds reappeared with Lady's cushion in his teeth. Carefully, he swept the kennel with his tail, and laid the cushion down just the way Lady liked it.

Lady smiled and lay down. And, do you know what? That night, they both had the sweetest dreams either one had ever had.

A Snappy New Ship

"My ship, my beautiful ship!" Captain Hook moaned. It had not been a good day for the pirate. Peter Pan and the Darling children had stolen his ship. And now, Hook was stranded on an island with Smee and the other pirates, their rowing boat having been chomped to bits by the crocodile.

"It's a very nice island, Captain," said Smee, trying to cheer up his boss. "And you could use a holiday."

Captain Hook turned to Smee with a furious look on his face. "Pirates don't take holidays! Pirates seek revenge! Which is precisely what we are going to do, as soon as we have a new ship to sail in."

Smee looked around. "Where are we going to find a ship around here, sir?" he asked.

"*We* aren't going to find one," Captain Hook answered. "You and the rest of this mangy crew are going to *build* one! And I don't mean a little one either. I mean a big, menacing, fit-for-a-magnificent-pirate-like-me one!"

For weeks, the pirates chopped trees and cut them into planks for the ship. They whittled thousands of pegs to use for nails, and crushed countless berries to use for paint. "You're not moving fast enough!" Hook complained as he sat in the shade, sipping juice out of a pineapple.

Finally, an exhausted Smee fetched Hook as he awoke from his afternoon nap.

"It's ready, Captain!" he announced.

Even Hook had to admit the ship was magnificent. Shaped like a giant crocodile, it was painted a reptilian shade of green. "No one will dare come near this ship. Not even that pesky crocodile. He won't want to tussle with anything this terrifying," Smee assured him.

Captain Hook was delighted. "We set sail tomorrow!" he crowed.

That night, Smee couldn't resist putting one more finishing touch on the ship. He painted a row of eyelashes on the crocodile's eyelids.

The next morning, Captain Hook and the crew climbed aboard and pushed off. The ticking crocodile soon appeared.

"Smee!" yelled a terrified Captain Hook. "I thought you said he wouldn't come near us!"

"But look how calm he is," said Smee, puzzled. "He's even smiling!"

Smee leaned over the side of the railing. "You know, it might be those eyelashes I painted. Maybe the croc thinks the ship is its mother."

Hook lunged at Smee. "You made my ship look like a *mother* crocodile? This vessel is supposed to be terrifying!"

"Mothers *can* be terrifying, sir," said Smee. "You should have seen mine when I told her I was going to become a pirate!"

Adventurous Imagination

Baymax, Hiro and the other heroes were all in costume, searching around Akuma Island for signs of trouble. There didn't seem to be very much going on, so Fred began to narrate what they were doing in an attempt to make it more exciting.

"The fearless Fred's Angels enter the mysterious fortress of the enemy," he said in a dramatic voice.

GoGo rolled her eyes. "It's just a hallway, Fred."

Fred laughed and pointed out that a real tech genius should know that nothing is really as it seems, and that danger could be lurking around every corner.

Suddenly, Fred gasped. "Did you hear that? We triggered a silent alarm!" he whispered. GoGo tried to ask how he could hear it if it was silent, but before she could finish they tumbled down into a hole.

"A trap is triggered, and Fred's Angels fall into emptiness!" cried Fred, as the others yelped and screamed around him.

They landed in a hi-tech underground complex, and quickly found themselves tangled in something sticky. "Oh no!" Fred said. "Our heroes have encountered a plasma coil trap!"

A cloaked figure stepped from the shadows. His rat-like face pulled into a sneer. "And there's nothing you can do about it!" he sniggered.

Wasabi tore through the bonds easily.

"Thanks to Wasabi and his deadly blades, Fred's Angels break free and are ready to fight!" Fred said.

"GoGo attacks first, and her brave leader, Fred, backs her up," he said, describing the battle unfolding before his eyes.

"Nothing can defeat Dr Rat," warned the villain, using a power blast to push them all back.

Fred gritted his teeth. "Baymax prepares to fight back with the help of his undefeatable leader," Fred shouted out.

GoGo tapped him on the shoulder. Fred blinked. The underground complex faded away, replaced by a crumbling sewer. He looked around. The plasma coil trap was just a lot of spider's webs, and the evil Dr Rat was just an ordinary little rodent. Fred had let his imagination run away with him again.

"If you hadn't tripped on your tail, we wouldn't have tumbled down this ramp!" GoGo said. "Reality is not like your comic books."

Fred grinned broadly. GoGo was right. Being a real superhero wasn't like the comic books. It was better! "Having narrowly escaped the evil Dr Rat, Fred's Angels have no idea what awaits them around the next corner...." said Fred. Then he raced up the ramp and off in search of the next adventure.

Disney
Aladdin
Market Day

"What's wrong, Abu?" asked Aladdin. The normally lively little monkey hadn't been himself lately. Abu sat at the window gazing longingly towards the village.

"You're right," said Aladdin. "A trip to the marketplace is exactly what we need!"

The pair had a wonderful afternoon visiting old friends. Abu played with Salim the goat, joked with Kahlil the ox and teased Gamal the camel. He and Aladdin stopped at each vendor's stall to say "hello". Aladdin saw how happy Abu was in the hustle and bustle of the marketplace.

"You know, Abu," said Aladdin that night, "you can invite your friends from the marketplace to the palace any time you'd like." The monkey jumped up and down, hugging Aladdin and knocking off his hat. "Okay! Okay! You're welcome!" Aladdin laughed.

The next day, Abu disappeared first thing in the morning. When he returned, Salim and Kahlil were with him. "Welcome," said Jasmine. "Please make yourselves at home." But they already had. The goat was chewing on the curtains, and the ox was wandering in the garden, eating the tops off the flowers.

"We can always buy new curtains or plant new flowers. The important thing is that Abu is happy again," Aladdin said to Jasmine, who sighed and agreed reluctantly.

The following day, Gamal and several other camels arrived. Jasmine was not pleased when they spat on the new carpet. "Think of Abu," Aladdin told her.

The day after that, the fruit seller rolled through the palace with his cart. Another vendor came with a pile of smelly fish. Next came the lady who sold dates, and the man who sold pottery.

"Isn't it wonderful that Abu has so many friends?" said Aladdin.

"It is," Jasmine agreed. "But have you noticed that we only see his friends coming and not going?"

"Now that you mention it, I have," Aladdin replied. "Let's find out what's going on." The couple followed Abu as he led his guests out to the garden. What they saw made them gasp. There was the entire marketplace! Aladdin burst out laughing. "I guess the next time Abu is feeling homesick, he doesn't need to go any farther than his own backyard!"

Jasmine sighed. "Aladdin, these people can't stay here." But, when Jasmine saw the sad look on Aladdin's face, she added, "Well, maybe they could come back next month."

And so began a new tradition – "Palace Market Day", which happened once a month. And *that* made little Abu *very* happy!

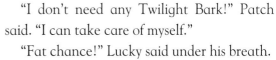

The Twilight Bark

Rolly, Patch, Lucky and the rest of the puppies were watching the end of *The Thunderbolt Adventure Hour.* As the credits began to roll, Pongo turned off the TV.

"Aw, come on, Dad!" Patch complained.

"We let you stay up late to watch the whole show," Pongo said.

Lucky sat staring at the blank television screen, hoping it would magically turn itself back on.

Perdy licked his face encouragingly. "Sit down, children," she said. "Your father and I need to speak with you."

"Uh-oh," Penny said worriedly.

"Oh, it's nothing like that," Pongo assured her. "We just think it's time to tell you about the legend of the Twilight Bark."

"Sounds cool!" Pepper cheered.

"What's the Twilight Bark?" Freckles asked.

"Legend has it," Perdy began, "that there's a special way that dogs can send each other messages. It stretches from the farthest side of the city all the way to the countryside."

"Wow!" Penny gasped. "Why would you need to do that?"

"Sometimes," Pongo began, "you need to communicate information from one place to another quickly, and you don't have time to go to the other place yourself."

"I don't need any Twilight Bark!" Patch said. "I can take care of myself."

"Fat chance!" Lucky said under his breath.

"What do you know?" Patch barked.

"If you ever get into any trouble," Perdy told the pups, "just go to the top of the highest hill you can find and bark out your message, and the members of the Twilight Bark will pass it along until someone can come and help you."

"That sounds like a bunch of baloney," Patch told his parents.

"Patch!" Pongo scolded his son. "That isn't very nice."

Just then, Lucky started howling at the top of his lungs.

"What's got into you?" Perdy asked.

"I'm trying out the Twilight Bark," Lucky said. "To get us rescued from Patch."

"Lucky," Perdy scolded him, "apologize to your brother."

"That's okay," Patch said. "I don't need his apology. I was right anyway. All that howling and no word from the Twilight Bark."

Just then, the doorbell rang. All of the puppies gasped and turned to look at Patch.

Perdy and Pongo smiled at each other, knowing it was actually Roger returning from the shop with milk for tomorrow's breakfast.

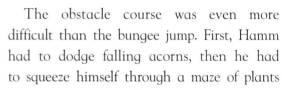

The Fairy Pig

It had been a bad day for Hamm. Bonnie had decided he should be fairy pig, the sweet, cuddly friend of Buttercup the unicorn.

As soon as Bonnie left, Hamm began to complain. "I can't be a fairy pig," he grumbled. "I'm evil Dr Porkchop!"

Hamm sighed when Buttercup whispered to him, "But now you can become a member of the Secret Unicorn Club."

"Enough fairy tales for today, Buttercup!" Hamm said bluntly, but Buttercup kept talking.

"The SUC is for secret unicorn agents, and you have to take three dangerous trials to become one."

Dangerous trials? Hamm didn't believe it, so he was surprised when Buttercup led him up onto the roof of Bonnie's house.

"I thought the trials were about cuddles or something like that?" he said.

"You thought wrong," said Buttercup, then he shoved Hamm towards the edge.

With a nervous cry, Hamm hurled himself off the roof. The rubber bands tied to his legs stretched like a bungee rope, twanging him upwards again. He bounced madly for a while, before Buttercup lowered him to the ground.

Hamm's first trial was complete, but he still had a long way to go. "Next comes the obstacle course," Buttercup announced.

The obstacle course was even more difficult than the bungee jump. First, Hamm had to dodge falling acorns, then he had to squeeze himself through a maze of plants and trees.

"Help!" he cried, getting stuck in a narrow gap. "I feel like a sausage!"

Hamm finally made it to the end of the course, puffing and panting. He had no idea it would be so hard to become a member of a unicorn club.

"And you haven't seen the third trial yet," Buttercup said. "The Washing Loop the Loop!"

Hamm spluttered as he was spun around inside the washing machine, flipping and twirling as he went round and round and round. "Hold on, Hamm!" said Buttercup. "After a while it's like a merry-go-round!"

That night, when all the trials were complete, Buttercup gave Hamm his badge. "I officially name you a Secret Unicorn Agent," he said. "But it will have to be a secret. To other toys, you'll always be evil Dr Porkchop!"

Hamm nodded and smiled happily. "I almost forgot our secret salute," said Buttercup. He wrapped his front legs around Hamm's neck. "The one-hour hug!"

"I knew it," sighed Hamm. He pretended to hate the special salute, of course, but – secretly – he loved every minute of it.

Lack of Staff

Dottie was driving around all in a dither. When Dusty and Chug rolled up, they asked her what was wrong.

"An old friend of mine is passing through Propwash Junction," she said. She explained that she hadn't seen her friend in over ten years. "I've got so much to tell her, but I can't leave the garage unattended."

Dusty and Chug exchanged a glance. "Why don't you take the whole day off?" Chug smiled.

Dottie frowned. "Who's going to mind the garage."

Chug told her that he and Dusty would watch the garage, and promised they could manage just fine without her for one day.

Delighted, Dottie thanked them, then sped off to meet her old friend. Dusty and Chug waited at the garage, enjoying the feeling of being mechanics.

Soon, their first patient arrived. Leadbottom had suffered a tear in his fuselage, and was looking for Dottie to patch him up. He was surprised to find Dusty and Chug waiting for him.

"Since when are you two mechanics?" he asked. "You know how to fix a torn fuselage?"

"No biggie! We'll have you fixed up in no time," said Dusty, confidently. He turned to Chug and whispered, "Now what?"

Chug had an idea. They would make a patch for Leadbottom's tear, using an old dishcloth they found in a pile of boxes.

Leadbottom dozed off as Chug and Dusty got to work. When he awoke, the repair was all done. "That was quick! Dottie would be proud of you boys," he said. "She should take more days off."

Leadbottom rolled out of the garage and began to spin his propeller. He was just about to take off when he spotted the patch on his side. It was bright pink, with a colourful pattern of flowers dotted all over it!

The patch looked ridiculous, and from the way it was blowing in the breeze, Leadbottom knew there was no way it would hold.

"Chuuuuug!" he bellowed. "Dustyyyyy!"

Luckily, Dottie returned a short while later, happy at having spent time with her friend. She set to work repairing the patch properly. When she was all done, Leadbottom let out a sigh of relief. "Thanks, Dottie. Without you, we'd all be lost!"

Dottie smiled. "No problem, Leadbottom!"

Even though they'd had fun being in charge of the garage, Dusty and Chug could only agree. They'd enjoyed carrying out repairs, but Dottie was definitely still the best mechanic in Propwash Junction!

Fillmore on the Run

Fillmore was enjoying a chat with his neighbour Sarge when Mater arrived with Lightning McQueen.

"Hey, Fillmore!" Mater cried. "Somebody's looking for ya!"

Fillmore was suspicious. "Who is? What for?"

"Beats me!" admitted Mater. "He just said it was about your organic fuel!"

"It must be that guy from last week," Sarge piped up. "That stuff must've given him indigestion."

Fillmore looked worried. "Then he won't be happy! I'd better disappear."

"Come on!" Lightning McQueen said. "We'll escape through the fields!"

"Go ahead," Mater added. "I've got an idea!"

As they were driving away, Fillmore thought he spotted the car searching for him and started to panic. "He saw us! What do we do now?"

"I've got it!" Lightning McQueen told him.

The two friends had arrived at the edge of a field full of dopey tractors that were grazing.

"Honk your horn," Lightning McQueen said.

"But Frank will get angry!" Fillmore frowned.

"That's what I'm hoping!" said Lightning McQueen, with a wink.

With a loud toot of Fillmore's horn, Frank the combine harvester kick-started his mighty engine and roared towards them.

Fillmore and Lightning McQueen bolted.

In town, Fillmore still felt uneasy. "What are we going to do?" he asked.

"Sally will know!" Lightning McQueen assured him.

But when they explained Fillmore's problem to Sally, she didn't know how to help.

"Doc is the best person to ask," she said.

They set off in search of wise Doc, but on the way, Fillmore spotted his unwanted guest rolling up the street. He looked like he meant business! Quickly, Fillmore hid behind a statue.

"Hello everyone!" said the car with a smart sheen to his paintwork. "I'm looking for...."

SMASH! A piece of the statue fell and shattered, drawing all eyes its way.

"I've found you!" cheered the smart car. "Congratulations, Fillmore! Your biological fuel was a real treat! I'd like to buy your stock for my service station."

Fillmore gawped in shock.

Just then, Mater rolled up. "Fillmore! I hid all the fuel!"

Fillmore blushed and turned to him. "There's been a bit of a mix-up, Mater. I need it back!"

"Um ... then you've got a problem," Mater confessed. "I've forgotten where I put it."

Fillmore sighed. "Come on, I'll help you look," he said, and together they set off on a fuel hunt.

Bambi

Sweeter than Clover

"Hi, Bambi," said a soft voice. Bambi looked up from the grass he was eating, and his friend Flower stopped searching for berries. Standing there was the pretty young fawn Bambi had met that spring.

"Hi, Faline," Bambi said. "It's nice to see you!"

"It's nice to see you, too," Faline said shyly.

"Faline!" a young male deer called across the meadow. "Come over and play with me!"

Bambi's eyes narrowed. He didn't like the idea of Faline going off to play with someone else.

Faline blinked in confusion. "Do you want me to go?" she asked Bambi.

"No, don't go," said Bambi. *But what could I say to make her stay?* he wondered. Suddenly, Bambi had an idea.

"I want to show you something special," he told her.

"Something special?" asked Faline.

"I know where to find the sweetest clover you'll ever taste," Bambi bragged. Thumper had shown him exactly where to find it.

"Where?" asked Faline.

"Just follow me!" exclaimed Bambi.

He led Faline across the meadow to the babbling brook. Then he followed the brook all the way up a steep grassy hill.

Finally they came to a big waterfall.

"The sweet clover is right here by this weeping willow tree," said Bambi.

Bambi couldn't wait to share it with Faline. But, when he got to the tree, there wasn't one single clover blossom left.

"Oh, that Thumper!" complained Bambi.

"What's the matter?" asked Faline.

Bambi shook his head. He felt very silly. He'd brought Faline all this way, and now he had nothing special to share with her! But, just then, Bambi looked up.

"Look," he whispered. "Up in the sky."

Faline looked up and gasped.

Shimmering bands of colour had formed an arch over the waterfall.

"It's so beautiful," whispered Faline. "I've never seen anything like it."

"Neither have I," said Bambi. "But I remember hearing my mother talk about it. I think it's called a rain ... bow."

"It's wonderful!" cried Faline.

"I'm glad you think so," said Bambi, a little relieved. "But I'm sorry you came all this way for no clover."

"Oh, Bambi," said Faline. "I came because I wanted to be with you. And, besides, a rainbow is a much sweeter surprise than some silly old clover, anyway!"

The Best Pilot

After saving Kevin from the wicked Charles Muntz, Russell, Carl and the dogs were flying home in Muntz's airship. Carl was at the wheel, gripping it confidently as the ship sailed through the sky.

"Are you sure you know what you're doing, Mr Fredricksen?" asked Russell. It was the fourth time he'd asked the question, and Carl was growing impatient.

"Yes, yes! Why do you keep asking me?"

Russell pointed out of the window ahead of them. "Because I've never been so close to a wave before."

Carl looked ahead and gasped. They were over the ocean and a towering wave was crashing towards them! Spinning the wheel, Carl managed to steer out of the way just in the nick of time – then almost crashed them into a passing plane.

They avoided the crash, but Carl decided that maybe Russell would have better luck steering.

"Don't worry, I'll take you home in just a moment," Russell said, strapping on a pair of flying goggles.

When the ship touched down, though, they definitely weren't back home. Carl looked at the blizzard blowing around them and realized they were at the South Pole.

"How long a moment do you think it'll be?" he asked.

"Hey, any explorer can make a mistake," Russell protested.

It turned out any explorer could make lots of mistakes! After the South Pole, they landed in Australia, where Dug chased the kangaroos.

Next, they wound up in India, and stopped to take some pictures of the Taj Mahal. Russell promised the next stop would be home, but instead the airship landed beside the Great Wall of China, which was about as far from home as they could get.

When he steered them to Paris in France, Russell decided enough was enough. "You can't quit," said Carl. "Who'll take us home?"

"I can, master!" said Dug. Carl and Russell both stared at him. "I'm a great tracker!"

Carl and Russell shrugged. What did they have to lose? Dug wriggled his head into the flying goggles and gripped the wheel with his paws. He spun it hard and the ship lurched sideways. Suddenly, Carl and Russell wondered if they'd made a mistake.

But soon they couldn't believe their eyes. Their town was below them. They were home!

Carl thought that maybe there was more to Dug than met the eye. "Of course," he said, as Dug scratched his ear with his back leg, then drooled on the ship's wheel, "I could be wrong!"

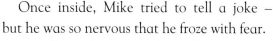

Mike's Dog Problem

It was business as usual at the new Monsters, Inc. Mike Wazowski was one of the top Laugh Collectors. He told funny jokes and made children giggle a lot, but lately, he was having problems at work.

"Oh no, this kid has a dog!" Mike groaned as he read the paperwork for his next assignment. Mike was terrified of dogs, but no one else knew.

Mike was pacing the Laugh Floor, trying to come up with a good excuse to skip work, when his friend Sulley arrived.

"What are you waiting for, buddy?" asked Sulley.

Mike couldn't think of an excuse, so reluctantly he walked into the boy's bedroom. He saw the dog straight away and jumped up on a stool to get away from it ... but this was a playful dog. It ran up to the stool and sat in front of Mike, who got so nervous he couldn't remember his jokes!

The boy didn't laugh at all, and Mike was very upset. He just couldn't relax when dogs were around. He would have to go back to work without any laughs.

The next day, Mike was assigned to the same room because he hadn't collected enough laughs. Sulley noticed that Mike didn't want to go, so he sneaked in behind him to find out why.

Once inside, Mike tried to tell a joke – but he was so nervous that he froze with fear.

Watching from outside, Sulley suddenly realized that his friend was afraid of dogs! That day after work, he asked Mike about it.

"I feel like a giant chew toy when I'm near them, like any second they might bite me!" cried Mike.

"Don't worry, pal," said Sulley, patting him on the back. "I'll help you out." Then he taught Mike all about dogs.

They read stories and watched videos together about friendly dogs.

"Remember, Mike," Sulley said. "Even though dogs slobber, have big teeth and make loud noises, that doesn't mean they're scary."

The next day, Mike and Sulley went to a room with a dog. Mike remembered what Sulley had taught him – to stay calm and let the dog sniff him. He took a deep breath. The dog bounded over and sniffed Mike, who tried to relax. The dog was friendly and Mike began to feel comfortable. Soon he was telling one joke after another! Thanks to Sulley's help, Mike became the top Laugh Collector again – and he even grew to like dogs.

"Maybe I'll get a dog," declared Mike.

"Maybe you should start with a hamster," Sulley said with a chuckle.

How to Unpack for a Holiday

One morning, Donald Duck heard a knock at the door. When he opened it, he found his friend Mickey Mouse standing there.

"Today is the day!" exclaimed Mickey.

"Today is *what* day?" asked Donald with a yawn.

"Don't you remember?" asked Mickey. "You're driving me, Minnie and Daisy to the beach for a week's holiday." Mickey held up his suitcase. "I packed last night. Aren't you packed too?"

"No," said Donald. "I thought we were leaving next week!"

"No," said Mickey. "We're leaving today. And Minnie and Daisy will be here in an hour."

"Oh, no!" cried Donald.

"Calm down," said Mickey. "You have time to get ready. Just pack your things now."

While Mickey relaxed in the garden, Donald went back inside.

"What do I pack?" Donald muttered to himself as he raced through his house. "I'll need my toys, of course, in case I get bored." Donald ran to his playroom and placed all his toys in boxes.

"What else should I pack?" Donald asked himself. "Clothes!" He ran to his bedroom and took out every suitcase he owned. Then he emptied all his drawers and filled his suitcases.

Finally, Donald calmed down. "That should do it," he said with a sigh of relief.

Mickey couldn't believe his eyes when Donald began packing up his car. Just then, Minnie Mouse and Daisy Duck arrived. They each had one small suitcase.

Minnie and Daisy took one look at Donald's car and gasped. Boxes and baskets were crammed into the back and front seats. Daisy opened the boot and found it overflowing with Donald's suitcases.

"There's no room left for *our* suitcases!" cried Daisy.

"Forget our *suitcases*!" exclaimed Minnie. "There's no room for us!"

Mickey put his arm around Donald. "It's okay, Donald," he said. "It's hard packing for a holiday. You have to leave some things behind. Even some of your favourite things. But they will all be here when we get back. I promise!"

"And besides," added Daisy, "don't you want to leave room in your car to bring back souvenirs, like seashells and T-shirts and sticks of rock?"

Donald brightened. "Seashells and T-shirts and sticks of rock!" he cried excitedly. "Oh, you bet!"

"Good," said Mickey. Then he pointed to Donald's overflowing car. "Now let's all help Donald *unpack* for this holiday!"

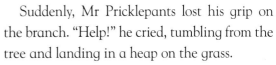

The Black Venus Panther

Buzz dashed for safety. "Run," he cried. "The Dino-Aliens have found us!"

He and a few of the other toys were the heroes in Bonnie's latest game. The dinosaurs, Rex and Trixie, were the villains.

Soon, Bonnie ran inside for lunch, leaving the toys alone on the grass.

Rex was upset – he was having great fun being a Dino-Alien.

"Don't worry, Rex," Buzz assured him. "Bonnie will be back soon."

Woody gulped nervously. "Guys? Do you feel like someone's watching us?"

Slowly, the toys turned round to see a fearsome-looking black cat staring at them, hungrily licking its lips.

Screaming, the toys ran in all different directions as the cat pounced at them.

"Jessie, bring them home safe," Buzz barked, pointing to Dolly, Trixie and some of the others. "We'll draw the cat's attention."

Buzz, Woody and Mr Pricklepants ran past the cat, waving and shouting. While it raced after them, Jessie got the others to safety.

"Quick! Climb the tree," Buzz ordered. Working together, the three friends frantically clambered up onto a low branch.

They were safe – or so they thought! The cat extended its claws and began to climb up the tree after them!

Suddenly, Mr Pricklepants lost his grip on the branch. "Help!" he cried, tumbling from the tree and landing in a heap on the grass.

The cat dropped to the ground and slowly approached, like a tiger stalking its prey.

Mr Pricklepants gulped. "Don't eat me. Please!"

The hedgehog toy closed his eyes. He could feel the cat's breath on his face. Any second now, it would –

SLURP!

The cat gave the toy a friendly lick on the cheek. Mr Pricklepants opened his eyes, then laughed with relief.

"Uh, guys? I think it's safe to come down," he cried.

The friends soon realized that the cat just wanted to play. They called Jessie and the others back out, and took turns tickling the cat's tummy.

Woody smiled at Buzz. "Are you thinking what I'm thinking?" he asked.

Buzz nodded. "I think so, Woody!"

The toys went back to playing their game again, but this time when the Dino-Aliens attacked, they were in for a big surprise.

"We've brought our new friend, the Black Venus Panther!" said Mr Pricklepants.

The Dino-Aliens took one look at the huge beast, then turned and ran away! The cat miaowed happily. Being a toy sure was fun!

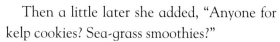

Nemo's Day Off

Nemo liked lots of things. But there was one thing he didn't like – rules. He thought his dad, Marlin, had way too many. *Don't play outside the neighbourhood. Never have more than one after-school snack. Do your homework as soon as you can. Go to bed at a reasonable hour....*

"I wish I could have a day without any rules!" Nemo said one morning.

"The rules are for your own good, Nemo," Marlin replied. "Someday, you'll thank me."

Just then, Dory swam up and Marlin had an idea. "Dory is going to babysit you, Nemo."

When Nemo told his friend Sheldon, he got very excited. "This means no rules!"

"Hey, Dory!" Sheldon said. "My friends and I are going to the coral reef to play hide-and-seek. Can Nemo come?"

"Sounds like fun!" Dory said cheerfully.

Nemo was having a great time until he tried to hide in a grumpy moray eel's home!

"Moray eels are not as friendly as I expected," said Dory, ushering Nemo away.

Then it was time for an after-school snack. "How about plankton pizzas?" Dory said.

"All right!" Nemo and Sheldon shouted.

A few minutes later, Dory exclaimed, "You boys haven't had your after-school snack yet! How about some seaweed sandwiches?"

Then a little later she added, "Anyone for kelp cookies? Sea-grass smoothies?"

After all that, Nemo and Sheldon felt ill. Nemo knew he should be doing his homework.

"Oh!" Dory said. "I just remembered something. I think it's time to –"

"Play kick the clam!" said Sheldon.

"Yes," said Dory. "That must be it!"

"Now I think it's time to –" Dory began.

"Play splash tag with Bruce!" Nemo suggested.

"Now I'm pretty sure it's time to –" Dory said after Bruce had left.

Nemo and Sheldon looked at each other. They had run out of ideas.

"Play toss the sea disc!" shouted Dory.

A few hours later, Nemo was ready to go home. But Dory was still having fun. "I think it's time to go home for real," he told Dory.

When they got home, Nemo was sleepy.

"Well, I guess it's time for bed," he said with a yawn. "Goodnight!"

"Five more minutes?" Dory asked. "Please?"

"Nope, it's one of the rules. And sometimes you have to stick to them," said Nemo.

Marlin smiled. "You sound just like me."

"Daddy, I'm so glad you're home!" Nemo cried. He paused. "Maybe ... rules aren't so bad after all."

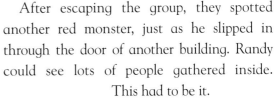

The Fear Party

Randy had found a half-torn invitation for a party some other students had organized, and was trying to convince Mike to go with him.

"We're not invited," Mike said. "Besides, I have to study."

"But we have half of the invitation, and we know the dress code," Randy insisted, pointing to where it said guests should wear red fur. "The only thing we don't know is the location."

Randy reminded Mike that there would be senior scare students at the party, who could know some secret scaring tips.

That was all the convincing Mike needed. If there was a chance he might learn some new scare techniques, he was willing to give it a try.

When Randy dressed him up in red fur, Mike felt like a walking carpet. Still, Randy realized, the fur was the trick to finding their way to the party. They just had to find another monster with red fur and follow it.

Soon, they spotted a furry red monster striding towards one of the fraternity houses. This had to be it! They scurried after him and raced in the door before he could push it closed.

Instead of finding the most exclusive party of the year, though, they found a support group for homesick students. Before they knew what was happening, the big slug-like group leader gave them a big hug, smearing them in slime.

After escaping the group, they spotted another red monster, just as he slipped in through the door of another building. Randy could see lots of people gathered inside. This had to be it.

Or maybe not.

As they entered, Mike and Randy were given a warm welcome to a Recycled Cooking Course. A bin full of smelly rubbish was dumped on them. "Choose your ingredients," the teacher said encouragingly.

Mike and Randy choked on the smell as the rubbish rained down on them, but then they spotted something among the litter – a party invitation, and this one showed the location!

The two monsters raced to the party and threw open the door ... only to find it had already finished. They were too late. They had missed the most exclusive event of the year.

Randy seemed to be taking it very hard. He knelt down, staring at the floor. "Randy ... are you okay?" Mike asked gently.

"I can't believe it," Randy said. He held up another torn-up invitation. This one was for an even more exclusive party next week.

As Randy tried to convince him they should go, Mike rolled his eye. He turned and walked off. After tonight, his partying days were well and truly over.

Sarge, Expert Strategist

Spring had blossomed in Radiator Springs. Red's pots were bursting with beautiful flowers. But Doc was nowhere near as cheerful as the other townsfolk.

"Got a problem, Doc?" wondered Sarge.

Doc frowned at the splodges of tarmac all over the floor. "I was hoping to hold Spring Fest in town, but Bessie broke down and made a mess. There's no time to clean it all up now." Doc turned to his friend. "I'm putting you in the driver's seat, Sarge."

Sarge accepted the challenge to find a new home for the Spring Festival. "I'll take care of everything, sir. We'll have a team together right away!"

Not too far away, Sarge found Mater. "Recruit Mater!" he barked, then explained the Spring Fest problem.

"I know the right place," Mater insisted. He led Sarge beyond the border into a clear opening surrounded by cacti. "Well?"

"Excellent job. This year's Spring Fest is gonna be a picnic," Sarge said. "But these cactus flowers need watering or they won't bloom in time. This calls for reinforcements!"

Sarge and Mater quickly fetched Red, who simply loved caring for plants. But just as Red prepared to hose the cactus flowers down, the sky grumbled and rumbled loudly.

"Typical!" said Mater. "As soon as I've had a carwash it starts raining."

"Fear not. There's still hope," promised Sarge as their friends appeared, all eager to help and celebrate Spring Fest together.

"We need a few things I've got at my place," said Sarge. "Only a real champion will be able to bring them here in time."

Lightning McQueen appeared, revving his engine. He was always keen to help a friend. Especially if it involved speed!

"You've picked the right car, pal," Lightning McQueen said. He listened closely to Sarge's whispered instructions. "I'll be back in a flash!" the race-car promised.

The storm continued to threaten and the cars became edgy as they glanced at the black clouds.

"Here comes the rain!" groaned Doc.

"Buck up! Nobody's going anywhere. Lightning'll be right back!" Sarge told him.

And he was, in no time at all! Together the cars erected one of Sarge's big green field tents.

The cars laughed as they huddled together, safe and dry beneath the tents, just as the rain started to pour down and the clouds thundered.

Luckily for them, Sarge was always the expert strategist!

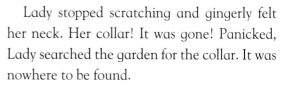

Lost and Found

Lady stretched and rolled over. It was so cosy on the window seat. Sunlight shone through the glass and glinted on her diamond-shaped name tag. Lady sighed contentedly. The tag was her most prized possession. Besides her owners, of course.

Jim Dear and Darling were very good to her. Just last night, they had given her and Tramp steak bones to munch on. There were so many, they had not been able to eat them all.

The bones! Lady had almost forgotten them. Leaping off the window seat, she hurried to the kitchen. Luckily, they were still right next to her food bowl.

Lady began to carry the bones into the garden. It took three trips, but soon the bones were lying in a heap on the grass.

Then she started to dig. The soil piled up behind her as Lady dug yet another hole. She carefully nosed the last bone into the hole and covered it with soil. After prancing delicately on top to pat down the soil, she collapsed in an exhausted heap. Burying bones was hard work!

Rolling over, Lady let the sun warm her belly. The garden was the perfect place for a late-afternoon nap. She was just dozing off when, suddenly, her neck itched.

Sitting up, Lady gave it a scratch. But something was missing.

Lady stopped scratching and gingerly felt her neck. Her collar! It was gone! Panicked, Lady searched the garden for the collar. It was nowhere to be found.

I must have buried it with one of my bones! Lady realized. She looked at all the freshly dug holes. It would take her all night to dig up the bones. But she just had to find her collar!

Tramp will help, Lady thought. She ran inside to get him. He was playing with the puppies, but ran outside as soon as he heard what was wrong. Soon the two dogs were busy undoing all of Lady's hard work.

"I see something shiny!" Tramp called. Lady was by his side in an instant, but it wasn't the collar. It was just an old bottle cap. Lady dropped her head sadly.

Lady and Tramp got right back to digging. And, just as dusk was falling, Tramp found a thick blue band with a golden tag. Lady's collar!

Lady let out a happy bark. Then she carried the collar into the house and sat down at Jim Dear's feet.

"Your collar came off, Lady?" Jim Dear asked as he fastened it around Lady's neck. "It's a good thing you didn't accidentally bury it with your bones!"

Pinocchio

A Bright Idea

One day, Geppetto told Pinocchio, "I am off to deliver these puppets. I will be gone for a few hours. Stay out of trouble!" But Geppetto had not even been gone for 15 minutes before Pinocchio became bored. "I have nothing to do," he said.

"You could clean the shop," said Jiminy Cricket.

"That's no fun," said Pinocchio. "I'll paint a picture instead."

"Where will you get paint?" Jiminy asked.

"From the workbench," said Pinocchio.

"You know you're not supposed to go near Geppetto's workbench," warned Jiminy. But the cricket's warning came too late.

"Oops!" Pinocchio cried.

He'd spilled red paint all over the workbench. Hurriedly, he grabbed a rag and tried to clean up the mess, but the paint just smeared. He'd made the mess even bigger!

Pinocchio looked around desperately. When he noticed Geppetto's kitten, Figaro, sleeping by the hearth, he had an idea.

"I'll say Figaro did it," Pinocchio said.

Jiminy shook his head. "That would be wrong," he said.

"What else can I do?" Pinocchio asked. "The workbench is ruined, and my father will be furious!"

"Why don't you paint it?" suggested Jiminy. "That's a very good idea!" said Pinocchio.

So he set to work. First, he painted the bench top bright red. Then he painted the drawers green and yellow. Figaro woke up and investigated, getting paint all over his whiskers.

Soon, the job was done.

"It looks wonderful," said Jiminy.

"Yes, it does," Pinocchio agreed. But he did not feel proud at all.

"It's a work of art!" Geppetto cried when he got home. "It's so colourful it makes the whole shop cheerful."

Then Geppetto saw the paint on Figaro's whiskers. "Did Figaro knock over the paint?" he asked. "Is that why you painted the workbench?"

"No," Pinocchio said. "I spilled the paint. I couldn't clean it up, so I painted the whole workbench. I'm sorry."

Geppetto was quiet for a moment, and then he said, "I'm proud of you, Pinocchio."

"Because I painted the workbench?" Pinocchio asked.

"No," said Geppetto. "I'm proud of you because you told the truth and apologized instead of telling a lie. That takes courage. Now, every day, when I see my workbench, I'll remember you did the right thing, and that will make the colours seem even brighter!"

Dusty's England Adventure

Dusty Crophopper was in England for his good friend Bulldog's retirement party. Dusty couldn't understand why such a legendary plane would want to retire!

"I'm proud of my racing career," Bulldog explained with a sigh, "but I'm getting older. I don't have all those fancy gadgets that the newer race planes have."

But Dusty knew his friend could outrace almost anyone. "All right," Dusty said with a grin. "But first, let's do some sightseeing."

"That's a smashing idea!" Bulldog said happily.

They soared over fields to Wingsoar Castle and then Hoverton Court Palace.

Bulldog then took Dusty to Flownhenge. The planes took turns timing each other as they weaved through the ancient stones. Dusty marvelled at how Bulldog always managed to beat the time Dusty had set.

"I don't suppose an old-fashioned plane like yourself would be up for one last race?" Dusty asked.

"You're on!" said Bulldog. "The first plane to land back in Hatfield wins!"

Dusty and Bulldog took off, racing as fast as their engines would allow. Every plane they zoomed by was amazed at the speed of the two racers. Dusty started out in the lead, but then Bulldog swept out ahead of him. By the time they reached the coast, the sun was setting and both racers were nose to nose.

But as the darkness settled in, so did a wall of thick fog. In an instant, the fog became so dense that Dusty couldn't see his navigation instruments. In fact, he didn't have the foggiest idea where he was!

"Uh, Bulldog?" Dusty called out nervously.

Then he heard Bulldog shout, "Pull up, lad! Hurry!"

Dusty reacted quickly to Bulldog's orders and saw he had nearly hit a cliff!

Dusty was thankful to land safely back in Hatfield behind Bulldog. "How did you know I was so close to that cliff?"

"I know the area like the back of my wing," Bulldog said. "I simply used my instincts."

"What good are instincts?" Dusty teased. "Sure, you can navigate mazes, fly through fog like a pro, but you're still grounded without those fancy gadgets and gizmos, right?"

Bulldog chuckled. "Maybe I should reconsider retirement."

All Bulldog's friends came to his party that night. And everyone was overjoyed to discover that the retirement celebration was now a comeback celebration!

The veteran plane made a toast. "Here's to all the racing we've done together and all the racing that's yet to come!"

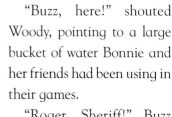

One Too Many

Bonnie was having a birthday party, and her friends were having great fun playing with her toys in the garden. There was only one thing better than playtime – birthday cake!

When Bonnie and her friends ran inside to eat, the toys chatted excitedly about the party.

There were dozens of brightly coloured helium balloons tied with string all around the garden. Mr Potato Head took a few strings in each hand. "I love balloons," he said. "They're so light...."

"Look out!" gasped Mrs Potato Head, as her husband lifted off the ground and began to drift up into the sky.

"We need to do something!" Woody cried.

Buzz quickly leaped into action. Snatching more balloons, he tugged the strings free and rose quickly into the air. "I'm coming, my friend!" he called.

Mr Potato Head gulped nervously. "Great. Then what?"

"You'll see!" said Buzz. He waited until his balloons were level with Mr Potato Head's, then he jumped.

For a moment, it looked like Buzz would fall, but he wrapped his arms around Mr Potato Head and they both swung wildly on the breeze.

"We're heavier together," Buzz explained. "So now we'll come back to the ground softly."

Softly? Not quite! Together, the two toys were too heavy. They plunged down towards the garden, the balloons doing little to slow their fall.

"Buzz, here!" shouted Woody, pointing to a large bucket of water Bonnie and her friends had been using in their games.

"Roger, Sheriff!" Buzz called. He knew just what to do. His wings opened, knocking the balloons out of Mr Potato Head's hands.

"What are you doing?" Mr Potato Head gasped. "You can't fly!"

"Perhaps not to infinity and beyond," Buzz admitted, swooping towards the bucket. "But enough to make a perfect splashdown!"

With a splash, Buzz and his passenger landed safely in the bucket – and not a moment too soon. Bonnie and her friends came racing out, still munching on slices of cake.

"My balloons!" Bonnie gasped, as she watched them all float off into the sky.

"Don't worry, we have plenty more!" said her mum.

Unnoticed, Buzz and Mr Potato Head climbed out of the bucket and onto the grass.

"The most important thing is all the toys are here," Buzz said.

Mr Potato Head smiled. "With their feet firmly on the ground!"

July

6

Disney MICKEY & FRIENDS
A Summer Day

It was a hot summer day and Mickey Mouse and his friends were relaxing in Mickey's living room. The friends were just deciding what to do with their day when – *pop!* – Mickey's air-conditioning broke!

"Maybe there will be a breeze outside," said Minnie. But there wasn't.

"What are we going to do now?" asked Daisy.

Minnie looked around. "Hmm," she said. "Maybe we could make fans. Or we could try sitting in the shade under the tree...."

"Gosh! Those sprinklers look nice and cool!" said Goofy, pointing at Mickey's lawn.

Donald nodded. "But there isn't enough water coming out of them to keep us all cool!" he said.

As Mickey watched his friends looking at the sprinklers, he had an idea. "I've got it!" he shouted. "Let's go to the lake! There's always a breeze there and there's so much to do!"

"What a great idea!" said Minnie.

Mickey's friends raced home to pack and soon they were on their way. They were really excited about a day at the lake!

"What should we do first?" Minnie asked when they got there.

Before anyone could stop him, Donald raced off towards a little boat. He'd decided he wanted to go fishing.

Donald was about to hop into the boat when Mickey called out to him. "Wait, Donald!" he said. "I don't think we can all fit in the boat. Let's do something together, first."

"But the water looks so nice," said Donald.

"Why don't we go for a swim?" said Minnie. "We can all do that."

Donald really wanted to go fishing, but finally he agreed. After all, they had come to the lake to do something together.

"Aah," said Donald as they got into the water. "You were right, Mickey. This was a good idea!"

Mickey smiled to himself. He was glad he and his friends had found a way to cool off.

"I could stay in this water all day!" Daisy said. And that is just what they did.

As the sun set and the day started to get cooler, Mickey and his friends got out of the water. And Mickey had one last surprise for his friends ... marshmallows!

"Gee, Mickey," said Minnie as they roasted the marshmallows over a campfire, "you really do know how to plan the perfect day!"

Finally, it was time to leave. Mickey and his friends packed their bags and got into the car.

"That was so much fun!" said Donald as they drove home. "Let's do it again tomorrow!"

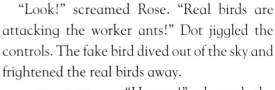

The Flying Blueberries

Everyone in the ant colony was in a good mood. The grasshoppers had been driven off once and for all, and none of the ants had even been hurt. But Flik's amazing fake bird had taken quite a beating, and the Blueberries were determined to mend it.

"Fixing that bird is a big job," said Mr Soil, Dot's teacher, "but I know the Blueberries can do it."

The Blueberries stared at the fake bird. It was a mess!

"I'll be back in a while to see how you're doing," said Mr Soil before he left.

"How can we ever fix this thing?" one of the Blueberries cried.

"We can do it!" said Dot. "I bet we can make it even better this time!"

With a cheer, the Blueberries went to work. Some picked new leaves to cover the frame. Others glued those leaves into place with sticky honey.

After hours of hard work, the bird was finally mended.

"Let's sit in it!" Dot said.

But, just as the Blueberries crawled inside the bird, the wind began to blow. Suddenly, the breeze caught the wings. The bird took off!

It was up to Dot to save the day. She hopped into the pilot seat and took control. The Blueberries flew around Ant Island once, then twice. Soon they weren't afraid any more.

"Look!" screamed Rose. "Real birds are attacking the worker ants!" Dot jiggled the controls. The fake bird dived out of the sky and frightened the real birds away.

"Hooray!" cheered the Blueberries. "We did it!"

"Don't cheer yet!" Dot cried. "This contraption is out of control!"

With a bump and a crash, the bird hit the ground and skidded to a halt.

"Everybody get out!" Princess Dot commanded. One by one, the Blueberries escaped from the bird.

"It's wrecked again!" said Rose. "And here comes Mr Soil! He's going to be so mad!"

But, surprisingly, Mr Soil was smiling. "You're heroes!" he told them. "You saved the worker ants."

"But the bird is wrecked again," said Rose.

"And you can fix it again too," he replied.

"Yeah," said Dot, "and when it's fixed again we'll go up for another flight."

"Hooray!" the Blueberries cried.

"And here is a merit badge for you, Princess, in honour of your first flight," said Mr Soil.

Dot was confused. "I've already made my first flight," she said, fluttering her tiny wings.

"Ah, but this is a special badge," Mr Soil replied. "It is for making your first flight, not using your wings, but using your head!"

Double Surprise

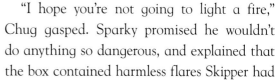

Mayday the fire engine was practising his water-shooting skills outside the main hangar. Dottie was impressed – Mayday could knock tin cans off a fence from a very long way away with just a single blast.

"A little training wouldn't hurt you, either," Dottie said to Dusty.

Dusty thought some fire and rescue training was a great idea, so Sparky and Chug set to work preparing a way for him to practise. "We'll set up a target," they said. "And you'll have to hit it, like in a real emergency situation!"

"Cool! What kind of target?" Dusty asked.

"That's a surprise," said Sparky. "It's your job to find it."

Dusty took off and thought back to the training he'd done with Mayday up on Piston Peak. He knew that when it came to fighting fires, planes had two options – fill up with flame retardant at base, or load up with water from a nearby river.

Banking left, Dusty flew low over the river running past Propwash Junction. His landing gear had been fitted with two large tanks, which filled up quickly as he skimmed across the surface of the water.

Back at the hangar, Chug was getting worried. Sparky was carrying a large box full of what looked like explosives!

"I hope you're not going to light a fire," Chug gasped. Sparky promised he wouldn't do anything so dangerous, and explained that the box contained harmless flares Skipper had collected from his navy days.

"How do they work?" Chug wondered.

Setting the box down, Sparky took out one of the flares. "It's easy. All you gotta do is break 'em like this," he demonstrated. The old flare went off with a flash and a puff of thick smoke.

Spluttering, Chug rolled backwards – right over the box containing the other flares. As the flares all broke, thick black smoke began to billow up into the air. Dusty spotted it at once and turned back to base.

"Target sighted!" he cried excitedly.

Passing over the smoke, Dusty opened both his tanks. Water gushed out, falling on the smoke like a rainstorm. As he flew on, he could have sworn he saw two shapes half-hidden by the smoke....

Touching down, Dusty grinned proudly. "I didn't expect a fake fire right in front of Skipper's hangar, guys!" he said. "I was really impressed."

Sparky and Chug flicked on their wipers, clearing away the river water that dripped down their faces. "Yeah," they spluttered. "So were we!"

101 DALMATIANS

One Lucky Pup

"Where are we going?" Penny asked. "Why do we have to get in the car? We're going to miss *Thunderbolt*!" Pepper pouted. The puppies all hated to miss their favourite dog hero TV show. They groaned in disappointment.

"This will be even more fun," Perdy said soothingly as she coaxed the puppies into the car. "I promise."

Roger and Anita got into the front seat. It didn't take long to get out of the city. Soon the car was winding down a country lane. The puppies smelled all kinds of good things. They smelled flowers and hay. Then they smelled something sweet – peaches!

"Here we are!" Anita opened the car door.

"Where's here?" Freckles asked Lucky.

"It looks like an orchard!" Lucky yipped. He loved to eat fruit.

Roger stretched. "You dogs run and play," he said. "We'll call you when it's picnic time."

"Don't eat too many peaches," Pongo barked, but the puppies were already running off.

All morning, the puppies ran around and played in the grass until Pongo and Perdy came to call them.

"Time for lunch!" Pongo barked.

"I'm not hungry," Rolly said, rolling over in the grass.

"I hope you didn't eat too much," Perdy said.

The big dogs herded their puppies up the hill towards the spot where Roger and Anita were laying out a picnic.

Perdy scanned the group of puppies. "Wait a minute," she said to Pongo. "Where's Lucky?"

The black-and-white pack stopped in its tracks. Pongo counted them. Lucky was definitely missing!

Perdy sighed and began to whimper.

"Don't worry, Mother," Pepper told her sweetly. "I have an idea." He turned to his brothers and sisters. "Hey, everyone, let's play Thunderbolt!" he barked encouragingly. "We have to find Lucky!"

All of the puppies yipped excitedly and tumbled over one another to find Lucky's trail. Soon every nose was sniffing the ground.

Penny sniffed around a tree and behind a patch of tall grass. She'd caught the scent! "Here he is!" Penny barked.

The rest of the dogs gathered around to see the puppy asleep in the grass.

Lucky's ears covered his eyes, but there was no mistaking the horseshoe of spots on his back, or the pile of peach stones by his nose!

"Lucky is lucky we found him," Perdita said with a relieved sigh.

"And," Pepper joked, "he'll be *really* lucky if he doesn't wake up with a tummy ache!"

El Materdor

ater and Lightning were out for a drive. Mater stopped to look at some grazing bulldozers. "I was a famous bulldozer fighter in Spain," he began. "They called me 'El Materdor'...."

El Materdor stood in the centre of a packed arena. With a nod of his head, he signalled that he was ready. A door at the side of the ring opened, and an angry-looking bulldozer rolled out. El Materdor raised his tow hook. One glimpse of the red cape dangling from it and the bulldozer charged towards the cape. El Materdor stood his ground.

Again and again, the bulldozer charged. Each time, El Materdor dodged him with a last-second move. Until the bulldozer finally surprised him. He came up behind El Materdor and pushed him across the ring, driving him right into the ground! The crowd watched in silence. Then the tow truck's hook poked out from a pile of dirt. At the end of it was El Materdor's red cape. The battle would go on!

El Materdor dusted himself off and bravely faced the huge bulldozer again. Through narrowed eyes, they studied each other. Suddenly, the bulldozer smacked his front blade on the ground. Two doors at the side of the ring opened and two more bulldozers drove out. Now it was three against one!

The bulldozers charged!

For a time, El Materdor fought off all of them. But then the three bulldozers circled him and began to close in. There was nowhere for El Materdor to go. Nowhere but up, that is....

El Materdor waited until the last moment. Then, with a mighty leap, he jumped out of the path of the charging bulldozers, who collided and collapsed in a heap.

"*Olé!*" El Materdor cried, landing on top of the wrecked bulldozers. But the celebration was short-lived. Soon more bulldozers rolled into the ring. It turned out that the wrecked ones had some friends.

"There I was, surrounded," Mater told Lightning. "Bulldozers all around me."

"What did you do?" Lightning asked.

"Don't you remember? You was there, too!" Mater said. In the arena, Lightning gasped. His paint job was red – just like El Materdor's cape! The bulldozers revved their engines and began their chase.

Back in Radiator Springs, Lightning interrupted the story. "Mater," he said, "that didn't happen."

"Well, try telling that to them bulldozers," Mater replied, pointing behind Lightning. The bulldozers that had been grazing were now surrounding Mater and Lightning!

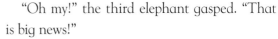

DUMBO

'Elephone!

"Did you hear the news, my dear?" one of the circus elephants said to another.

"What is it?" the second elephant asked.

The first elephant looked around carefully to make sure that no one was listening to them. "Well," she whispered in the second elephant's ear, "you know Mrs Jumbo's son, Dumbo, right?"

"Of course," the second elephant said. "The small fellow with the big ears. The one who became a –" she shuddered with distaste, "– a clown."

"That's right," the first elephant said. "Well, a little bird told me that the first show was a hit! Everyone loved the 'Building on Fire' act. Dumbo leaped off a platform 20 feet high. And they're going to raise it up much higher next time!"

"Oh my!" the second elephant said.

"But you musn't tell a soul!" the first elephant warned.

But, as soon as the first elephant turned away, the second elephant turned to another of her friends. "Listen, dear," she said, "you'll never believe what I just heard!"

"What is it, dear?" the third elephant asked.

The second elephant lowered her voice to a whisper. "Oh, you'll never believe it!" she began. "It's Dumbo – 20 clowns had to hit him with a tyre to get him to leap off a platform!"

"Oh my!" the third elephant gasped. "That is big news!"

"But don't breathe a word to anyone!" the second elephant exclaimed.

"Certainly not!"

Soon, the third elephant was whispering to another friend. The fourth elephant gasped with amazement as she listened.

"... and so Dumbo set the platform on fire, and it took 20 clowns to put out the flames," the third elephant told the fourth.

The fourth elephant told a fifth, and a fifth told a sixth. Soon, the whole circus was buzzing with the news of Dumbo's first clown show.

A little bird was flying over the big top when he saw a pair of elephants chattering below.

He flew down to see what was going on, landing on one elephant's trunk. "Good day, ladies," he said. "What's the word around the circus this evening?"

"It's about Dumbo," one elephant said excitedly. "It seems he fell off a platform in the last show, and hit 20 clowns. Now they're talking about setting him on fire next time!"

The little bird didn't stick around to hear the end of the discussion. "I can't wait to spread this news!" he squawked, fluttering back up into the sky. "Wait until everyone hears – they'll never believe it's true!"

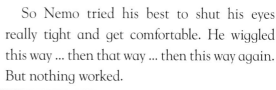

Sleep Tight, Nemo

It was late at night at the bottom of the sea – but little Nemo was wide awake.

"Nemo," said Marlin, poking his head into the anemone, "you should be asleep!"

"But I can't sleep," Nemo complained. "I need another story."

"No more stories," said Marlin sternly. "I told you five already."

"Then maybe another snack?" said Nemo.

But Marlin rolled his eyes. "No, Nemo. You just had a plankton snack five minutes ago. What you should do now, young clownfish, is go to sleep!"

"Okay, Dad," said Nemo. Then he did as his dad told him and closed his eyes. But, seconds later, they popped open again.

"Dad!" Nemo called out. "Daaaad!"

"Nemo!" Marlin groaned. "I'm beginning to lose my patience!"

"But, Dad," said Nemo, "I ... I ... I heard a noise."

"What kind of noise?" Marlin asked.

"Um ... a ... a spooky noise," answered Nemo.

"*Hmph.*" Nemo could tell Marlin did not like this reason for being awake either. But still, Marlin stopped and listened ... and listened ... and listened.

"I don't hear anything, Nemo," he said after a moment.

So Nemo tried his best to shut his eyes really tight and get comfortable. He wiggled this way ... then that way ... then this way again. But nothing worked.

"Daaaaaaaaaaaad!" he called out.

"Nemo," Marlin said. "For the last time, it's time to go to sleep. If you call for me again, it had better be a good reason or ... or ... or else. Goodnight!"

Now, Nemo knew his father well, and he knew when Marlin was just a teeny, tiny bit angry with him. But Nemo also knew that when you can't go to sleep, you can't go to sleep. And no matter how many moonfish or angelfish or sea stars you count; no matter how tightly you close your eyes; no matter how mad your dad gets – you'll never go to sleep until you're absolutely, positively, no-doubt-about-it ready. And Nemo wasn't. But why not?

Suddenly, Nemo bolted up. "Dad!" he shouted. "Dad! Oh, Daaaaad!"

"All right. That's it, Nemo!" Marlin said.

"But, Dad," Nemo said. "There's one more thing I really, really, truly need. Then I promise, I'll go to sleep."

And with that, he snuggled into Marlin's fins for a great big goodnight hug.

"I love you, Dad," he smiled. "See you in the morning."

The Little Lightning

One evening, the rain was pouring down on the Sunnyside Daycare Centre. Chunk, Twitch and Stretch were safe and sound inside, happily playing a board game together.

"It's a pity that Sparky didn't come," said Chunk. They'd invited their robot friend to join in, but he'd been busy playing with some of the other toys in the Butterfly Room.

As the game drew to a close, the friends all yawned and stretched. "It's late," said Twitch. "Let's go to sleep."

Stretch agreed. They

had to be wide awake for playtime next day. They had just packed away the game when the lights flickered and went out, plunging the centre into darkness. "Oh, no! A power cut!" said Twitch. "How can we find our way back to the Butterfly Room?"

Chunk took a few steps forward. "Don't worry! I know the way like the back of my hand," he said, but then he walked straight into a table leg and bumped his head!

"It's lucky you have such a hard head," Stretch giggled.

There was a bright flash of lightning outside, and a rumble of thunder. Twitch's wings quivered in fright. He was terrified of thunder and lightning. "If a bolt of lightning got in, it would turn us into puddles of plastic!" he said.

Chunk shook his head. "Calm down! That's impossible. Sunnyside is safe. No lightning could get in here!"

Twitch swallowed nervously. "Maybe a little bit could," he whispered. "Like that over there!"

Stretch and Chunk both gasped. Across the room they could see the flashes and sparks of a tiny lightning storm.

"Let's hide!" Chunk said, and they all took cover behind some building blocks. They peeked out and watched the flashing and sparking. "It really is lightning," Chunk whispered.

"And it's coming towards us," Twitch said, but as it drew closer, he realized it wasn't a lightning storm at all. It was Sparky, their toy robot pal with the light-up action feature!

"Hi, friends!" he said. "I realized you might be lost and came to your rescue. I brought a torch!"

Chunk took the torch and clicked it on, lighting up their path.

"Why didn't you switch on the torch from the beginning?" Twitch wondered.

Sparky's eyes flashed happily. "A robot with a personal lightning supply doesn't need one!" he said, and the four friends laughed. Maybe a little bit of lightning wasn't a bad thing, after all.

Disney
THE
LION KING

Runaway Hippo!

One morning, Simba, Timon and Pumbaa were eating breakfast.

"Mmm, crispy, crunchy bugs," said Pumbaa.

"Try the big red ones," said Timon. "They have lots of legs. They come with their own toothpicks!"

Suddenly, they heard a sad cry from the jungle.

"Sounds like somebody is in trouble," said Simba.

"The sound is coming from over here," said Pumbaa. He led them to a muddy pond full of thick vines. In the middle of the swamp was a baby hippo. He was tangled up in vines and half buried in mud.

"Help!" the hippo cried as he struggled against the vines. The more the hippo squirmed, the more tangled he became, and the deeper he sank into the mud.

When the little hippo saw Simba, he became very frightened. "Oh, no, a lion! He's going to eat me!" he cried.

"Take it easy," Simba replied. "These guys have got me on an all-bug diet."

Timon grabbed a vine and swung over to the hippo. He began digging the little hippo out of the mud.

Meanwhile, Simba jumped onto the hippo's back and began tearing at the thick vines with his teeth.

That made the hippo even more afraid!

"You *are* trying to eat me!" he shouted.

Finally, Simba and Timon got the hippo unstuck. Free at last, the hippo started to cry. "P-p-please don't eat me," he said to Simba.

"I'm not going to eat you, I promise," said Simba. "I just want to know how you got stuck in the mud."

"I was angry at my little brother and I bit his tail and made him cry. I was afraid my parents would be upset, so I ran away from home," said the little hippo.

"I'll bet your parents *are* upset," said Simba. "Because you're gone and they're worried about you."

"They won't care," the hippo said.

"Come on," said Simba. He led the little hippo to the edge of the river. When they got there, they could hear the other hippos calling.

"Oyo! Oyo! Oyo!"

"Listen," said the hippo. "Oyo's my name. They're calling me! They miss me!"

"Sure," said Simba. "You can't just run away without being missed. When you're part of a family, no matter what you do, you'll always belong."

"What about *your* family, Simba?" Timon asked as they watched the little hippo rejoin his family. "Do you think they miss you?"

"I didn't used to think so," Simba replied thoughtfully, "but now I wonder...."

Island Adventure

Disney Mickey & Friends

Mickey, Minnie, Donald and Daisy were on their way to their seaside holiday. As soon as they arrived, they put on their bathing costumes and ran down to the beach.

They came to a lovely cove. "I'm going to relax here!" Minnie declared as she spread out her blanket.

"Me, too," said Daisy, opening her umbrella.

"Those waves are just perfect for surfing," said Donald, looking out to sea.

"You boys run along," Minnie said.

"We're happy right here," said Daisy.

Mickey and Donald surfed and swam until the sun went down.

The next day was sunny too. On their way to the beach, Mickey and Donald spied a boat for hire. "Let's go fishing!" cried Donald.

But Daisy and Minnie shook their heads. "We want to relax," they said.

So Donald and Mickey went fishing alone.

On the third day, Mickey and Donald wanted to go for a long swim.

"No, thanks," said Minnie. "I want to take it easy."

"Me, too," said Daisy. "We're going to the cove to relax."

The boys went off to swim. Daisy and Minnie headed for the cove.

While she and Minnie were lounging under the palm trees, Daisy spied a bottle floating in the water. There was a map rolled up inside. She waded into the water to get it.

"It's a treasure map!" she exclaimed.

"The treasure is on an island!" announced Minnie, pointing to an X on the map.

Minnie and Daisy decided to follow the map. They went up one hill and then down another. They crossed a stream and reached a dock with a boat tied to it.

"That's the island," said Daisy, pointing out to sea. They hopped into the boat and started to row.

They rowed and they rowed until they reached the island. Minnie and Daisy were very tired and very hungry.

"Look!" Minnie cried. "I see a fire!"

"Pirates!" exclaimed Daisy.

But there were no pirates. Just Donald and Mickey, waiting for Daisy and Minnie to arrive. A campfire was roaring, and fish sizzled on the grill.

"Looks like they found our map!" Donald exclaimed.

"*Your* map?" cried Minnie.

"It was the only way to get you two to have an adventure with us!" Mickey replied.

"Now, sit down by the fire," said Donald. "Lunch is served!"

DISNEY·PIXAR
MONSTERS, INC.

The Last Laugh

"Feeling funny today?" Sulley asked Mike on the Laugh Floor one morning.

Mike smiled. "You bet!"

Just then, laughter filled the Floor, catching Mike off guard. A group of employees were standing around another monster.

"Who's the comedian?" Mike asked.

"Stan, our newest recruit," Sulley replied. "I'll introduce you."

"Good morning!" Stan said when he saw Sulley.

"Hey, there's someone I'd like you to meet." Sulley turned to Mike. "Mike Wazowski, this is Stanley Stanford. And Mike here is our top Laugh Collector."

Mike and Stan shook hands. "What were you guys laughing about before?" Mike asked.

"I was just telling them about the time I met the Abominable Snowman and his mother. I said to him, 'Hey, Mr Snowman, where's your mother from?' And he said, 'Alaska'. And I said, 'Hey, don't bother. I'll ask her myself!'"

Everyone burst out laughing all over again – everyone except Mike, who couldn't help feeling green with envy. He felt like his position as best Laugh Collector was being challenged!

"Hey, good one, Stan," Mike said when the laughter had died down. "But have you heard the one about the skeleton who decided not to go to the party?" All eyes turned to Mike.

"He had no body to go with!" Mike exclaimed. Everyone laughed. He was back on top!

But Stan had another joke. "That's funny, Mike," he said. "Have you heard the one about the big elephant that wouldn't stop charging? The only way to stop him was to take away his credit card!" Now everyone was laughing at Stan again. Mike knew this was joke war. As the jokes came fast and furious, the employees gathered around the two jokesters.

The joke-off carried on until, in a moment of panic, Mike's mind went blank! He began to jump up and down, hoping to jump-start his brain. Then, in one of his panicky little jumps, Mike landed on the edge of a wheeled trolley.

"Waaaah!" Mike cried as the trolley took off, travelling across the room and carrying him with it! The employees watched as Mike rolled wildly across the Laugh Floor. They fell down, laughing their heads off! When Mike landed in a pile of cardboard boxes, the joke-off was over, and Mike was the winner. "You're a funny guy, Mike Wazowski," Stan said.

Mike smiled. Stan wasn't such a bad guy, after all. *And with two hilarious monsters on the Laugh Team*, thought Mike, *just imagine all the laugh energy they could collect!*

Disney · PIXAR
WALL·E
The Sore Loser

One sunny day, a few weeks after the Axiom space cruiser had landed on Earth, WALL•E was showing EVE one of the strange things in his trash collection.

WALL•E had spent years building up the collection, gathering together all the strange things he had found among the junk that fascinated him. He was very proud of it.

The thing he wanted to show EVE was a little rectangle of plastic with some buttons on each side.

As EVE pressed the buttons, a little square screen lit up and a voice chimed, "Welcome! Do you want to start a new game?"

WALL•E gasped. The thing had never done that before. He tried to take a look, but EVE turned away. The thing was a handheld games console, and on-screen was a tiny robot that looked a little like her.

"Play!" EVE said, as she pushed the button that started the game.

Immediately, the screen was filled with rows of angry-looking villains. EVE's fingers jabbed at the buttons, making her on-screen character open fire. Laser blasts pinged around the screen, and as WALL•E's home was filled with bleeps and bloops, he tried once again to get a look.

"Walleeee!" he said, raising up onto his wheels to try to get a peek at the game, but EVE didn't

want to give it up yet. When her character was blown up, she immediately hit the start button again, and launched back into the game.

EVE's metal fingers clicked frantically, making her character fire faster and faster. It was no use, though. A sneaky laser blast got through her defences, blowing her up.

"You lose!" the game announced.

WALL•E hoped that meant it was his turn, but EVE was determined to beat the game.

"Play!" she snapped, starting all over again.

Every time EVE lost the game, WALL•E hoped it was his turn, but EVE refused to hand it over. She growled angrily as she restarted for the fifteenth time. This time she was going to win, she could feel it.

"You lose," said the game, as she was blown to pieces once again. "Game over, loser!"

That did it! EVE knew one way she could beat the game for sure.

She took aim with her blaster arm and opened fire, turning the console into a smouldering pile of melted plastic.

Victorious, EVE finally passed the game to WALL•E so he could have his turn.

WALL•E sighed as he looked at the blackened plastic. Suddenly, the game didn't seem so much fun, after all.

The Winning Cup

At Flo's V8 Café, business was booming. Tourists from all over were bustling to get a seat and all of them were after one delicious, mouth-watering thing.

"We'd like the house speciality!" a cheery customer requested.

"I'm afraid we're all out," said Flo. "But how about a nice oil-shake? You'll love it," she suggested.

In the kitchen, Flo sighed under the pressure. Ramone couldn't help but overhear as he drove by. He hated to see Flo miserable.

"What's the matter, Flo?" he asked. "Your place is buzzin' with all these thirsty tourists!"

"But everyone orders the house special," Flo complained.

"So?" said Ramone, confused.

"The café doesn't have one!" she moaned.

Sheriff, sneaking in for a quick shot of his favourite oily drink, caught the end of Flo's conversation. "That your problem?" he piped up. "Then all you have to do is pick one from the menu!"

"Yes! Like your Antifreeze Ice Cream. Or the Pick-Uppuccino!" Ramone said.

"I want something more original," admitted Flo. "With a real knock-out name."

"Then do what we always do when advice is needed," said Ramone.

Flo knew exactly what he meant. She shot off, leaving her friends to man the café in her absence, and found Doc in his garage.

"Have you got a minute?" she wondered.

"Sure do, Flo! Come on in," invited Doc.

"I've got a problem," she explained. "I ... ooooh!" she paused. A thought had rendered her speechless for a moment. "I should have thought of that myself!" she said.

"Huh?" frowned Doc. What had just happened?

"Thanks, Doc!" she cried over her shoulder. "You've been a big help!"

"But I didn't say a word...." he murmured.

"You've given me the perfect idea though! Just come to V8 later, you'll see!" she called.

Later that day, the crowd around Flo's café was five cars deep and full of excitable whispers. A big sign had been placed high in front of the shop for the entire world to see.

Doc grinned in appreciation. "You're right, Flo, this really is a winner."

The sign proudly displayed a trophy full of bubbling juice – the new Piston Cup.

"You've always said your trophies are just empty cups," said Flo, blushing.

Doc agreed. She'd certainly come up with the best way to fill his trophies and a grand way to remind the town of his achievements too!

RATATOUILLE
(rat·a·too·ee)

Remy's Day Off

The restaurant was closed for the day, and Remy was thrilled to have the whole kitchen to himself. With everyone else gone, he could experiment with new some recipes.

Just as he was about to get started, his brother, Emile, showed up. He told Remy he wanted to help him cook.

"Cooking is not easy, Emile. Are you really sure?" Remy asked, but Emile was positive.

Remy explained how important it was to be clean when cooking, and they both scrubbed their paws with soap. Next, Remy chose a recipe for them. Emile liked the sound of Gusteau's Special Cream Cake, and the brothers set to work.

"First, break four eggs," said Remy, reading from the recipe. Behind him, Emile smashed the eggs together, spilling their gooey contents all over the worktop. "In a bowl!" Remy groaned.

They only needed the yolks of the eggs, so while Remy tried scooping one up in a piece of broken shell, Emile wrapped his arms around one of the wobbly yellow blobs and carried it to the bowl.

Eventually, all four yolks were in the bowl. Remy poured in flour and sugar, then added a little pinch of baking powder. "That's to make the cake big and soft," he explained, and Emile licked his lips hungrily.

Emile was helping to mix everything together by trampling on it. As the ingredients merged, though, Emile found himself sinking in the sticky dough. Luckily, Remy grabbed his paw and pulled him free.

Remy went to get the electric mixer to whip up the cream. He told Emile not to touch anything, but Emile couldn't help thinking about that baking powder. If a little pinch made the cake big, a whole packet would make it huge!

When Remy returned he put the cake mix in the oven, leaving Emile to whisk the cream with the mixer. As the mixer rattled and shook, it took off across the table, dragging Emile with it and spraying cream in all directions. "This is fun!" Emile cried.

After saving Emile again, Remy and his brother sat down on the floor, waiting for the cake to bake. Remy asked Emile what he thought of cooking and Emile looked down at his sticky fur. He thought you were supposed to be clean to cook, but he'd never been so dirty.

Suddenly, there was a sound from the oven. The door flew open as a huge blob of dough forced its way free. Remy and Emile ran as the expanding dough chased them across the kitchen. Cooking wasn't just messier than Emile had thought – it was more dangerous, too!

Bonnie's Birthday Surprise

Bonnie's mum had been hard at work, busily preparing the food for Bonnie's birthday party. While she and Bonnie went out for some last-minute supplies, the toys admired the delicious-looking spread.

"It's gonna be a great party," Woody whistled.

Rex and Trixie, the dinosaur toys, pushed past. "Hey! I wanna see the cake," said Rex. Trixie agreed, and they both began to scramble up the table.

"Well, I don't think that's a good idea, guys," began Woody, but it was too late. Rex and Trixie had already made it onto the tabletop and were racing towards the box containing Bonnie's birthday cake.

"I can't wait to see it!" Rex cheered.

Woody was nervous. Rex had a habit of being clumsy. "We'd better go after them," he said, and he and Dolly hurried to catch the dinosaurs up.

"Be careful, Rex," Woody warned, climbing up onto the table beside the cake box.

Rex nodded. "Don't worry, I'll be super careful," he said, as he slowly lifted the lid of the box.

The cake was beautiful! There was pink and white frosting, sweet sprinkles and Bonnie's name written in pretty icing. Bonnie was sure to be delighted with it.

"Let me see it, let me see it!" demanded Trixie, shoving Rex out of the way. Rex flapped his stubby arms as he lost balance and – *SPLURT!* He landed face first in the cake, messing it up.

Rex pulled his head free of the frosting and gasped. "What will we do now?"

The toys couldn't let Bonnie's birthday be ruined, so they quickly set to work. Trixie searched the Internet for cake decorating tips, but they were all too difficult for them to even attempt.

Woody had an idea. "What about using jelly beans and candies?" he suggested. Bonnie loved jelly beans, and the toys quickly agreed. The only problem was, the frosting was still a mess. No amount of candies would fix that.

Rex waggled his tail. "Maybe I can do something about that."

In no time, Rex used his long tail to smooth over the pink frosting, and the toys set to work decorating. They finished just as Bonnie and her mum returned from shopping.

Bonnie cheered when she saw her cake. "Wow! This is the best cake ever!" she said.

Her mum nodded. "Yes ... it's even better than I remembered," she said.

Down on the floor, Dolly whispered quietly to Rex. "Well done. Everything turned out fine, thanks to you and your dinosaur tail!"

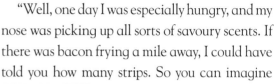

A Tramp Tale

It was a warm evening, just about the time that the first star comes out to shine, and long past the time for Lady and Tramp's puppies to go to sleep.

"Just one more story, Dad," begged Scamp.

Tramp rolled his eyes.

"Well ..." he said, "okay, but just one."

Happily, the puppies snuggled down onto their cushion. Tramp stretched out beside them.

"Did I ever tell you kids about the time I stole my very first sausage?" he asked.

"*Tramp!*" Lady warned him from her seat across the parlour. "That hardly sounds like a proper story for the children."

"Oh, tell it, Dad!" Scamp urged him.

"Well, maybe 'stole' isn't exactly the right word," Tramp reassured his wife. "And besides, it's got a great moral!" And with that, he began his tale.

"Now, this all happened way back when I was just a little pup, already living on my own in the big city. I hope you puppies know just how good you have it living here in this nice house, with Junior and Jim Dear and Darling. Your old dad, though, was not so lucky. Oh, I had a lot of friends. And I had a lot of fun. But I'd be lying if I said I wasn't hungry – just a little – nearly every day.

"Well, one day I was especially hungry, and my nose was picking up all sorts of savoury scents. If there was bacon frying a mile away, I could have told you how many strips. So you can imagine the interest I developed in a certain, spicy smell coming from the butcher's shop. Well, I followed my trusty nose, which has still never let me down and, sure enough, there was a heaping tray of steaming sausages. Can you believe it?"

"So you jumped up and gobbled them all up! Right?" Scamp broke in.

"That's my boy!" Tramp laughed. "But no. Don't forget, I was just a little guy. Couldn't reach the tray. All I could do was think about how to get that sausage ... when up walked a lady with a kid in a carriage. Well, at first I was irate. Competition! But then I noticed the crumbs all over the carriage. *Hey!* I thought to myself. *This might be the ticket – this kid obviously can't hang on to anything.* Sure enough, when the lady handed the kid a piece of sausage, the kid dropped it, and down it fell into my waiting mouth! Delicious!

"See, Lady," Tramp added with a grin, "no stealing!"

"And what exactly is the moral of that story?" Lady asked.

Tramp laughed. "Why, good things come to those who wait, of course!"

THE DISNEP
HUNCHBACK
of NOTRE DAME

Laughter is the Best Medicine

"I hope Quasi is okay out there!" Laverne said fretfully.

The other two gargoyles in the bell tower, Hugo and Victor, nodded in agreement. Their friend Quasimodo had just left Notre Dame to help the young soldier Phoebus search for the Court of Miracles. It was certain to be a dangerous mission.

"The only thing we can do is stay strong, and be hopeful," Victor said.

Hugo smirked. "How can we *not* be strong?" he asked. "We're made of stone, remember?"

"Good one!" Laverne giggled. "Rock solid."

"You know that's not what I meant." Victor frowned at Hugo. "And both of you – don't you have any sense of the seriousness of this situation? Our dear compatriot is out there somewhere, facing grave peril...."

"*Grave* peril?" Laverne said. "Way to be optimistic, Victor – you've already got poor Quasi in his grave!"

"Hoo-hoo!" Hugo whooped. "You slay me! If I were alive, I'd be dying right now!"

As the two of them rolled around on the tower floor, laughing loudly, Victor glared at them.

"I see," he said sternly. "So you two would rather mock me and crack bad jokes than join me in my concern for poor young Quasimodo."

Laverne stood up and brushed herself off. "Why does it have to be an either-or thing, Victor?" she asked. "Just because we're laughing, doesn't mean we're not worried, too."

"But our friend could be in real danger!" Victor exclaimed.

"That's right," Laverne said. "And standing around here all stone-faced isn't going to help him any."

Hugo nodded. "If we spend all our time thinking about how terrible everything is, we'll go nuts."

Waving his arms to help make his point, he accidentally hit a bird's nest that was tucked into one of the eaves. The occupant of the nest squawked and flew upwards. Laverne ducked just in time to avoid the bird flying straight into her face, but then she tripped and fell and landed on the ground. The bird banked upwards, still squawking as it flew over Hugo.

Hugo leaped backwards – and landed on Laverne's hand. She yelled and yanked her hand out from under him. Hugo lost his footing, and landed in a heap on top of Laverne.

Victor stared at his friends, who were trying to untangle themselves.

Then he started to laugh. He laughed harder and harder, until he could hardly speak.

"You know," he said finally, "I think you just might be right. I feel much better already!"

Peter Pan

A Feather in His Cap

Peter Pan and Tinker Bell were off on an adventure and the Lost Boys were bored.

"Never Land is a dull place without Peter Pan," Slightly complained.

Then Rabbit spoke up. "We can play pirates! That's always fun."

"Can't," said Slightly. "I lost the feather off my pirate hat."

"We could find another feather," Tootles suggested.

"An extraordinary feather," Cubby said. "Like Captain Hook's."

"That's it!" Slightly cried. "I'll steal Captain Hook's feather!"

A short time later, the Lost Boys were sneaking aboard Hook's pirate ship. Luckily for them, the pirates were taking a nap!

There, hanging from a peg on the mast, was Captain Hook's hat.

"There it is," whispered Tootles. "Get it!"

"M-m-m-me?" stammered Slightly.

Smee, Hook's first mate, awoke with a start. He thought someone had said his name. "Smee, you say! That be me. But who be calling Smee?"

He opened his eyes and spied the Lost Boys. "Ahoy!" he cried, waking up the others. Quick as a flash, the Lost Boys were caught.

Captain Hook burst from his cabin. "Lash them to the mast!" he commanded. "We'll catch Peter Pan when he comes to save his friends."

Floating high on a cloud, Peter Pan and Tinker Bell saw their friends being captured.

They flew down to Pirates' Cove and landed on the ship's mast. Peter cupped his hands around his mouth and made a most peculiar sound.

"Tick tock," Peter went. "Tick tock!"

Down on deck, Captain Hook became very frightened. "It's that crocodile!" he cried. "The one that ate my clock and my hand! Now he's come back to eat me!"

"Tick tock ... tick tock," went Peter.

"Man the cannons!" Hook cried. "Shoot that crocodile!"

The Lost Boys, tied to the mast, were forgotten. As the pirates ran in circles, Tinker Bell began to flap her wings. Fairy dust sprinkled down onto the Lost Boys. Soon they floated right out of the ropes and up into the clouds. On the way, Slightly snatched the feather from Hook's hat and stuck it in his own.

Peter Pan, Tinker Bell and the Lost Boys met on a drifting cloud.

"Thanks for saving us!" exclaimed Tootles.

"You helped me scare old Hook!" Peter Pan cried. "That's a feather in all your caps."

"But the best feather of them all is in mine," Slightly said, as he showed off Captain Hook's prized feather!

DISNEY·PIXAR
MONSTERS, INC.

Back to School for Boo

Mike was sitting in Boo's bedroom, telling jokes and acting silly. He was collecting laughs to help power the city of Monstropolis.

Boo was happy to see Mike, but she wasn't laughing quite as much as usual.

"Is something wrong, Boo?" Mike asked.

"School starts!" Boo said. "No photos!"

Luckily, Mike quickly worked out what Boo meant. School was about to begin again and she wanted to tell her class what she'd done over the holidays – but she needed pictures.

"Why don't you come to Monsters, Inc. with me?" Mike said. "We'll surprise Sulley."

Boo jumped up in excitement. "Yay!"

Boo and Mike went to Monsters, Inc. by stepping through Boo's wardrobe door. Mike found an old camera in the storeroom and started to take pictures of Boo.

Then Mike led Boo to the Laugh Floor. "Oh, Sulleeey!" he called out to his blue, furry friend. "I have a surprise for you."

"Kitty!" Boo exclaimed.

Sulley was so happy to see Boo! He gave her a big hug.

Then, all night long, they raced from one place to another, all over Monsters, Inc. – and Monstropolis – taking photographs!

By the end of the visit, Boo had taken lots of photos. She and Mike were trying to decide which were the best ones to take to school.

Sulley's eyebrows shot up. "School? What do you mean 'school'?"

Mike explained that Boo needed great pictures to share with her class.

Sulley was not happy.

"You know that's not allowed!" he exclaimed.

"Gee, Sulley, I was just trying to help," Mike said.

Sulley softened. "I know, Mikey, but it's my job to protect Monsters, Inc. We have to keep the monster world a secret from the human world."

"How are we going to tell Boo?" said Mike.

Sulley looked over his shoulder. Boo was already looking sad.

Sulley hated to see Boo so disappointed.

"Please, Kitty?" she said.

"Okay," Sulley finally told her. "I'll let you take back one photo. But I get to pick it."

Mike grinned, and Boo cheered!

At school the next day, Boo told her class all about her special adventure.

Her classmates didn't believe her. Her teacher didn't believe her. So Boo pulled out the picture....

The teacher gasped. "That looks just like Bigfoot!" she cried.

Boo giggled. "Not Bigfoot. That's Kitty!"

Training Memories

Dusty was telling Sparky and Chug all about the fire and rescue training he'd done up at Piston Peak.

He told them that when he'd first arrived, the national park had seemed like a peaceful place, but all that had changed when the fire team had raced into action to put out a forest blaze.

Dusty had got a close look at the action. Too close, in fact – he'd almost been blinded by the flame-retardant spray!

A blast of a high-pressure hose had washed the red powder off, but he still shivered when he remembered how icy-cold it had been!

From there, things only got worse. His landing gear was cut off and replaced by two large pontoon tanks, which could be filled with water!

Those things were hard to get used to, and on his first try at filling up from a river, Dusty almost plunged over a waterfall! Luckily, the helicopter, Blade, saved him just in the nick of time.

"I was so tired every night," Dusty recalled. "But next day I was always ready to go again!"

He told Chug and Sparky about the firefighting classes he attended every day, where he learned lots of different ways to be useful in an emergency.

He had to pay very close attention to what was being taught, as people's lives could be depending on it.

Along with the lessons, he practised hard for hours at a time. He'd go through the same exercises over and over until he got them right every time.

It wasn't easy – when trying to put out practice fires he'd often swoop in too late and miss completely, or drop too early and crash right into them.

For a while, he thought he'd never make it as a firefighter, until one day he managed his first direct hit on a blaze.

Unfortunately, it had been a campfire, and Blade the helicopter had laughed at him. "Congratulations, you just saved a family from a nice holiday!"

Still, Dusty kept learning and kept practising, until he was ready for action.

And not a moment too soon! Dusty had been called on soon after, and thanks to his new skills and quick-thinking, he'd been able to save a lot of vehicles from a forest fire. At last, he was a real firefighter!

When Dusty finished the story, Chug cheered. "Now the citizens of Propwash Junction can feel safe," he said.

Sparky giggled. "As long as they aren't camping!"

THE INCREDIBLES

A Super Summer Barbecue

One hot summer afternoon, Helen Parr stood in the kitchen icing a cake. It was almost time to leave for the barbecue.

"Hey, Mum," said Helen's eldest son, Dash, running into the room at Super speed. "Why do we have to go to some silly neighbourhood barbecue?"

"Dashiell Robert Parr," said Helen. "We're lucky to have been invited. You know we're doing our best to fit in here. And remember – no Super powers outside the house."

A while later, the Parrs walked around the block to their first neighbourhood party. Helen placed her cake on the dessert table. Her husband Bob headed over to the grill to help out. Her daughter Violet looked around for someone to talk to and Dash watched some children compete in a sack race. He couldn't join in because it might reveal his Super speed.

"Are you too chicken to play?" a boy teased. Dash scowled. When the mean boy hopped by, he mysteriously tripped and fell. Dash smiled to himself and brushed off his sneaker. His speed had come in handy, after all.

Meanwhile, out of the corner of her eye, Helen saw Jack-Jack on top of a high brick wall. He was about to topple off! In a flash, she shot her arm all the way across the yard and caught him. She sighed with relief and cuddled

Jack-Jack. Another mother rubbed her eyes and mumbled something about not sleeping much the night before. *Oops*, Helen thought to herself.

A while later, Helen saw the neighbours enjoying her cake. She looked around the yard and spotted Dash telling a story. Violet was eating an ice-cream cone with a girl her age. *Wow, it looks like we really fit in here*, Helen thought. But just then, she overheard one of the neighbours.

"There's something strange about those Parrs," he said.

Had someone discovered them? Were their Super powers about to be revealed?

"All that may be true," someone else added, "but that Helen sure makes a terrific cake!" Everyone agreed, and the conversation ended.

The Parrs chuckled to themselves. Their cover wasn't blown after all! Maybe they were a little strange compared to the average family, but they were doing their best to act normal.

Bob and Helen rounded up their children and headed for home, pleased with the way things had gone.

As they reached their house, Helen gave Bob a great big kiss, which the kids did their best to ignore.

Moon Mater

Mater and Lightning McQueen were looking up at a large full moon.

"Yep," said Mater, "I've been up there."

"*Pffft!* You have not," Lightning said.

But Mater insisted. He began to tell a story about the time he went to the moon. Mater described driving past NASCA, the National Auto-Spacecraft Administration. Inside, a monitor showed the surface of the moon. On-screen, a moon buggy named Impala Thirteen was stuck on the edge of a crater!

"He needs a tow!" cried one of the forklifts who worked at NASCA. Then Roger the space shuttle saw Mater driving by and Mater agreed to help.

On the day of his flight, he made his way to the shuttle launchpad. He was wearing a spacesuit and rocket jets. He rolled onto the space shuttle and strapped in.

At the base of the launchpad, smoke spilled out of the booster rockets. Then fire, followed by even more smoke. Finally, blast-off! The shuttle launched into the sky.

"And we have lift-off!" announced Mission Control.

As Roger rocketed up into space, he cheered with joy. "Woooo-hooo!"

Inside the shuttle, Mater looked out of the window. "See ya later, Earth."

Soon Roger's rockets had carried them deep into space. They were nearly at the moon!

"Operation Tow Mater is a go!" Mission Control said over the radio. It was time for Mater's moon landing. He floated out of the shuttle and into space.

"Good luck," Roger said. "See you on Earth." The shuttle began the trip home. The rescue mission was up to Mater now. Using his jets, he steered to the surface of the moon. He bounced over to the Impala Thirteen.

"Connect your rescue apparatus to the frontal structural component of the linear axle assembly," instructed Impala Thirteen.

"Uhh," Mater replied. "How 'bout I just give you a tow?" He fastened his tow hook, blasted his jets and pulled the moon buggy free!

"Mission accomplished!" Impala Thirteen said. "Now take us home!" Mater fired his jets and rocketed towards Earth with Impala Thirteen on his tow rope.

In Radiator Springs, Mater had just finished his story. "Oh, come on," Lightning said. "That did not happen."

Suddenly, Roger the shuttle set down next to them. "Suit yourself," Mater said, and then he drove up a ramp into the shuttle.

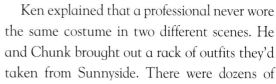

Space Comedy

One night, while Bonnie was fast asleep, Jessie and some of her friends set to work making a movie!

Jessie wanted to make a thrilling space adventure film for Buzz, and Ken and Chunk had come all the way from Sunnyside to help her out.

Ken and Chunk worked the camera, while Mr Pricklepants directed the action. Jessie and the aliens were the stars of the show, with Rex dressed up as a scary alien monster for them to battle.

The stage was set for the most amazing space adventure story ever – but things didn't quite go to plan.

"Space Ranger Jessie is in danger!" Jessie announced, as Ken pointed the camera her way. "We need the help of our hero...."

"The Claw!" chimed the aliens.

"Stop!" cried Mr Pricklepants. "Who is this Claw? It's not in the script! You have to say 'Buzz Lightyear'."

The aliens smiled. "The Claw!"

Jessie gave a sigh. "Let's move on to the next scene," she suggested.

Ken raced excitedly out from behind the camera. "Did you say next scene? Stop! Change of costumes!"

"Already?" frowned Jessie. "But we only just started filming."

Ken explained that a professional never wore the same costume in two different scenes. He and Chunk brought out a rack of outfits they'd taken from Sunnyside. There were dozens of them – and those were just for the first three scenes!

"We have to wear all these?" Jessie asked. "But we'll never make it!"

Just then, Rex came charging onto the set, wondering if it was his turn in front of the camera. His swinging tail knocked part of the set, bringing it crashing down on Mr Pricklepants.

As Jessie pulled the hedgehog out from under the set, the aliens raced up to the camera holding a sign which read: 'The End'.

"The Claw!" they said again, giggling into the camera lens. Jessie shook her head sadly. Her movie was terrible!

Next day, she decided just to go ahead and show Buzz the movie anyway. "I'm so sorry," she said, when the film had finished. "I wanted to give you an adventure movie, and instead –"

"It's the funniest comedy I've ever seen!" Buzz laughed. He planted a kiss on Jessie's cheek. "Thanks, Jessie," he said. "I like it a lot!"

Buzz had loved his present. Jessie blushed, making a note to thank her friends – for being such disasters!

Safe Swimming

In the depths of the ocean, Marlin the clownfish emerged, ready for a day of adventure with his son, Nemo.

"Nice to see you're up early," he said, finding Nemo already outside.

"I've been waiting for this all week!" Nemo cried excitedly. "Let's go!"

"Nemo, wait!" Marlin shrieked as Nemo dashed off. He caught his son by his littlest fin. "What are you doing? You can't swim off into the ocean willy-nilly. It's dangerous!"

"Aww, c'mon, Dad," said Nemo, unfazed. "I've been lost in the ocean before and came home fine."

"Just because you were trapped in a fish tank doesn't mean you know how to survive the ocean," Marlin warned him. "We can still have fun together. Safe fun ... Nemo!" His eyes bulged out of his head when he realized his son had left him again.

Nemo swam upwards towards a pair of orange legs swishing in the water. Pelican legs! Marlin powered after him and snatched him from harm's way, just as the pelican ducked its beak into the water to swallow Nemo whole.

"Just because you've met a friendly pelican before and had a ride in his mouth, doesn't mean others won't try and eat you," Marlin scolded.

"That was so cool," marvelled Nemo.

"This is no laughing matter!" said Marlin, losing patience. Nemo needed to be smart in the ocean. Everything could be an enemy....

"Hey, Dad! I've found something."

Nemo had swum off again in the brief moment Marlin had looked up to see if the pelican's legs had gone from above them.

"This is awesome," Nemo declared, rubbing a fin across the shiny glass surface of a discarded bottle from the human world.

"Stay away from that. It could be dangerous!" snapped Marlin, rushing over. He glanced at the surface of the object. His jaw gaped open. In the reflection, bolting towards him and his son was a....

"BARRACUDA! We'll never outswim him!"

Thinking on his fins, Nemo dived into the narrow opening of the bottle.

"Follow me!" he yelled.

"But we'll be trapped," panicked Marlin.

"I know," said Nemo.

The barracuda swam directly at the bottle and slammed its face into the glass as it tried to eat the little clownfish inside. In pain, it whimpered off into the ocean with a few teeth loose and wobbling.

"You did it!" Marlin high-fived Nemo.

Nemo hoped his Dad had learned his lesson – that sometimes being trapped in a glass tank could have its advantages!

Disney
Bambi

A Manner of Speaking

Bambi and his mother were out for a summer's walk. As always, they stopped by the rabbit den where Thumper lived.

"And how are you today, Thumper?" asked Bambi's mother.

"I'd be better if my mum didn't just give me a dumb old bath," he said.

"Thumper! Please, mind your manners!" his mother scolded him.

"I'm sorry, Mama," Thumper said. He looked back at the doe. "I'm fine, thank you," he replied.

Bambi and Thumper were given permission to play, so they headed off into the woods.

"So, what do you want to play?" Bambi asked Thumper.

"How about hide-and-seek?" Thumper suggested. "I'll hide first, okay?"

Bambi turned his back to Thumper, closed his eyes, and started to count. "One ... two ... three ... four ... five...."

"Save me! Help! Bambi, save me!" Thumper cried. Bambi whirled around to see Thumper hopping towards him with a terrified look on his face. A moment later, a mother bear emerged from a nearby cave with three small cubs toddling behind her.

Though he was terrified, Thumper *still* managed to make a rude comment. "That's the meanest-looking creature I ever saw!"

"I beg your pardon?" the mother bear said. "First, you come into my home and disturb my children while they're sleeping. And then you have the nerve to call me mean? I think you owe me an apology!"

"Do it!" whispered Bambi. "Apologize."

"I'm sorry you're mean," Thumper said.

"Thumper!" Bambi cried. "That isn't funny."

Thumper was confused by Bambi's outburst. "I wasn't trying to be funny," he said.

"Try again!" the mother bear boomed.

"Um," Thumper tried again. "I'm, um, sorry I disturbed your cubs ... and, um, you look just like a bear mum should look ... which is big. And nice. Yup, you sure look nice."

Before the mother bear let Thumper and Bambi go, she said, "Like I always tell my children – manners are important!"

Bambi and Thumper ran home as quickly as they could. When they arrived at Thumper's, his mother said, "Just in time for a nice lunch of greens." Thumper was about to tell his mum how awful he thought the greens tasted, then changed his mind. "Thank you, Mama. That sounds wonderful," he said.

Thumper's mother beamed. "What lovely manners! I guess you have been listening to me, after all!" she said, as pleased as could be.

Disney
The Fox and the Hound

The Chase

"Whoopee!" Tod cried as he tumbled head over tail towards the water. He hit the surface with a splash. A second later, his friend Copper landed right next to him.

"It certainly is a beautiful day," Copper said.

"It sure is," Tod agreed. The two friends swam to the edge and climbed up on the bank. As they sat in the warm sun, a great big blue butterfly landed on Copper's tail.

"Looks like you've made a friend," said Tod.

But the butterfly was scared away by a loud voice.

"Copper!" the voice rumbled. It was Amos, Copper's master. Amos was usually grumpy, and right now he sounded angry too. "Where are you, mutt?" he shouted.

Tod silently climbed out of the water. He could tell that Amos was nearby, and that his other dog, Chief, was with him.

Copper creeped up beside Tod. "I'd better go," he said. "Amos sounds awfully mad."

"Why don't you sneak back to your barrel so you're there when he gets back," Tod suggested. "He can't be mad if you're already home when he finds you."

Copper scratched behind his ear. "But he's right in my path, and Chief is with him. Chief will hear me or smell me for sure."

Tod grinned. "You just leave that to me."

He winked at his friend and dashed up the hill, right past Amos and Chief.

"There's that varmint fox!" Amos cried as Chief took off after Tod, barking like mad. Amos gave chase, running as fast as he could on his long, skinny legs.

Tod darted around trees and leaped over branches. More than once, Chief got close, his hot breath on Tod's tail. But Tod was smart. He led Chief towards a rocky outcrop and dashed into a small cave. Chief stuck his snout into the opening, growling away. But he was too big to fit.

"Never mind, Chief," Amos said when he finally caught up. "We'll get him later."

Chief gave a final growl into the cave, but Tod had already escaped at the other end and was dashing home.

Exhausted, Amos and Chief started home. By the time they got there, Tod was napping next door in front of the Widow Tweed's fireplace, and Copper was sitting in his barrel. Next to him, his supper bowl was empty.

"There you are," Amos grumbled. He shook his head. "And I suppose you've been sitting here almost the whole time. We could have used your help catching that dang fox – it's almost as if you're trying to avoid hunting him!"

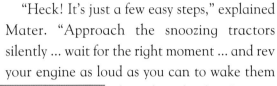

Tractor Tipping!

Mater and Lightning McQueen were trundling through the streets of Radiator Springs in hysterics. They couldn't remember the last time they'd laughed so hard.

"Did you see those tractors jump?" Mater chuckled, tears of joy in the corners of his eyes.

Lightning McQueen's body shook as he giggled. "That horn from Sarge worked like a charm!"

"Let's do it again tonight," Mater suggested.

"Okay, sure!" agreed Lightning McQueen. "I'll see you after practice."

As they turned to leave, a voice sounded behind them. "So, tell me, what's so funny?"

Mater and Lightning McQueen turned to find The King rolling up the street with a smirk on his face. "I've come for a visit," The King said. "I'm curious though. What's so amusing?"

"The tractors!" Mater giggled. "They spend all day grazing in the fields, so every once in a while we stop by to wake them up a little!"

The King considered this. "I've never tried anything like that."

"Why don't you tag along tonight? We'll make it a special expedition, just for you!"

"You've got yourself a deal!" cried The King.

Later that night, in a quiet field, the cars kept a beady eye out for lazy, sleepy tractors.

"Now what?" whispered The King.

"Heck! It's just a few easy steps," explained Mater. "Approach the snoozing tractors silently ... wait for the right moment ... and rev your engine as loud as you can to wake them from their slumber!"

The King nodded. They all creeped forwards.

"All set?" Mater asked in a hushed tone.

The noise from their horns and engines gave the tractors the fright of their lives, and each one rolled backwards onto their behinds in alarm.

Lightning McQueen laughed unstoppably, his friends weak at the wheels from giggling too.

Suddenly, a light flashed from behind them. An engine deeper, louder and fiercer than any of their own rumbled and roared in the night.

"What on earth is that?" shrieked The King.

"That's Frank!" Lightning McQueen cried. Frank was the combine beast of the field, with the tools to churn up and crush anything in his path. "We've gone too far this time!"

"Now what?" The King demanded.

Mater was already way ahead of them, bolting for the edge of the field. "We run for it!" he yelled over the sound of Frank's growling.

The cars took off across the field, their laughter lost beneath the sound of Frank's roaring revenge, and the tractors returned to their grazing, happy once more.

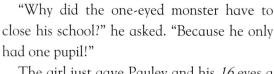

Monster Laughs

Sulley was worried. As the new head of Monsters, Inc. it was his job to make sure the power levels stayed high. But none of the monsters seemed to be getting enough laughs.

"Mikey, we've got a power problem," Sulley said to his friend. "It's been a year since we switched from scare power to laugh power and the monsters aren't funny any more. All their routines are old and dull."

Mike thought for a moment. "I got it!" he said, snapping his fingers. "I'll write some new jokes for all the monsters!"

Mike spent the next few nights writing jokes and inventing gags. He put on a show for the other monsters....

"Back in the day when I was scary, I gave 'eye-scream' a whole new meaning! But honestly, can you believe kids were afraid of me? I'm just 50 per cent eye. That's not scary – that's just an eye sore!"

He wrapped up the performance with the perfect impression of a bowling ball!

After he finished his act, Mike handed out comedy scripts to each of the monsters and told them to perform the jokes just like he had – those kids would be laughing in no time!

But things didn't go so well. A monster called Pauley tried one of Mike's jokes on a little girl.

"Why did the one-eyed monster have to close his school?" he asked. "Because he only had one pupil!"

The girl just gave Pauley and his *16* eyes a blank stare.

"They're terrible!" said Mike. "I need to round them up for some practice. If they can learn to perform the jokes just like me, our power levels will go through the roof!"

"But Mike, that's the problem," said Sulley. "The other monsters can't perform the jokes like you, because they're not you."

The next day, the monsters were feeling downhearted. Then, suddenly, a very tall monster called Lanky slipped on a banana skin. When he landed, his arms and legs were all tangled up. Lanky started to laugh, and so did all of the other monsters!

Mike thought for a moment. "That's it!" he cried. "Instead of copying me, you just have to be yourselves! That's how to be funny!"

"That's right," said Sulley. "If you've got 16 eyes – use them! If you have really long limbs – use them! Be proud of who you are!"

A few days later, the Laugh Floor buzzed with activity. Behind wardrobe doors, kids roared with laughter.

"Great job, Mikey," said Sulley. "Power levels are going back up!"

A Jump in the Smoke

All the crop dusting was over and done with for the day, and some of the planes had gathered in the hangar to chat.

"Hey, Dusty!" called Leadbottom. "Tell Alice about the planes and the Smokejumpers on Piston Peak." Alice, a young truck, rolled closer to listen in.

"There's not much to tell, actually," said Dusty. "When a call comes in, the Piston Peak air attack team heads to the fire and puts it out."

Leadbottom smiled encouragingly. "Aren't you forgetting something? I also asked you about the ground crew...."

"The Smokejumpers are special," Dusty began. He told Alice about how the wheeled firefighting crew were always joking around and playing pranks, but when an emergency call came in, they turned deadly serious.

Although they were all ground vehicles, the Smokejumpers started most jobs in the air. They would leap out of a carrier plane above a fire and parachute into action. Dynamite, the leader, would issue the orders and the team would race wheels first into danger.

Each member of the team had their own special set of skills.

Pinecone's digger arm could clear paths through the undergrowth. Blackout's pincers were perfect for cutting through trees – even if he occasionally sliced through other things by mistake!

The loud-mouthed Avalanche and second-in-command, Drip, rounded out the rest of the crew, making them ready for any emergency.

It was their job to stop fires spreading through the forest by cutting, hacking and chopping down the surrounding plants and trees. With nowhere for the fire to go, it made life much easier for the planes and helicopters above to put out the flames.

"It's a risky business," said Dusty. "Once, the Smokejumpers were trapped in a fire with no way out."

It had looked as if the brave ground crew were in serious trouble, but luckily, Dusty explained, he'd been flying overhead right at that moment, and was able to clear a path using his flame-retardant powder. Dusty's accurate aim had saved his friends, but it was all in a day's work for a firefighter.

"Some precision!" said Leadbottom, impressed. "Dusty learned it from me when he was a crop duster."

Alice giggled. "Yeah, right, Leadbottom!"

Dusty and the other planes joined in, too. "But don't go tryin' to put out any fires with Vita-minamulch!" they advised, and everyone – including Leadbottom – laughed.

Disney
HERCULES

A Not-so-relaxing Holiday

There was no doubt about it – Hercules badly needed a holiday! All these trials and challenges were very tiring.

"But what about your training?" argued Phil. "You can't stop now! If you're gonna be a god, you've got to train like one!"

"If I don't take a break," said Hercules, "I'm never going to become a god, because I'll be so burned out. Sorry, Phil, but I've got to go."

And, with that, he put away his dumbbells and his javelins, cancelled his Herculaid Sports Drink TV advert, and rounded up Pegasus.

"We're off to the Greek Islands, my friend," he told the winged horse. "Sandcastles, beach blankets, umbrella drinks ... here we come!"

And, before you could say 'Mount Vesuvius', there they were, at the finest resort in the ancient world, soaking up the sun and doing absolutely nothing.

"A hero could get used to this," said Hercules as he bobbed in the water, sipping a smoothie and adjusting his sunglasses.

Suddenly, a cry rang out from the beach. "Shark! Shark!"

"Shark?" said Hercules. "In the Aegean Sea?"

But sure enough, a big, grey dorsal fin was speeding towards the crowded shore!

"Help!" cried the people in the water.

"Help!" cried Hercules ... until he realized he was the one who could save them.

He swam up to the shark, grabbed it by the tail and tossed it up into the sky, all the way to the Atlantic.

"Whew," said Hercules, as the people clapped and cheered.

But not five minutes later, another frightened scream rang out – this time from the hills.

"Volcano!"

From the centre of the island's mountain rose a plume of thick, black smoke and fiery bursts of molten lava.

"Help!" cried the people.

Hercules knew what he had to do. He raced around the island until he found the biggest boulder. He rolled it all the way to the mountain top, then with one great push, he tipped it over the edge and into the bubbling mouth of the volcano. A perfect fit. The volcano was stopped.

"Hooray!" cheered the people.

Before any more natural disasters could occur, Hercules decided it was time to pack up and head back home.

"Back so soon, Herc?" asked Phil, looking pleasantly surprised.

Hercules shrugged. "Let's just say that for a hero, sometimes work is easier than holiday!"

An Important Role

At the stadium, Lightning McQueen was revving himself up for a race with the help of Fillmore. Sometimes the best way to prepare for the track was to remind himself he could do this!

"Speed! I'm pure speed," Lightning McQueen chanted determinedly.

"Definitely," Fillmore enthused. "Just keep cool and do your thing."

Fillmore was wearing one of his inventions – a hat fitted with two canisters of his infamous bio-fuel. With a straw at either side, he could sip his drink with ease.

Later that day, when Lightning McQueen was prepping at the starting line, Fillmore wandered aimlessly around the car park, enjoying the sun and his bio-fuel hat.

"Ha! Look at that!" came a cruel chuckle.

"Check out this practical joke!" came another voice.

Fillmore turned to see two forklift trucks. One of them scooted up beside Fillmore and with a vicious swipe of his arm, he stole the hat straight from Fillmore's head.

"Ha! Bruiser strikes again," he cackled.

"Hey, watch it!" cried Fillmore. "You scratched me!"

Both the forklifts ignored him, throwing the hat backwards and forwards.

Fillmore got dizzier as he watched his hat getting meanly thrown about ... when out of nowhere, Lightning McQueen zoomed through the air, catching the hat mid-flight.

Lightning McQueen handed it back to his friend.

"Thanks a bunch, man," said Fillmore gratefully.

"You two better steer clear of my friends," warned Lightning McQueen. But as the words left his mouth, Bruiser speared Lightning's barrel of fuel with a long lifting arm, making oil spew out onto the road in a black puddle.

"Try racing without fuel, champ!" Bruiser sneered. His brother laughed at his side as they left together.

"Now there isn't enough fuel to finish the race," Lightning McQueen fretted.

"I might have a solution," said Fillmore.

Later, on the track, Lightning McQueen whizzed ahead in first place, only this time there was something different about the way he looked. On his head was Fillmore's fuel-guzzling hat invention and as he raced around the track, he chugged down enough fuel to keep his engine running.

"Great idea, Fillmore," Lightning McQueen praised at the finish line, a new trophy in hand.

Fillmore and Lightning McQueen looked out for each other, always.

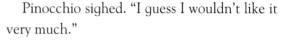

In a Tangle

One night, while Pinocchio was sleeping, a loud crash woke him. He jumped up and raced downstairs to Geppetto's workshop.

"Is anybody here?" Pinocchio called.

"Miaow!" It was Geppetto's kitten, Figaro.

"I hear you, but I can't see you!" called Pinocchio.

Suddenly, the puppets sitting above Geppetto's workbench began to move.

"Yikes!" cried Pinocchio, startled.

Pinocchio looked up to see Figaro tangled in the puppets' strings. Pinocchio began to laugh.

"That's funny!" he said.

"Miaow!" cried Figaro. He didn't think it was funny! The kitten struggled to get free, but he only became more tangled in the strings.

Pinocchio just laughed harder.

Jiminy Cricket hopped down from the hearth. He rubbed his tired eyes. "What's going on?" he asked.

Pinocchio pointed to the little kitten.

"Pinocchio, maybe you should help poor Figaro instead of laughing at him," Jiminy said.

"Maybe I should leave him there," replied Pinocchio. "Then Geppetto can see how naughty he's been."

"Miaow!" poor Figaro wailed.

"That's not very nice," said Jiminy. "How would you feel if you were all tangled up?"

Pinocchio sighed. "I guess I wouldn't like it very much."

He was about to free the kitten, when he suddenly exclaimed, "Hey, Jiminy, look at that!"

Figaro's paws were now wrapped around the puppets' strings in such a way that when his paws moved, the puppets began to dance!

"That's a neat trick," said Pinocchio. "Figaro can work the puppets!"

The kitten moved his paws some more, and all the puppets danced on their strings.

"I have an idea," said Jiminy Cricket. "Do you want to hear it?"

Pinocchio and Figaro both nodded.

The next morning when Geppetto awoke, he got a surprise.

"Look, Father!" Pinocchio said. "Figaro can make the puppets dance!"

Pinocchio winked at Figaro, and the cat leaped onto the puppet strings again.

"Amazing!" Geppetto cried. "We can put on a puppet show for all the children of the town!"

Pinocchio was thrilled to see Geppetto so happy.

"But when did you discover Figaro's talent?" asked Geppetto.

"Last night," said Pinocchio, "when I found him in your workshop ... uh, hanging around."

Disney · PIXAR

TOY STORY

Shampoo Time

The toys were having fun playing in Bonnie's room when – oh no! – a glass of orange juice spilled all over Mr Pricklepants the hedgehog.

"Look at me! I'm soaked!" he groaned.

Buzz grabbed a towel. "Don't panic. I'll dry you up in a minute," he promised.

After Buzz had finished drying him, Mr Pricklepants looked even worse! The orange juice had made his hair sticky.

"You need a shampoo to wash it away," said Buttercup the unicorn.

Mr Pricklepants raised an eyebrow. "A shampoo?" he said. He'd never had a shampoo before, but before he knew what was happening, the other toys had dragged him to the bathroom and dropped him into the sink.

"The shampoo's coming," announced Buzz, glugging the sweet-smelling green goo over the hedgehog's head.

"And here's the water," added Dolly, turning on the tap.

The basin quickly began to fill with water and bubbles. Soon, Mr Pricklepants was struggling to stay afloat.

"Heeelp!" he spluttered.

Buzz got ready to jump in and save their friend, but Dolly had a better idea. Thinking fast, she pulled out the plug, letting the soapy suds drain away. Mr Pricklepants was safe but he was covered from head to toe in frothy white foam.

"I've got a super plan!" Buzz said. He turned on the shower, blasting Mr Pricklepants with a jet of icy-cold water. The force of the water almost knocked him off his feet.

"It's too powerful!" he spluttered.

"Hold on. Almost done," Buzz promised, rinsing away the last of the soap.

When he was clean, Dolly used the hairdryer to give the hedgehog a blow dry. Mr Pricklepants sighed as the hot air hit him in the face, swishing his hair all around.

At last, it was over. Mr Pricklepants looked at himself in the mirror and gasped. He looked like an enormous ball of fuzzy fluff! Still, at least he was clean, and he wouldn't have to be washed again for a very long time.

Or so he thought!

That night, when Bonnie was called for bath time, she grabbed Mr Pricklepants and tucked him tightly under her arm.

"Let's pretend I'm a hairdresser!" she said, carrying him through to the bathroom.

Buzz and the others giggled quietly. Something told them that Mr Pricklepants would be having another shampoo session very soon indeed!

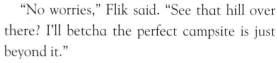

Happy Campers

It was a warm, sunny day on Ant Island – the perfect day for Princess Dot and her fellow Blueberries to go on a camping expedition! Flik volunteered to be their leader.

"Single file! Forward march!" called Flik. "Follow me, Blueberries. Watch out for those twigs!"

"This is gonna be so much fun, Flik!" said Dot, marching behind him. "Pitching our tents! Making a campfire! Telling ghost stories all night long!"

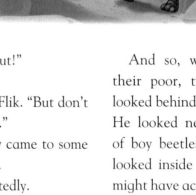

"Well, we've got to get to our campsite first," Flik reminded her. "The perfect campsite for the perfect campout!"

"Where's that?" asked Dot.

"I'm not exactly sure," said Flik. "But don't worry! I'll know it when I see it."

So on they hiked, until they came to some soft moss beside a quiet stream.

"Is this it?" asked Daisy excitedly.

Flik shook his head. "Definitely not," he said. "Too out in the open."

"We're getting tired," Dot said.

"Chins up, Blueberries," said Flik. "We'll find the perfect campsite soon. I'll bet it's just across that stream."

Flik guided the Blueberries onto a broad leaf. Together they rowed across the water. But the other side of the stream was not quite perfect enough for Flik either.

"No worries," Flik said. "See that hill over there? I'll betcha the perfect campsite is just beyond it."

The Blueberries followed him up the grassy hill and down the other side.

"We made it!" the Blueberries cheered.

"Not so fast," said Flik, frowning. "The ground is too damp here. We'll have to keep looking."

"But, Flik! We can't go any further," they moaned.

"Nonsense!" said Flik, tightening his backpack. "You're Blueberries!"

And so, with the Blueberries dragging their poor, tired feet, Flik hiked on. He looked behind a big rock, but it was too dusty. He looked near a hollow log, but a troop of boy beetles was already there. He even looked inside an old, discarded shoe, which might have actually worked … if it hadn't been so stinky.

Just when the Blueberries thought they couldn't walk another inch, Flik suddenly froze in his tracks. "The perfect campsite! We've found it! Let's pitch those tents, Blueberries, and get a fire started!"

But instead of cheers, Flik heard only silence. He turned around and saw that those poor Blueberries, still wearing their backpacks, were already fast asleep!

Land Lost in Time

Carl and Russell hadn't been in South America long, and were just setting off towards Paradise Falls, pulling Carl's house behind them. They had a long journey ahead, and Russell announced that, to pass the time, he'd tell Mr Fredricksen everything he knew about tepuis, the table-top mountains, like the one they'd landed on.

"This trip is going to be even longer than I thought," Carl muttered.

Russell started by telling Carl about the sudden changes of weather which were common in the area.

As he spoke, the heavens opened and heavy rain poured from the sky. Carl and Russell took shelter under the house, hoping to wait out the storm, but Russell suddenly remembered something.

"Um, I forgot to tell you," he said, as a gush of water washed past his legs. "There might even be flash floods!"

The warning came too late! A surge of flood water swept Carl and Russell off their feet and rushed them towards a sheer drop. That was something else Russell knew about tepuis – they were very high up!

Screaming, Carl and Russell plunged over the edge of the mountain. They flapped their arms, trying to stop themselves falling.

Then, the ropes they'd used to tie themselves to the house went tight and they floated gently down into the rainforest below. They were safe ... but not for long!

As Russell pointed out the different types of plants, something much more dangerous creeped out of the jungle. A jaguar edged towards them. Carl backed away, but Russell had never been so excited. As well as the big cat, there was also a fearsome anaconda slithering towards them. He'd only ever seen them in books before!

"I take it all back," said Carl. "I want to know more – like how we get out of this mess!"

Russell's mind raced. He thought about climbing up to the house, but there was no time. The animals were both getting ready to attack. Suddenly, he knew what he had to do – the Wilderness Explorer Call!

Throwing back his head, Russell cried, "*CAW, CAW, ROAR!*"

Startled, the jaguar and snake turned and darted into the jungle. Carl breathed a sigh of relief. "Scaring them off was a great idea!"

Russell explained he'd been trying to talk to the animals, not scare them, and Carl laughed. The Wilderness Explorer Call may not have worked as Russell had planned, but he was happy it had worked, all the same.

Peter Pan

Tiger Lily

It was a hot summer night in Never Land – so hot, in fact, that the poor Lost Boys couldn't sleep. And so it was decided that instead of trying to stay in their hideout in Hangman's Tree, Peter Pan and the Lost Boys would camp out for the night in the wild wilderness.

Certainly, they thought, the woods would be cool and shady, and the trees would catch any breeze kind enough to blow through. But little did they know how mysterious – and spooky – a forest could be once the sun went down.

"It's dark out here," said Cubby.

"And awful quiet," said Tootles.

"Won't you tell us a story, please, Peter?" asked Slightly, who was shivering in his fox suit despite the sticky heat.

"Very well," agreed Peter. "If it will make you all be quiet! I will tell you the story of the very first time I ever camped out in the wilderness – which, by the way, was the first time I met Tiger Lily...."

"I had made myself a fire, a great big one, 'cause it was autumn and the nights were getting cool. I'd just laid my head down on a patch of nice, soft moss when all of a sudden I heard a rustling in the shadows."

"*Indians?*" the Lost Boys gasped.

But Peter shook his head.

"Not Indians," he told them. "That's what I thought at first too. No, this was something bigger. It was a *bear!* It jumped out of the trees, growling and waving its big paws in the air like Captain Hook tryin' to swat blue flies. I've never seen such a mean, angry beast, before or since!"

"So wh-wh-what did you do?" asked the Lost Boys.

"Told him to get lost, of course. To *scram!* But, apparently, he didn't understand English, 'cause he just kept charging.

"Well, I'm not going to lie to you – I started to get nervous. And then, there she was – Tiger Lily – as quiet as a mouse. Without a 'hi' or 'how do you do?', she grabbed a stick from my fire and waved it at the bear. The next thing I knew, the bear had turned around and was running off crying! I suppose Tiger Lily saved my life that night," said Peter. "And it wasn't the last time either. The end."

"Um ... Peter," said Cubby, peering out into the darkness, "do you know whatever happened to that bear?"

Peter thought for a moment. "Nope," he said and shrugged. "Probably still out there, wandering around, I guess." He yawned a big, mischievous yawn. "Now stop yer yammerin' and close your eyes and go to sleep!"

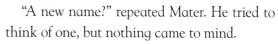

Heavy Metal Mater

Everyone was gathered at Flo's V8 Café for karaoke. Lightning McQueen looked over at Mater. "Why don't you get up there and sing?" he asked.

"I don't want to steal the show," Mater replied. "I was a big rock star once."

"What?" Lightning couldn't believe it.

"I started out in a garage band...." Mater described how his rock band, Mater and the Gas-Caps, rehearsed in a garage. Soon Mater and the Gas-Caps had a gig at the Top-Down Truck Stop. When the band finished, all the trucks cheered.

"That rocked!" called a waitress named Mia. "Do you guys have a record?"

The guitar player shook his head, but Mater smiled. He had an idea.

Soon, Mater and the Gas-Caps were in a recording studio. Mater sang so loudly that everyone in the recording studio could hear him. Doors began to open. Cars peeked out. "What's that sound?" someone asked. A music agent named Dex knew the answer. "It sounds like angels printing money to me!" He liked the song.

Dex rolled into Mater's recording booth. "You boys are good," Dex told the band. Then he noticed their name on the drums. "All you need is a new name."

"A new name?" repeated Mater. He tried to think of one, but nothing came to mind.

At that moment, a delivery car entered the studio. "Where do you want this heavy metal, Mater?" he asked.

"That's it!" Mater cried.

Heavy Metal Mater were an overnight success. They packed stadiums and had thousands of fans. Their concerts instantly sold out. Word had spread quickly about their amazing performances. A giant Mater balloon with wings lifted up from behind the stage and floated over the audience.

In Radiator Springs, Lightning interrupted the story. "You were Heavy Metal Mater?"

"No," the tow truck replied. "We was Heavy Metal Mater!" Then he continued his tale. Except this time Lightning was in the band, too. Mater described how he was onstage at the concert. Then a platform rose up. Lightning was on it, wearing sunglasses. "Are you ready to rock?" Lightning yelled. Then he jumped down and joined Mater.

At Flo's V8 Café, Lightning interrupted again. "I'm sorry," he said with a laugh, "that did not happen."

"Well, suit yourself," Mater replied, motioning to the sky. Lightning looked up. The balloon from the concert was flying overhead! Had Mater been telling the truth...?

A Rolling Gift

Gusteau's Restaurant had just closed for the evening, and the kitchen staff were busily tidying up. Linguini was getting ready to scrub the floors, but his friend, Colette, stopped him just in time.

"You'd better wait until they've all left," she said, pointing to the other chefs. "Or they'll walk all over your wet floor."

Colette was right. She had saved Linguini from having to wash the floors twice. Linguini was lucky he had her there to help him.

"I have to find a way to repay her for all the help she's given me," he said. In his hidey-hole, Remy folded his arms and sulked. What about all the help *he'd* given Linguini?

Later, at home, Linguini paced the floor, trying to think of the perfect present to give Colette. He thought about getting her a box of chocolates or a bunch of flowers, but they were both far too obvious.

Remy stood on his couch, trying to mime some suggestions for gifts, but Linguini didn't pay him any attention.

"I wish someone would give me some good advice," Linguini said, and Remy just sighed in despair.

The next day, Linguini and Colette went outside to get some fresh air on their break. A young couple whizzed by on roller skates, laughing as they chased each other down the deserted Paris street.

Colette watched them go. She'd always wanted to learn to skate, but had never managed to. Linguini's eyes lit up. He knew the perfect gift for her.

A few days later, Colette roared up to the park on her motorbike. Linguini jumped out of the way, startled by her high-speed entrance.

"So, why did you want me to meet you here?" asked Colette, taking off her motorcycle helmet.

Linguini held up a pair of roller skates and told Colette he was going to teach her how to skate to repay her for all the help she'd given him. Colette said she didn't think she'd be able to learn, but Linguini reassured her. "Don't you know? My friends call me the Skate Master!" he said.

When Colette slipped on the skates, she immediately started to fall. Linguini caught her hand and steadied her. They both smiled, and the lesson began.

Just a few hours later, Colette zoomed and twirled on her skates like an expert. "It's all thanks to my teacher," she said.

"You think so?" asked Linguini.

"Of course," laughed Colette. "Don't you know? They call him the Skate Master!"

Linguini blushed, and they chased each other on their skates until the sun went down.

THE ARISTOCATS

The Cosiest Carriage

One day, O'Malley took Duchess and her kittens down to the rubbish dump to visit O'Malley's old and dear friend, Scat Cat.

Scat Cat lived in a broken-down carriage that had once been very grand indeed. But the wheels had fallen apart long ago, and the cushions were shredded.

To top it all off, there was a huge hole right in the middle of the worn, tattered roof.

Still, as far as Scat Cat was concerned, his home was perfect. "I feel free here," he told the kittens. "I can come and go as I please. And when I stretch out on the cushions at night, I look up and there are the stars, a-twinklin' and a-winkin' back at me!"

The kittens had a grand time playing with Scat Cat in the junkyard. But they were glad to return to the soft pillows, cosy blankets and warm milk waiting for them back at Madame Bonfamille's mansion.

But a few days later, who should appear at Madame's doorstep but Scat Cat himself.

"You'll never believe it," he said. "I went into town to stretch my legs, and when I got back – *poof!* – the carriage was gone!"

"Well, naturally," said Duchess, "you will have to stay with us! I'm sure Madame would be delighted to have you as our guest."

But after only one night, Scat Cat began to feel sad. Everything at Madame Bonfamille's happened according to a schedule. Scat Cat missed doing as he pleased.

"But you know what I miss most?" Scat Cat told O'Malley and the kittens. "My old carriage. What I wouldn't give to be able to look up at the sky and count the twinklin' stars...."

The kittens decided to help Scat Cat. For a while, Madame had been complaining about her old carriage. So, Berlioz climbed into it and began clawing at the old cushions. Toulouse and Marie joined him, and soon, the cushions looked just like the ones in Scat Cat's old carriage!

Finally, Toulouse came crashing down through the carriage roof, making a huge hole. "Oh, my!" exclaimed a voice. The kittens turned, and there was Madame. She surveyed the damage ... and smiled! "At last I have an excuse to buy a new carriage," she said. "Let's take this one out to the junkyard at once."

"I don't believe it!" cried Scat Cat, when the kittens led him to his new home, back in the junkyard. "It's purr-fect! How can I ever thank you?" he asked the kittens.

"It was our pleasure," said Berlioz. He flexed his claws. "It's not every day we're thanked for clawing something to pieces!"

Speedy Emergency Drill

One morning, two vehicles came trundling onto the runway. Dusty recognized the larger one as Ryker, an inspector from the Transportation Management Safety Team. The smaller truck beside him was his assistant, Kurtz, who was making notes of everything Ryker said.

Dusty was worried. Ryker only appeared if something was wrong.

"Take it easy, Dusty," Mayday the fire engine assured him. "He's only here to time you."

That didn't relax Dusty one bit! He'd thought the airfield was in for an inspection – he hadn't realized the inspection was for him!

"I have to verify how fast you are in emergency situations," said Ryker, as Kurtz marked a spot on the runway. Dusty was told to pretend there was a fire on that exact spot, and to put it out as quick as he could.

Much as Dusty hated tests, he knew he could do this. Zooming off, he scooped up water in his pontoons, then dropped the first load on the red 'X' Kurtz had made. "Bullseye!"

"Nice goin'!" admitted Kurtz over the radio. "Great time."

Dusty hoped the test was over, but Kurtz told him there were three more targets near the old silo. Banking steeply, Dusty hurried towards his next targets.

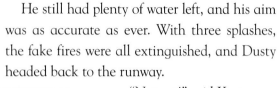

He still had plenty of water left, and his aim was as accurate as ever. With three splashes, the fake fires were all extinguished, and Dusty headed back to the runway.

"Not yet!" said Kurtz.

"There's a third test," said Ryker. "The last 'fire' is near Mount Aileron."

Dusty gasped. Mount Aileron was miles away. There was no way he could make it there in time. He was sure to fail this test, unless.... Maybe one of his old racing tricks would work.

Climbing sharply, Dusty punched up through the clouds. When he was high enough, he angled his wings to catch the air currents, letting them push him towards the distant mountain.

"Target hit!" he announced, as he emptied the last of his water onto the target.

When he returned to base, Ryker and Kurtz were staring in amazement. "That was incredible. Nobody's ever passed that test before," said Ryker.

"So is the airport going to stay open?" asked Dusty, screeching to a stop.

Ryker laughed. "I think you're mistaken. We're not here as part of the safety team. We're off duty today."

"We came as judges for the single engine air tanker state competition," added Kurtz. "And you won – you're our new champion!"

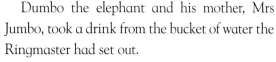

DUMBO
Lend Me Your Ears

"I think I can, I think I can, I think I can," chugged Casey Jr, the circus train. The train moved slowly around a bend. "I think I can. I think I ... *AH-CHOO!*" he sneezed.

Suddenly, he came to a halt. "I know I can't," he admitted finally. The animals and the performers poked their heads out, wondering what was wrong.

"Well?" asked the Ringmaster.

"Casey Jr here has a cold," the engineer replied. "He's going to need some rest before he can take us any farther."

The Ringmaster frowned. "But we're due at the fairground in a few hours. What will we do? After all, the show must go on!"

The engineer just shrugged and turned his attention back to the sneezing, coughing and spluttering little engine.

The Ringmaster went down the train, swinging open the doors to all the cages and cars. "Come on, everyone," he said. "Might as well stretch your legs."

The animals lumbered, scampered and pranced onto the wide open field. Next, the clowns and acrobats and animal trainers sauntered out. Some set up crates in the grass and played cards, others rehearsed and a few pulled out packed lunches and sprawled on the ground.

Dumbo the elephant and his mother, Mrs Jumbo, took a drink from the bucket of water the Ringmaster had set out.

Mrs Jumbo gazed around. "Looks like we're in the middle of nowhere," she said. "I do hope poor Casey Jr is feeling better soon."

"Me too," Dumbo's friend Timothy Q. Mouse said hopefully.

Just then there was a clap of thunder. Rain began to fall from the sky. The animals and performers ran for the shelter of the circus wagons. Dumbo held on to his mother's tail, but just then, the wind picked up. The gust caught Dumbo's huge ears and sent him flying backwards.

"That's it!" yelled the Ringmaster over the howling wind. "Dumbo, come with me!" He led Dumbo over to the train, climbed onto the front wagon, and motioned for the little elephant to join him.

"Now, spread out those great ears of yours!" the Ringmaster said. Dumbo's ears billowed out, catching the wind like giant sails and pushing Casey Jr along the tracks. "The show will go on!" the Ringmaster shouted happily.

"I know I can, I know I can, I know I can," chanted Casey Jr. And then he added, "Thanks to Dumbo!"

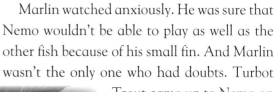

Nemo's Best Shot

"Come on, Dad! We're going to be late!" cried Nemo. Nemo and Marlin were hurrying through the busy swimming lanes of the colourful Great Barrier Reef.

"Are you sure you want to play pearl volleyball?" Marlin asked his son nervously. "There are lots of other things you can do. Sponge jumping, for example. Or maybe you could try reef dancing."

"Reef dancing!" cried Nemo, horrified. "No way! That's for babies! I want to play pearl volleyball!"

At Sea Urchin Stadium, Mr Ray made the opening announcements. "Hello and welcome, everyone! Thank you for coming to watch the match. Before we get started, let's give a big thank you to Ms Esther Clam for donating today's ball."

Everyone applauded as Esther opened her shell and spat out the pearl.

"Let's play pearl volleyball!" cried Mr Ray.

"Good luck, son," said Marlin. "Just remember what I told you –"

"I know! I know!" said Nemo, rolling his eyes. "When you give it your best shot, even if you lose, you win."

The players lined up on either side of the sea fan net. Ray's Raiders were on one side, and Nemo's team, the Fighting Planktons, were on the other.

Marlin watched anxiously. He was sure that Nemo wouldn't be able to play as well as the other fish because of his small fin. And Marlin wasn't the only one who had doubts. Turbot Trout came up to Nemo on the court.

"Coach may be letting you play today," Turbot snapped, "but you'd better not mess up the Planktons' winning streak."

Turbot didn't know Nemo had spent many hours smacking around pebbles in a dentist's fish tank.

"Just watch and learn," murmured Nemo.

Suddenly, the pearl came right to Nemo. *Smack!* Using his good left fin, Nemo sent the pearl flying right over the net. The pearl flew so fast, the other team couldn't return it. Nemo scored his first point for the Planktons!

Nemo played like a pro. He scored again with his good fin, then with his tail. And, just to show his father and Turbot Trout, he scored the winning point with his little fin.

"Go, short fin!" cried Turbot Trout. "With a player like you, we're going to go all the way to the Lobster Bowl Clam-pionship!"

"Wow, Nemo!" said Marlin after the game. "That was amazing."

"Thanks, Dad," said Nemo. "I gave it my best shot, like you said. And we actually won too!"

The Hic-hic-hiccups

"What a day!" Pumbaa said as he led Simba and Timon through the forest.

"What a day, indeed," Timon agreed.

"*Hic!*" said Simba.

"What was that?" Timon cried.

"Don't be scared. It's just that I have the – *hic!* – I have the hiccups," Simba explained.

"I'll tell you what to do," Timon assured him. "Forget about it! They'll go away – eventually."

"Forget about it? *Hic!* But I can't roar when I have the hiccups," Simba explained. And to demonstrate, he opened his mouth really wide. But, just as he was about to roar, he hiccupped!

"See?" he said sadly.

"Have you tried licking tree bark?" Pumbaa asked.

"Licking tree bark?" said Simba.

"It always works for me," Pumbaa explained. "That or closing your eyes, holding your nose and jumping on one foot while saying your name five times fast – backwards."

Timon watched Simba hop around on one foot, holding his nose with his eyes closed. "Abmis, Abmis, Abmis – *HIC!* It's not working!" Simba cried.

"Maybe there's something caught in his throat," Timon offered.

"There's nothing caught in his throat," Pumbaa said.

"How do you know?" Timon asked.

"I just know about these things," Pumbaa answered confidently.

Suddenly, right on cue, Simba interrupted their argument with the biggest hiccup of all.

"*HIC!*"

And, wouldn't you know, just then the biggest fly you've ever seen came soaring out of Simba's mouth. It flew right into a tree and crashed to the ground.

The fly stood up groggily and shook itself off.

"It's about time, buddy!" the fly called up to Simba.

Simba was about to reply, but he was interrupted by two voices, shouting in unison,

"DINNER!"

The fly gave a frightened squeak and flew off, as Timon and Pumbaa both pounced on the spot where it had been sitting just a moment earlier.

The Doughnut Kart

During races, everyone drove at top speed around the Sugar Rush tracks. Off the tracks, though, there was a strict speed limit. If anyone broke it, it was up to the doughnut cops, Wynchel and Duncan, to stop them.

No matter how fast the cops ran, though, the cars always got away. There was only one thing for it – Duncan and Wynchel had to learn to drive.

Vanellope, who was now the president of Sugar Rush, agreed to teach them, but first they'd need to make themselves a kart. After leading them to the kart factory, Vanellope left them to build the vehicle themselves.

Everything went fine to begin with, but before long the cops began to bicker and argue. They couldn't agree on the right type of body shape for their kart, and spent a long time fighting over who was right.

When they'd finally settled on the shape, they then fought over the correct temperature to bake it at. The two cops almost came to blows, with one saying the temperature was too high, and the other insisting it was far too low. They fought over the controls, turning the heat up and down as they squabbled.

And still the arguments continued. They wrestled over which type of icing to use, and how much of it to put on. They battled over the amount of sugar to use, and what colour the sprinkles should be.

Whatever Duncan wanted, Wynchel seemed to want the opposite. Finally, though, the kart was ready. They asked President Vanellope to come and take a look. Her jaw dropped open as she looked at the kart the officers had built.

"It's the craziest kart I've ever seen! Cool!" she said, giving it a thumbs-up. "But I don't think it will run."

Wynchel's face fell. All their hard work was for nothing. They'd never be able to chase speeding drivers now.

As Vanellope looked the kart over, though, she broke into a broad grin. She'd had an idea.

Next day, Vanellope checked in with the doughnuts to see if the plan had worked.

"Now that we've got our kart, nobody goes over the limit," Wynchel laughed. He pointed down to where two speeding drivers were approaching the bend.

The drivers took one look at the hideous kart and mistook it for a monster. They immediately slowed to a stop.

"They just take one look at it and hit the brakes!" Wynchel laughed.

It might not have worked out how they'd expected, but the monstrous new kart had certainly done the trick.

Hair Clip Mission

Bonnie was getting ready to go out, but there was something missing.

"I've lost my hair clip with the flower," she said, hunting through a box of accessories.

Her mum used a different clip to fasten Bonnie's hair back. "We'll look for it later. Put this other one on for now."

Bonnie trudged out of the room behind her mum. "That hair clip is my favourite," she sighed.

As soon as Bonnie and her mum were out of the room, the toys jumped into life. "Did you hear that?" said Woody. This was an emergency. Bonnie was their kid, and they knew they had to help.

They searched under the bed, in the toybox and all over the floor, but with no luck.

"Let's think this through," said Woody. "Where did we last see it?"

"Right here on this shelf we're on," said Buzz. He spotted a narrow gap at the back of the shelf. "The hair clip could have fallen back here! We'd better check."

Mr Potato Head snorted. "How do you plan to do that? It's really dark back there."

Woody smiled. "I have an idea!"

Moments later, he lowered one of Mr Potato Head's eyes down behind the shelf on a piece of string. For a while, the eye swung around in the gloom, but then Mr Potato Head let out a cheer. "Hey, guys, I can see it! The hair clip is right there!"

He patted Woody on the back to congratulate him on finding it, but Woody lost his grip on the string, and Mr Potato Head's eye landed on the floor right beside the hair clip!

"Well, that's just great!" Mr Potato Head groaned. "Now we have to recover the hair clip *and* my eye!"

Woody tried to force his way into the narrow space behind the shelf. "Maybe I can slip into this gap...."

With a sigh of effort, Woody squeezed into the gap – but then got stuck! Buzz tried to pull him out, but the cowboy was wedged in tight, and Bonnie was coming back up the stairs! The toys went limp just as Bonnie bounced into the room.

"Let's play!" she said, grabbing Woody by the arm. She tugged, but he was still stuck fast. "Mummy!" she cried. "I can't get Woody out. He's stuck behind my shelf!"

Bonnie's mum moved the furniture, and Woody sprang free. At the same time, Bonnie spotted her missing hair clip and Mr Potato Head's eye!

She had no idea how everything had ended up behind the furniture, but she gave Woody an extra cuddle for helping her find her favourite hair clip.

The Birthday Surprise

Today was Mickey's birthday! He jumped out of bed and saw Pluto staring out of the window. Mickey looked outside and saw his friends walking by.

I wonder what they're doing, he thought.

Donald's arms were full of cups and plates. Daisy had lemonade. Goofy was holding balloons. And Minnie was carrying a cake.

"Could they be having a birthday party ... for me?" Mickey said to Pluto.

Mickey and Pluto sat and waited for their friends. When the bell rang, Mickey raced to the door. He threw it open, but it was only Donald – and he looked upset.

"What's wrong?" Mickey asked.

"My favourite hammock is broken," Donald told Mickey. "Can you help me fix it?"

"Sure, Donald," Mickey said.

So Donald, Mickey and Pluto set off. As they walked, an idea popped into Mickey's head. *Maybe there is no broken hammock. Maybe Donald is really taking me to my party!*

Donald led Mickey to his garden. There was the broken hammock. Mickey looked around. There were no balloons and no cake. So Mickey helped Donald fix his hammock.

"That should do it," Mickey said, as he finished tying the hammock's rope round a tree.

"Thanks, Mickey!" Donald said.

I guess there wasn't a party after all, Mickey thought, sadly. Just then, he heard Minnie and Daisy calling him.

The girls led Mickey to their garden. Mickey looked around. The garden was full of pretty flowers, but no party. He was disappointed.

Suddenly, Goofy ran up. "Mickey!" he shouted. "You've got to see this!"

Goofy seems very excited, Mickey thought. He guessed Goofy must be taking him to his party!

"Look, Mickey," Goofy said, pointing to a large rock. Mickey looked, but there was no sign of a party. Then he saw two snails racing on the rock. Mickey and Pluto watched the snails for a while. Then they headed home.

"Oh, well, Pluto," Mickey sighed. "I guess there won't be a party after all."

Mickey opened the door to his house....

"Surprise!"

Mickey's friends jumped out at him. They had planned a party after all!

"I don't understand," he said, almost speechless. "How did you ... at my house ... without me finding out?"

Minnie giggled. "We took turns keeping you busy," she explained.

Mickey smiled. He loved surprise parties!

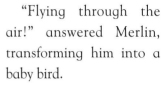

The Sword in the Stone

In the depths of the woods, somewhere in England, Merlin the Magician was waiting for a very special visitor. His name was Wart, a clever but reckless young boy....

"Watch out, Wart! You're climbing too high." And sure enough – *CRASH!* – Wart tumbled and landed on a chair in front of Merlin, just in time for tea!

"A great destiny awaits you, my boy," Merlin said to Wart. "But first you need to learn a few things....

"There's no great destiny without a great teacher – and I will be that person! Just let me pack my case and then we'll be off."

First lesson – the world of water. Merlin touched his wand to Wart's head and the boy turned into a fish! Merlin transformed himself, too, and they swam in deep water. Wart waved his fins and made bubbles.

Then suddenly, they saw a monstrous fish coming straight for them! Quickly, Merlin changed back into human form and saved Wart from the jaws of the pike.

Second lesson – exploring the forest in the form of a squirrel! Wart immediately made a friend – a charming female squirrel who really liked him.

But, just when a wolf was about to attack him, Wart changed back into a child.

"I'm sorry, Miss, I'm a boy, not a squirrel," Wart said to the disappointed girl squirrel.

"What's the third lesson?" Wart then asked his teacher.

"Flying through the air!" answered Merlin, transforming him into a baby bird.

In the company of Archimedes, a grumpy old owl, Wart launched himself into the air. What fun it was to fly!

But in the air, too, danger lurked. Suddenly an eagle appeared and threatened the two friends!

Panic-stricken, Wart dived into a chimney. But he fell into the clutches of Madam Mim – a wicked sorceress who lived in the forest!

Luckily, Merlin appeared in the cottage. To overpower the sorceress, he changed himself into a germ and gave her the measles! Well done, Merlin!

Later on, Wart came across a mysterious sword thrust into an anvil. Engraved on the sword were the words:

"Who so pulleth me out will be King of England."

To everyone's astonishment, the boy effortlessly pulled the stone out!

Wart, or rather Arthur, was to be King of England. Long live King Arthur!

Disney
101
DALMATIANS

Patch's Plan

"Whoa!" Patch said, "Look at all these other puppies!"

His brothers and sisters were still whimpering with fear. They had just been dognapped, and after a long, bumpy ride in a car, they had arrived at a big, draughty house. But Patch was already trying to work out a way to get back home. He looked around the large, shabby room.

"Hey," Patch asked the closest stranger. "Where are we exactly?"

The spotted puppy smiled at him. "Oh, you must be new!" he said. "Which pet shop did you come from?"

Patch scowled at the strange new puppy. "We're not from a pet shop – we were stolen from our house."

Several other puppies heard him and moved closer. "Stolen? Really?" they exclaimed.

The first puppy shrugged. "Well, bought or stolen, we're all stuck here now."

"Maybe *you're* stuck here," Patch said boldly. "Our parents and their human pets will be here soon to rescue us, just see if they aren't!"

"I hope so," Patch's sister, Pepper, said. "I wonder why someone would want to steal us, anyway?"

Patch didn't know. But he was sure that their parents would find them soon. In the meantime, he wanted to make sure he and his siblings stayed well away from all the pet-shop puppies, so there wasn't any confusion.

"We don't know why there are so many of us," the strange puppy told Pepper. "I guess Cruella just really likes puppies."

Patch gasped aloud. "Cruella?" he cried. "Do you mean Cruella De Vil?"

His brothers and sisters shuddered. Their parents had told them scary stories about that nasty woman. Could it be true?

"Yes, she's the one who bought us." Several of the other puppies spoke up, while others nodded their heads.

This changed everything! "We have to get away," Patch declared.

Rolly sighed. "We know," he said. "Mum and Dad will be here soon. I just hope we get home in time for breakfast...."

"No, you don't understand!" Patch shook his head. "Cruella is bad news – that's what Dad always says. We have to get away from her now – all of us!" He gestured to the entire group of puppies, bought and stolen. It didn't matter where they'd come from. What mattered was they were in this mess together. "We have to work as a team."

The first puppy smiled at him. "I'm with you!" he exclaimed. "When we're done with her, Cruella will be seeing spots!"

Heli-Mater

"The state road isn't much farther, troops!" declared Sarge. They were planning on helping him collect a delivery from a truck, waiting at a service station.

"Great!" said Mater, with a toothy grin. "These canyons remind me of the time Lightning McQueen was lost and I rescued him."

Lightning McQueen glanced at him, confused. "I don't think I've ever been lost and rescued by...."

"Happens to everyone in these parts!" Mater interrupted him. "It was a big rescue operation. I was way up in the hold of Dinoco Helicopter, keeping a close eye on the town when a call came through from base camp, telling me that Lightning McQueen was lost in the canyons."

Sarge and Lightning McQueen gave each other a knowing look. When Mater shared what he believed to be a memory, it was better to just let him roll with it.

"You'd just come to Radiator Springs and didn't know your way around," continued Mater. "Somewhere out there in the wilds, you were thirsty and overheated. There were only a few drops of gas left in your tank."

Mater pictured the moment he'd spotted Lightning McQueen in the canyons – a streak of red, stark against the grey rocks and brown dirt. "I called base to tell them I'd found you! You looked so exhausted, but I had fuel supplies on board waiting."

"How did the Dinoco Helicopter land? The gorges are narrow. The roadways would be too thin for a helicopter to land on," pointed out Lightning McQueen.

Mater grinned. "There was only one thing to do!" he said. "I attached my tow rope to the handrail and dived bravely into open air. For a moment, it felt like I was free-falling through a sky-blue infinity, until I slipped between the rocky crevices and stopped ... right in front of your very eyes!"

"Are you and that cable really any good?" challenged Sarge.

Mater turned to him. "Even better. Wanna see another trick o' mine?" He spun his cable in a circle. *SWISH, SWISH, SWISH* and then *SPROING!*

Mater shot into the air.

"Is he flying?" gasped Lightning McQueen.

"Nope...." said Mater. He was swinging from a branch growing from the rock face, the tow cable wrapped tightly around it. "But there's an awesome view from up here."

His friends belly-laughed. Mater was probably the only Helicopter Rescue team member in Radiator Springs who didn't actually need a helicopter!

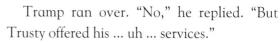

Trusting Trusty

"Tramp!" cried Lady one morning. "One of our puppies is missing!"

"Don't worry," said Tramp with a yawn. "Scamp is always getting into mischief."

"It's not Scamp," said Lady. "It's little Fluffy! She never gets into trouble. Tramp, do you think we should do?"

"You look inside. I'll look outside," said Tramp worriedly. He searched their back garden. Then he went to the next garden, and the next.

From a neighbour's garden, Trusty the bloodhound called, "Howdy! Whatcha looking for?"

"My daughter, Fluffy! She's missing," said Tramp.

Trusty's long floppy ears pricked up. "A missing puppy – now that's serious! And I should know. I used to help my grandpa track down missing persons through the swamps!"

"I know," said Tramp. He'd heard Trusty tell that story 100 times.

"Have you found a trail yet?" asked Trusty.

Tramp shook his head.

"Well, let me at it!" Trusty ran over to Tramp's garden. He put his big nose to the ground. *Sniff, sniff, sniff....*

"Tramp, have you found Fluffy?" Lady called from the dog door.

Tramp ran over. "No," he replied. "But Trusty offered his ... uh ... services."

"He can't smell any more," Lady whispered. "I know he tracked that dogcatcher's wagon and saved you – but he hasn't tracked anything since."

"He helped us once," said Tramp. "I think we should trust him again."

Just then, Trusty shouted, "Look at this!"

He had spotted a bluebird's feather below a window. "That's the window the puppies look out from," said Lady.

"Look! A bit of puppy fur," said Trusty. "And footprints!" Trusty followed the trail of footprints to the back of a shed.

And that's where Trusty found the missing puppy! Fluffy was fast asleep under a big tree.

"Fluffy! What happened?" Lady cried.

"I woke up and saw a bluebird," said Fluffy with a yawn. "And I didn't want Scamp to bark and scare it away, like he always does. So I didn't wake anyone. I followed the bird all the way to this tree. Then I guess I got sleepy."

Lady walked over and gave Trusty a kiss.

"Thank you," she told the bloodhound.

"Aw, shucks," said Trusty, blushing. "It weren't nothin'."

As the bloodhound trotted home, Tramp turned to Lady. "See that?" he said with a grin, "I told you we should trust Trusty!"

Loud Escape

A big fire was raging near Piston Peak, and the fire crew was gearing up to sort it out.

Blade told Dynamite that her crew had a very important role to play. A herd of deer was caught in the gap between two fires, and there was a real danger they might run into one of the blazes while trying to avoid the other.

Once aboard Cabbie, Dynamite dished out orders to the rest of the team.

"You two clear the ground along the path of Fire Number One," she told Pinecone and Drip. "Blackout, cut the trees in front of Fire Number Two."

With their orders given, the three Smokejumpers hurled themselves off the back of the plane. Activating their parachutes, they drifted down through the smoke and immediately set to work.

Back aboard Cabbie, Avalanche frowned. "Aren't we gonna jump?" he asked, his booming voice shaking the aircraft's metal walls.

"Not yet, Avalanche," said Dynamite. She knew their jump had to be timed perfectly. "We'll wait until we're over the area behind the herd. Which is ... NOW!"

Together, the two brave Smokejumpers drove off the plane into thin air. They tumbled in freefall for a while, before their parachutes opened and brought them safely floating to the ground.

Although being surrounded on both sides by a blazing inferno wasn't exactly safe!

The herd of deer was up ahead of them. They were snorting worriedly and looking like they might jump straight into the flames at any moment.

"We need a plan," said Dynamite.

Avalanche gasped. "What? You don't have a plan?" he boomed. "You always say we've got to move quickly once we're in action on the ground!"

Dynamite smiled. "It's working," she said knowingly. "Keep talking."

"What's working?" Avalanche demanded.

"Look at those deer!" Dynamite laughed. "Your voice is scaring them! They're running in the opposite direction towards the river and safety!"

With the deer saved, the rest of the team quickly put out the fire. Back at base, Blade congratulated Dynamite on a job well done.

"I couldn't have done it without Avalanche," she said. "Every time he opens his mouth he makes more racket than a jet engine!"

"Not true! I'm as quiet as a mouse!" said Avalanche, and as his voice shook the ground, all his friends laughed.

Disney · PIXAR

WALL·E

As Special as the Sea

After hundreds of lonely years of cleaning up Earth, WALL•E had finally found a special friend to share his life with. WALL•E and EVE worked together, as the humans and robots of the Axiom restored Earth and its environment.

One day, EVE decided to celebrate WALL•E's hard work by giving him a gift to add to his collection of treasures. EVE knew that WALL•E loved Earth, so she gave him a model of the planet. WALL•E was delighted with EVE's kind gift and happily added it to his collection.

EVE felt a little disappointed – she hadn't realized that WALL•E already owned two models of Earth!

EVE looked thoughtfully at the models. She was determined to give WALL•E a very special present. Gazing at the bright blue model, she suddenly knew what she needed to do.

The next morning, EVE had mysteriously disappeared. WALL•E was very sad and he hoped his friend wasn't upset. WALL•E looked all over the Axiom for EVE. He asked all the other humans and robots but no one had seen his friend. WALL•E sat on the bow, longing for his friend to come back ... when EVE suddenly flew past!

"EEEVE!" WALL•E shouted as he watched his friend fly away.

If EVE wanted a race, then WALL•E would follow her! He zoomed after her as fast as he could. Soon he was just behind her. EVE giggled as she watched WALL•E whizz past her. WALL•E looked back at EVE through the dust cloud behind him. He was enjoying the race and he was very to happy to have his best friend back.

But WALL•E wasn't watching where he was going as he raced forward, and suddenly he went over the edge of a cliff and landed in a huge pile of rubbish!

"EVE?" WALL•E called as he poked his head up.

"Behind you!" EVE laughed as she covered his eyes with her arms.

EVE had a surprise to show WALL•E. She uncovered his eyes and WALL•E blinked. All he could see in front of him was bright blue! That's why she was racing away, EVE had found the most special present of all – the sea!

EVE took hold of WALL•E's hands and carried him out across the sea. WALL•E and EVE giggled with delight as they zoomed over the water.

The sea seemed to go on forever. It was big and blue, just like WALL•E's models. But it was even more beautiful than he could ever have imagined! WALL•E would treasure this special moment with his friend forever.

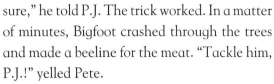

A Prize-winning Pair

Max and his dad, Goofy, were sitting at the breakfast table. Max looked at the funny pages, while Goofy leafed through the rest of the paper. "Listen to this!" said Goofy. "Channel 10 sponsors the Father & Son of the Year Contest. The father and son who can prove that they have achieved something truly incredible together will appear on national TV on Father's Day to accept their award."

"Too bad Bigfoot ruined that video we took of him last summer," said Max. "Finding him and living to tell about it – now that was incredible!"

Max paused for a moment. "Hey, I know! Why can't we go back and find him again? And this time we'll make sure we have proof."

"Okay, Maxie. Count me in!" said Goofy. "And we can even get a little fishing in, too."

Goofy and Max reached the campsite that night, pitched their tent and went to sleep. Soon they were awakened by a loud crash.

"It's him!" cried Max. "Get the camera!" But, when they poked their heads out, they saw it wasn't Bigfoot at all, but Pete and P.J.

"I'm sorry," said P.J. "I told my dad about your trip, and now he wants *us* to win that prize. We're out here looking for Bigfoot, too."

The next day, Pete set up a barbecue with several juicy steaks. "This will lure him out for sure," he told P.J. The trick worked. In a matter of minutes, Bigfoot crashed through the trees and made a beeline for the meat. "Tackle him, P.J.!" yelled Pete.

Though he was scared, P.J. did as he was told. Bigfoot threw him around while Pete turned on the camera. "The judges are going to love this!" he cried.

"Help!" P.J. begged.

Goofy and Max heard P.J.'s cries and came running from the lake. Without saying a word, Goofy jabbed the monster with a fishing rod while Max threw a net over the its head. Howling, the monster dropped P.J. to the ground.

"You were awesome," Max told Goofy.

"Right back at you, son," Goofy replied.

"Got it!" Pete said triumphantly. "Here, P.J., take some footage of me." He struck a hero's pose in front of the captive monster.

Back at home, Pete sent the video to Channel 10. But, after viewing the tape, the judges decided it was Goofy and Max who deserved the award instead.

But on Father's Day – the day they were to appear on TV – Goofy and Max decided to go to the beach together instead. They realized they didn't need anybody to tell them what an incredible father-and-son team they were. They knew it already!

Monster Hunt

Bonnie was going to play at a friend's house, and had decided to bring Buzz and Woody with her. The two friends were very excited. They loved meeting new toys, and as soon as Bonnie and her friends ran off to watch cartoons, they leaped out of her bag.

A little rabbit toy and a sailor action figure raced towards them.

"Hide yourselves!" he warned. "Hurry up, before the monster comes out!"

Woody and Buzz exchanged a worried look.

"A space monster?" asked Buzz.

The rabbit shook his head and pointed to a colourful box. "No, a monstrous monster!"

The new toys explained that within the box lurked a terrifying creature. When there was no one around, it would pop out of the box and frighten all the other toys.

Just then, the lid of the box flew open and out popped a green snake-monster with huge, pointed teeth.

"BOO! Flee!" the monster cried, then it frowned. A flickering red light lit up the end of its nose. "Huh? What's this?" it demanded.

"It's a space laser," Buzz told the monster, keeping the button on his arm pressed down.

The monster snorted. "A space what?"

But before Buzz could answer, a lasso looped over the monster's neck.

"Caught!" cheered Woody. "Thanks for distracting him, Buzz. You did a great job!"

Buzz shut off his laser. "You can come out, friends," he announced, and the other toys crept out from under the bed. They cheered happily. At last, the scary monster had been captured.

The monster groaned. "I didn't want to do anything bad," he said. "I just wanted to have some fun because nobody ever wants to play with me."

Woody stroked his chin thoughtfully. He and Buzz knew what it was like for a toy who didn't get played with. Maybe there was something they could do to help....

When Bonnie and her friends returned, the toys had all gone limp. Buzz sat by the monster's box holding the pop-up switch.

"What are we going to play?" Bonnie asked, grabbing Buzz. As she did, the monster popped out of its box. Bonnie giggled. "A snake! Cool!"

Bonnie's friend looked surprised. "Really? I never play with him. He's frightening."

"That's what makes him fun!" Bonnie smiled. Holding the box, she chased her friends, making scary hissing sounds, and they laughed as they ran away.

In his box, the snake-monster sighed happily. Maybe being scary wasn't such a bad thing, after all.

DISNEY · PIXAR

MONSTERS UNIVERSITY

Child Invasion

It had started off as a day just like any other at Monsters University. Students and staff had spent the morning going about their business, learning and teaching and discovering new ways to scare.

All that changed when a piercing alarm began to ring loudly across the campus. The monsters yelped and gasped in panic. They began to run, waving their arms and tentacles, and screaming at the tops of their voices.

It was the child alarm, and that meant only one thing – a human kid was loose in the university!

"We're doomed!" wailed one fearsome fanged creature, running around in panicky circles. He and the rest of the monster stampede raced past the Dean and Professor Knight, who watched with growing concern.

"It's coming from that direction," said the professor, pointing across the campus. "We must call the CDA."

The Child Detection Agency was made up of a fearsome bunch of experts, trained to capture, contain and dispose of any human children who managed to find their way into the monsters' world.

"Wait! You can't do that!" cried Mike, hurrying over to the staff. Sulley grabbed him by the arm and pulled him in the direction

Professor Knight had pointed. "I can't explain now," Mike cried. "Just don't call the CDA!"

Mike and Sulley shoved their way through the fleeing crowds until they spotted a little boy wandering towards them. He wore thick gloves and thicker glasses, and had a mop of curly brown hair.

Without hesitating, Mike and Sulley made a dive for the boy, arms outstretched. The Dean and the Professor watched in disbelief. "They just touched a human kid!" Professor Knight gasped.

Meanwhile, Mike and Sulley wrestled with the boy. Sulley's big paws pinned him to the ground, while Mike's fingers searched in the child's curly hair. "Where is it?" Sulley cried.

After a few panicked moments of searching, Mike and Sulley found what they were looking for. There was a zip on the boy's head, and it was stuck fast. Taking hold of the material, Sulley tore it apart, revealing the child's head to be just a mask.

Squishy let out a deep breath as the mask was pulled away. "Thank you, guys," he wheezed. "I got it stuck and couldn't breathe."

Mike and Sulley both smiled, relieved they had managed to save their friend. Squishy smiled, too. "This is the last time I wear a kid costume to practise our scaring skills," he laughed.

Living Paintings

Flo was serving up a storm of delicious drinks at her quirky café, when Ramone burst in, clutching a sheet of paper.

"Great news, Flo! I'm an artist!" Ramone announced proudly.

"We know that, dear," said Flo. Ramone was the town's body-artist after all!

"So what's the news?" wondered Doc.

"I mean a real artist. I got a letter from a famous art dealer!" boasted Ramone. "He noticed my work while passing through Radiator Springs and wants to organize an exhibition."

"I'm proud of you." Flo beamed at him.

"I'm heading out to get some canvases and brushes," decided Ramone. He was bubbling with enthusiasm.

After he had gathered the items he needed to paint a masterpiece, Ramone conjured up his artistic magic. But it seemed the more he swiped the brush across the crisp white canvas, the more he disliked the artwork before him.

"That's no good," he murmured. Frustrated, he scrapped the canvas and got a new one.

Again, he swished and swirled his brush over the white surface and scowled at the results.

"It's horrible!" he grumbled in disgust.

"How's things, Mr Artist?" asked Lightning McQueen from the doorway to Ramone's place. Flo was beside him, peering in curiously.

"How many paintings have you done?" she asked.

"None," whined Ramone.

His friends were stunned.

"Nothing good, that is. Looks like my talents are best expressed on car sides and hoods. Not canvases."

"You're not going to call off the exhibition, are you?" Flo worried. This was a big opportunity for Ramone. Surely, he couldn't just throw it away now?

"There may be a solution," he said craftily.

The day of the big exhibition, Ramone donned a smart red and gold tie and bowed to his captivated audience.

"Wonderful," praised a renowned art critic.

"They're authentic masterpieces!" said a minibus with eyes as big as his wheels.

"Thanks," said Ramone, with a triumphant smile. He drove up and down his display of art that had been painted on the bodies of his friends!

"*Psst!*" whispered Lightning McQueen. "How much longer do we have to be still on these podiums?"

"Not much longer," Ramone promised. "Just until the gallery closes."

His friends sighed among themselves and Ramone grinned, drinking in the applause and appreciation for his ingenious 'living' art.

Disney
Bambi
Flower's Power

It was a warm summer afternoon in the forest, and a shy little skunk named Flower was playing a game of hide-and-seek, searching for his friend Thumper. He had been looking for quite a while.

"Come out, come out, wherever you are!" Flower called. "I give up."

"*Surprise!*" shouted Thumper, bursting out of a thicket. "Here I am! *Ugh!*" Thumper wrinkled his nose. "What's that *smell?*"

Flower blushed bright pink. "Sorry," he said miserably. "I sprayed. It happens when I get scared."

"*Whew!*" Thumper waved his paw in front of his face. "You should warn us before you let out that kind of stink!"

"Well, *you* should warn *me* before you jump out like that," Flower said. "Anyway, it'll go away ... in a day or two."

But a day or two was too long for his friends to wait. The smell was just too strong!

"Sorry," Bambi told Flower. "I, uh, think my mother's calling me."

"Me, uh, too," Faline gasped. "See you later, Flower ... in a day or two."

"Or three!" Thumper added, giggling.

And the next thing he knew, Flower was all alone.

Poor Flower. If only he weren't a skunk, he thought. If only he didn't *stink* so much whenever he got scared. What was the point? It only drove his friends away. But now it seemed he couldn't even play hide-and-seek!

No matter what his mother and father said, being a skunk stunk!

And that's why Flower wouldn't have been very surprised if, two days later, his friends had still stayed away. But, to his bashful pleasure, there, bright and early, were Bambi and Faline – with Thumper hopping close behind.

"Want to play?" Bambi asked Flower cheerfully.

"Sure! Anything but hide-and-seek!" said Flower.

"How about tag?" said Thumper. "Ready or not, you're It!"

But before the game could begin, a soft *crunch* of leaves made the friends turn.

"Wh-wh-what's that?" Bambi stuttered, staring straight into a hungry-looking, red face.

"That's a fox!" said Thumper.

"A fox?" shrieked Flower. "Oh no!"

He spun around and lifted his tail and buried his head in fear ... and the next thing the friends knew, the hungry fox was running away, whimpering and rubbing his nose.

"Sorry," Flower sighed, blushing.

"Don't be!" said Bambi and Thumper. And do you know what? Flower wasn't!

Cruella Sees Spots

Cruella looked around the living room of the old De Vil mansion and rubbed her hands together. The room was full of Dalmatian puppies. Everywhere Cruella looked she saw spots, spots, spots! At last, her dream was coming true! Cackling with glee, Cruella thought back to the day this had all started....

It had begun as a perfectly miserable day. Cruella had been shopping for fur coats all morning and she hadn't found a single thing she liked.

"Too long! Too short! Too black! Too white!" she screeched, knocking an armload of coats out of the shop assistant's hands. "I want something unusual! I want a coat that has never been seen before!"

Cruella stormed out of the shop, slamming the door so hard that the glass cracked. She needed something to cheer her up. Just then she remembered that her old school friend, Anita, lived nearby.

Soon Cruella stood at the door, ringing the buzzer impatiently. She could hear cheerful piano music coming from an open window.

Just then, a pretty brown-haired woman answered the door. Her eyes opened wide when she saw the skinny woman, covered in fur, standing on her doorstep. "Oh, Cruella!" she cried. "What a surprise!"

"Hello, Anita, darling," Cruella said, walking into the sitting room. At that moment, a tall, thin man strolled down the stairs. But, when he caught sight of Cruella, he leaped back in fright!

"Ah, Prince Charming," Cruella said, smirking at Anita's new husband. Roger scowled. Then something else caught Cruella's eye. Two black-and-white spotted dogs were sitting in the corner of the room.

"And what have we here?" Cruella asked.

"Oh, that's Pongo and Perdita," Anita explained. "They're wonderful pets." But Cruella wasn't looking at the dogs. She was looking at their coats. Their glossy fur wasn't too long or too short. It wasn't too black or too white. Cruella had never seen anything like it. It was perfect.

"And soon we'll be even happier," Anita went on. "Perdita is going to have puppies!"

"Puppies!" Cruella shrieked. Suddenly she had an idea that made her smile an evil smile.

"Oh, Anita, you have positively made my day. Now, you must call me just as soon as the puppies arrive. I think they are *just* what I have been looking for."

Pongo snarled, but Cruella didn't notice.

"What a perfectly *marvellous* day," Cruella said to herself as she strode out of the door.

... And *that* was how it all started.

First Day of School

It was the first day of a brand-new school year for Nemo and his friends.

"Hey, Tad! Hey, Pearl!" called Nemo as he swam into the playground. "Isn't it great to be back at school?"

"Well," said Tad, "I wouldn't go *that* far."

"What do you mean?" asked Nemo. "It's gonna be awesome! I heard this year we get to learn how to subtract and speak Prawn."

"Sure," said Tad, "but did you hear who's gonna be teaching us all that?"

"Who?" asked Nemo.

Just then, up swam Sheldon, Jimmy and Jib.

"Hey, Sheldon," Tad called out. "Why don't you tell Nemo here about our new teacher, Mrs Lobster?"

"Mrs Lobster?" said Nemo.

"Yeah," said Sheldon. "Ooooh, they say she's the worst!"

"Who says she's the worst?" asked Nemo.

"Well, Sandy Plankton, for one. He told me his cousin, Krill, had her last year – and that she was so mean, he'll never go to school again!"

"And you know what I heard from Sandy?" said Tad. "I heard she has these great big claws, and that she uses them to grab students real hard when they give the wrong answer!"

"Oh!" said Pearl. "Don't say that. You're going to make me ink!"

"Yeah," said Nemo. "That sounds awful!"

"I know," said Jimmy. "Sandy says Mrs Lobster never goes on field trips like Mr Ray did. And she sends you home with tons of homework, and makes you stay after school if you forget to bring it in the next day!"

Oh, no! shuddered Nemo. All summer long he'd been looking forward to this day. And now school hadn't even started yet and already he wished it would end!

"Don't look now," Sheldon whispered, "but I think she's coming!"

"I'm gonna ink!" whimpered Pearl.

Nemo shut his eyes and wished with all his might for his dad to come and take him back home....

"Hello there," said a warm voice. "You must be my new pupils! I'm Mrs Lobster."

Huh? thought Nemo. Surely this wasn't the Mrs Lobster the kids had been talking about. And yet, when he opened his eyes, there she was, taking the register.

"Jib, Jimmy, Nemo, Pearl, Sheldon, Tad ... my, what a smart-looking class. I do hope you kids are ready to have fun."

Nemo sighed. Silly Sandy Plankton – they should know by now not to believe everything he said. Because Nemo was pretty sure this was going to be a great year, after all!

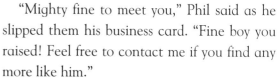

Family Reunion

Meg paced up and down the room. "What's wrong?" Hercules asked his girlfriend.

"We're going to visit your parents," Meg told him. "I want to make a good first impression."

"You're smart and kind and intelligent," Hercules said, smiling. "How could you make anything other than a great impression?"

"All right!" Phil cried. "Enough with the sweet talk. I have a cavity already. Can we get out of here?"

"Absolutely!" Hercules smiled at him. Pegasus galloped over and whisked them away.

Meanwhile, Hercules' parents, Amphitryon and Alcmene, were getting ready for their son's visit. Amphitryon was pacing, too.

"Is everything all right?" Alcmene asked.

"Yes, of course," Amphitryon answered. "Why wouldn't it be?"

"Maybe you're nervous because your son is coming home and you haven't seen him in quite a while," Alcmene said, with a knowing look at her husband.

Before Amphitryon could answer, they heard a sound.

"Look!" Amphitryon cried. "It's Hercules!"

And, sure enough, Hercules came charging up to the door. He leaped off Pegasus and gave a hearty hug to each of his parents. Then he introduced Phil.

"Mighty fine to meet you," Phil said as he slipped them his business card. "Fine boy you raised! Feel free to contact me if you find any more like him."

"And who is this?" Amphitryon asked.

"This is my friend Meg," Hercules said, blushing.

Just then, Pegasus snorted. "Oh, and how could I forget my pal Pegasus?" Hercules cried.

"All right, all right, enough with the niceties," Phil interrupted. "It's been a long trip. I'm hungry. Where's the grub?"

"Wait!" Hercules said. "I know you have prepared a wonderful meal, but first, I want to tell you what has happened since I left." He took a deep breath. "I've learned that I'm the son of Zeus and Hera. That's where I've got all my physical strength from. But, without everything I learned from you, my adoptive parents," Hercules continued, "all that would mean nothing."

Amphitryon and Alcmene beamed with pride at their son.

Then they all sat down for a feast worthy of the gods. Amphitryon and Alcmene were glad to have Hercules home. Hercules was happy to be home. Meg was honoured to be their guest. And Phil was thrilled to finally get to eat some home-cooked food!

Cheaters Never Prosper

The stadium was empty ahead of the Piston Cup championship. Nitroade was on the track, training hard for the race.

"I've got to improve!" he said to himself.

Nitroade was zooming round the corner when Chick Hicks suddenly cut in front of him. Nitroade hit his brakes in a cloud of smoke, narrowly avoiding hitting Chick Hicks.

"Hey, dude! You're just the guy I was lookin' for!" Chick Hicks yelled.

Nitroade knew that Chick Hicks was up to no good, as usual....

"I hear you're going to be starting in front of Lightning McQueen. My sponsor would be very grateful if you were to cut Lightning off and let me speed ahead," Hicks continued.

Nitroade was shocked that Chick Hicks wanted him to cheat and help him win the race. This wasn't why he became a racer – he wanted to train hard and race fairly.

"Certain proposals are unworthy of a true racer!" Nitroade said firmly before speeding off.

"If that's the way you feel about it ... then you'd better stay out of my way tomorrow!" Hicks said menacingly.

The next day, at the big race, Nitroade was determined to show everyone how hard he had been training. Chick Hicks revved his engine aggressively, trying to distract Nitroade.

"Ready, set, go!" the announcer boomed.

The cars zoomed off the starting line and onto the track. Lightning McQueen was leading the way, head-to-head with his long-time rival Chick Hicks. But thanks to his training, Nitroade was gaining on the leaders. He might just make a trip to the podium today.

"I warned you to steer clear of me today. You're about to take a turn for the worse!" Chick Hicks cried.

Chick Hicks's engine growled and his eyes narrowed as he swerved in front of Nitroade.

"Watch out!" yelled Lightning.

Nitroade dodged Chick Hicks just in time thanks to Lightning's warning. Chick Hicks's dirty trick backfired and he spun off course.

The rest of the cars sped past, with Lightning and Nitroade leading the race. The crowd cheered as Lightning flew over the finish line. But Nitroade wasn't far behind and came a very close second!

After the race, Nitroade joined Lightning on the podium. All his hard work had paid off, he'd come second in the Piston Cup.

Chick Hicks looked very angry. He hadn't finished the race after he tried to cheat.

Nitroade smiled down at his rival and said, "Chick, listen to me. Next time, you've got to remember to play fair!"

From Fire to Water

Dusty was very excited. His friends from the Piston Peak base fire crew were passing through Propwash Junction on the way back from a fire safety meeting, and they had all stopped by to say hello.

It was a wild and stormy night, and the friends were enjoying catching up inside the warm hangar, out of the wind and rain.

Suddenly, Mayday the fire engine screeched up. He looked worried. "The river's overflowed its banks. There could be flooding," he warned.

"Did you check out the situation?" asked the helicopter, Blade. Mayday explained that he'd tried, but the bridge across the river was almost completely underwater and he couldn't get across.

Dusty fired up his engines. "Luckily, those of us who can fly don't need a bridge," he said. He and Blade lifted off to find out how bad the situation was.

When they got to the river it was even worse than Mayday had said. Not only was the water rising fast, but a pick-up truck named Flap was stranded on an island in the middle of it all. If they didn't rescue him soon, he'd be swept away!

Without a bridge, there was no way to get to him by land. Luckily, the Piston Peak crew had a team of specialists who could help.

The Smokejumpers quickly parachuted in and set to work. Avalanche reinforced the banks of the island, stopping the water rising any higher – for a little while, at least.

"But I'm still stranded," sobbed Flap.

Dynamite smiled at him reassuringly. "Not for long!"

They all looked up in time to see a large green helicopter descending towards them. A platform swung from beneath him, held up by four strong cables.

"Our taxi is here! Climb aboard," said Dynamite, as Windlifter the helicopter lowered his platform all the way to the ground.

With his wheels shaking, the terrified Flap rolled onto the platform. He yelped in fright as Windlifter rose into the air, and safely carried the pick-up truck back to Propwash Junction.

A few hours later, it was time for the friends to say goodbye. The rain had stopped, and they were all gathered at the runway, ready to set off.

"Thanks to all of you," said a grateful Dusty. "We couldn't have done it without you."

"It was a pleasure, Dusty," Blade assured him. "Luckily everything turned out okay."

"That's the way it goes when you've got friends you can count on," said Mayday.

Dusty smiled. "Especially when they're experts in emergencies!"

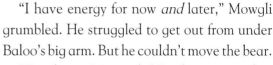

Mowgli's Nap

When Baloo yawned, you could almost see his tonsils. Mowgli leaned forward for a better look. The big bear blinked sleepily.

"Am I ever sleepy." Baloo stretched, leaned against a tree trunk and scratched his back as he slid to the ground. "I think it must be time for an afternoon snooze."

"Good thinking, my friend." High above them, stretched out on a branch, Bagheera dangled a limp paw. His golden eyes were half-closed in the heat of the day.

"A nap? Not for me!" Mowgli shook his mop of dark hair. "I'm not tired."

"Now, hold on a second there," Baloo said. "Don't you want to go hunting with us after it cools off? You're going to need energy."

"I have plenty of energy," Mowgli insisted. "I have energy right now!" He started to walk away from the bear, but Baloo stretched out a paw and grabbed the boy's ankle.

"Not so fast," Baloo said.

"You may have energy, but if you use it now, you will not have it to use later," Bagheera said wisely.

"Listen to the cat," Baloo yawned. "He knows what he's talking about." And with that, Baloo pulled Mowgli onto a pile of leaves and held him down with one great paw.

"I have energy for now *and* later," Mowgli grumbled. He struggled to get out from under Baloo's big arm. But he couldn't move the bear.

"Good nap, Man-cub," Bagheera purred at the scowling Mowgli.

A moment later, the panther and the bear were sleeping soundly. As soon as Mowgli heard their snores, he hoisted up the arm that was pinning him down.

"Good nap, yourself," Mowgli whispered. And he tiptoed off to swing in the trees and drop sticks on the animals below.

Baloo's snores shook the jungle for an hour, perhaps two, before Mowgli returned to the shady napping spot again. He'd had a grand time in the treetops, but the sun and the swinging had tired him. The great grey bear looked so soft and peaceful lying against the tree that Mowgli could not help himself. He curled up against his friend and closed his eyes.

Not two minutes later, Bagheera awoke and stretched his inky paws. The panther flicked his tail under Baloo's nose.

"I'm up. I'm up and ready to go!" Baloo sat upright. Then, spying Mowgli, the bear gave the boy a good shake. "How about you, Man-cub? You awake?"

But the only sound that came from Mowgli's mouth was a loud snore.

The Fancy Dress Party

Bonnie was very excited. She'd been invited to her first fancy dress birthday party!

At the kitchen table sat all of her favourite toys. They watched quietly as Bonnie prepared her rucksack.

"Do you like my bows?" she asked her toys. She was wearing a dress covered in ribbons. "I can't wait to go to the party," she told them. She placed a bow on the table, smiling happily. "Look what I made you. Isn't it beautiful?"

"Bonnie!" came a cry from the front door. "We've got to go shopping!"

"Can I keep my costume on, Mummy?" she shouted back, running from the room.

The toys waited until Bonnie was out of sight and then came to life.

"Hey, who is this bow for?" asked Jessie.

"She was talking to me!" insisted Buttercup the unicorn.

"Wrong! Bonnie's taking me to that party," Mr Pricklepants told them firmly.

"Calm down, folks," said Woody. "Why don't we each try the bow on and see who it suits best?"

The toys agreed it was a great idea.

Rex was the first to try the bow. "Do I look nice?" He placed it around his neck and twirled for his friends.

"You're so funny!" giggled Jessie.

Next, Mr Pricklepants pinned the bow to his dungarees. "I look like a clown," he mumbled.

Jessie placed the bow on top of her cowboy hat. "Oh! It's too big for me," she admitted.

"I'm sure it'll be perfect on me, though," Buttercup said, but the bow fell down over his eyes!

Finally, the aliens wandered over and lifted the bow above their heads in fascination.

"No, no!" laughed Woody. "You're supposed to wear it!" he explained.

Eventually, the toys gave up. The bow could be for any one of them.

"We just have to wait for Bonnie to tell us who the lucky toy is," Woody said.

A door slammed and the toys hurried back into their positions.

"I'll be in the kitchen, Mum!" Bonnie yelled.

The door swung open and she rushed in to find her beloved toys all sat waiting for her. She tipped her rucksack upside down on the table and a huge pile of multi-coloured bows tumbled out.

"You're all coming to the party with me!" she cheered. "Mum's going to help me carry some of you in her handbag."

And with that, she fixed a different bow to every toy, so they could all enjoy the party without anyone being left behind!

Peter Pan

We're Going on a Picnic

"Cap'n?" Mr Smee knocked softly on Captain Hook's door. There was no answer. He pushed his way inside, carrying a breakfast tray. "I've got breakfast, Cap'n."

"I'm not hungry!" Captain Hook replied. "Go away!"

"But, Cap'n. You have to eat," Smee worried. The Captain hadn't eaten in days. In fact, he hadn't even got out of bed! "I know you feel bad about Pe –" Smee stopped himself from saying the dreaded name just in time, "– that flying boy. And the croc – I mean – that ticking reptile, too." Captain Hook was really angry about being beaten by Peter again. Even worse, Peter had set the crocodile right back on Captain Hook's trail. "But we haven't seen hide nor scale of either of them for a week. I think the coast is clear."

There was no reply from Captain Hook.

Smee thought for a minute. "I know how to cheer you up!" he cried. "We'll have a nice old-fashioned picnic! Won't that be lovely?"

Again, silence from Captain Hook.

"Ah-ah-ah! No arguments!" Smee left the breakfast tray and hurried down to the galley. A picnic on Mermaid Island was just what the doctor ordered!

Smee whistled merrily as he made herring-and-pickle sandwiches (Captain Hook's favourite) and packed them in a wicker basket. This was Hook's day! Smee carefully folded up a gingham tablecloth and placed it in the basket, along with his tin whistle. He was going to make sure that Hook had a good time, whether he wanted to or not!

Once the picnic basket was packed, Smee called down to Hook, "It's time to go, Cap'n!"

After a while, Captain Hook finally appeared on deck, blinking in the sunlight. "Fine," he said grumpily. "But I know I'm not going to have fun!"

Smee let the rowing boat down into the water and Hook began to climb down the rope ladder. Once he was safely in the boat, Smee picked up the picnic basket.

TICK TOCK, TICK TOCK , TICK TOCK.

"Smee!" cried Hook. "Help me!"

Smee peeked over the side of the ship. The crocodile was about to take a bite out of the boat!

In a panic, he threw the only thing he had to hand – the picnic basket. It landed right in the crocodile's open mouth. The crocodile stared at Smee in surprise. Then, without a sound, it slipped back under the water.

"My picnic!" cried Smee. "My tin whistle!"

"Next time you have any smart ideas about cheering me up," said the Captain, glaring at his first mate, "keep them to yourself!"

Mater the Greater

Lightning McQueen and his friends were enjoying a few oil cans at Flo's V8 Café when ... "Whoa!" Mater sped backwards over a ramp. He crashed into a pile of cans. "I used to be a daredevil," he explained. Mater began to tell the story of his days as a daredevil. One of the events was at a sports arena.

The announcer called, "Ladies and gentlecars, Mater the Greater!"

In the stands, fans waved signs and cheered. It was nearly time for Mater's big stunt. He would try to jump over a long line of cars!

"And he's off!" the announcer called out. Mater's wheels burned rubber as he drove towards the ramp.

THUD! Mater the Greater landed on the first two cars past the ramp. Each car in the line-up groaned as Mater the Greater tiptoed all the way down the row.

"'Scuse me!" he said. "Pardon me! Comin' through!" At last, Mater the Greater rolled over the last car.

"He did it!" the announcer cried. The crowd went wild! Mater the Greater had made his way over all the cars. It didn't matter to them how he had done it.

"I did all kinds of stunts," Mater told Lightning as he continued. He described being shot from a cannon through a ring of flames.

In another stunt, Mater the Greater dived from a high platform into a tiny pool of water.

"The biggest stunt Mater the Greater ever did was jumping Carburetor Canyon," Mater said. He said, even with a rocket strapped to his hood, the jump seemed impossible.

Lightning was starting to doubt the story.

"Jumping Carburetor Canyon? No way!"

"Yes way," Mater replied. "You remember. You was there, too."

Mater continued his story, except now Lightning was with him.

Lightning had a fancy new paint job, and three huge rockets were strapped to his roof. He even had on Mater the Greater souvenir false teeth!

"Ready, buddy?" Mater the Greater asked.

But Lightning didn't really have a chance to answer. Someone lit his rockets and pushed him down the ramp!

Lightning shot down the ramp and launched into the air. He was about halfway across the canyon when his rockets sputtered ... and went out. By this time, everyone at Flo's V8 Café was listening. They were all waiting to hear the end of Mater's story.

"Well, what happened?" Lightning asked.

"You didn't make it," Mater replied. "Well, see ya later!"

Disney

Pinocchio

Boy's Best Friend

Like all little boys, Pinocchio wanted a puppy. And, like all little boys, he promised to feed it and walk it and do everything and anything required to care for it.

"Puppies are a lot of work," Geppetto told his son. "And puppies like to chew things, like slippers – and wood." The toy maker glanced over at the rows and rows of wooden toys on his workbench. "No, I don't think a dog is a good idea," he said finally.

That afternoon, when Pinocchio returned from school, Geppetto had a present waiting. The boy wasted no time in opening the box. "It's a dog," Pinocchio said, trying to hide his disappointment. "A wooden dog." Not wanting to hurt Geppetto's feelings, Pinocchio thanked his father and placed the toy on his bed.

A few days later, as Pinocchio was walking home from school, he heard a puppy whining in an alleyway. With a little coaxing, the puppy emerged. "Why, you look just like the wooden dog my father carved for me," Pinocchio said.

Pinocchio wondered what to do. "Well, I can't leave you here all by yourself," he decided. The boy went home and tied the dog to a tree a few doors up the street. Then he sneaked the puppy a bowl of food and went back inside.

After Geppetto had fallen asleep, Pinocchio slipped outside and scooped up the dog. "Now, you're going to have to be very quiet," he warned.

Once inside, the puppy sprang from Pinocchio's arms and made a dash for Figaro. As the dog bounded after the fleeing cat, they upset chairs and knocked over crockery. "Look out!" cried Pinocchio. Geppetto soon appeared in his night clothes. "What's going on here?" he asked.

"Well...." Pinocchio began. Suddenly, the puppy sprang onto Pinocchio's bed, knocking the wooden dog beneath it. Geppetto blinked. The puppy looked just like the toy he had made for his son!

"Could it be?" the toy maker asked. "Pinocchio! You wanted a puppy so much that the Blue Fairy must have turned your toy dog into a real one!"

Pinocchio just picked up the pup and brought it over to meet Geppetto. A day later, when Pinocchio finally found the courage to tell Geppetto the truth, the little puppy was in no danger of becoming an orphan again.

"Well," Geppetto said affectionately when he found the pup carrying the wooden dog around the house, "I suppose we have room for two dogs here – especially if one of them walks the other!"

Sports Day

The reef was teeming with vibrant fish all sensing the excitement in the water. Sports Day was here – a chance for the kids to have fun and take part in competitions, while their proud parents watched above their heads and applauded.

"Hooray! I love Sports Day. Don't you, Nemo?" asked Tad, Nemo's closest fishy friend. "Which events are you in?"

"I don't know. I'm not sure what I'd be good at," confessed Nemo.

"What do you mean?" wondered Tad.

Nemo looked sad. "Well, I know I'm not very good at sporty things," he said timidly.

"Come on," said Tad. "I'll find you something to take part in."

He took Nemo on a tour of the events that were taking place all over the reef. Lots of sea creatures were practising, ready for their moment to compete.

Tad brought Nemo to the football pitch. "What about football?" he suggested.

"Err, I'm not sure," he admitted, as Pearl expertly headed a ball into the back of the net. "I'm nowhere near as good as Pearl."

"Okay," said Tad, leading him away. "What about the obstacle course?"

Nemo watched as Squirt and his turtle friends dodged incoming bubble blasts and slipped through hoops made of seaweed at a staggering speed.

"I'll leave that to Squirt," Nemo said quietly.

"Hey! Weightlifting! That could be your thing!" Tad beamed at him.

Nemo studied the fish lifting rocks five times their own weight above their heads. There were gasps and cheers all round.

"Well, maybe not," said Tad, before Nemo could open his mouth. He didn't like to see his best pal so deflated. Then, he had a brainwave. "Actually, I know just the thing. Come on, Nemo!"

Tad found Nemo the perfect race ... so perfect, even Nemo couldn't believe his luck!

Stretching his littlest fin, Nemo focused on the finish line. Tad nodded encouragingly at his side. When the signal came for the fish to start the race, Nemo and Tad swam neck-and-neck the whole way round the sandy track.

"We won, we won!" cheered Tad.

"We did! I'd never have thought to enter the three-finned race without you," Nemo smiled.

Tad and Nemo high-fived each other and accepted their medals with smiles as big as a pelican's grin. Sports Day wasn't so scary after all. And Nemo couldn't wait to put his medal on the wall at home, to remember his unexpected but well-earned victory.

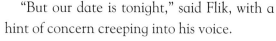

Flik's Big Date

Flik loved Queen Atta very, very much. So, he decided to plan the most romantic evening for the two of them that an ant could possibly imagine.

"I'll pick you up at eight tonight," Flik told Atta when he met her at the anthill early in the morning. Then off he hurried to get ready for their big date.

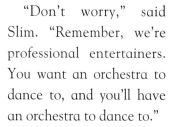

First, there was the dinner to prepare – sprouted wheat with sunflower seeds and wild truffles then free-range millet on a bed of dandelion greens, and, to finish, Queen Atta's favourite dessert – gooseberry mousse.

The perfect menu! Flik thought.

Then Flik went down to the stream to find the perfect leaf for a romantic moonlit cruise. "This elm leaf should do," Flik said as he tied the leaf to a root near the shore. "And I'll use this twig for my oar. Yes, Atta's going to love this."

But that wasn't all that Flik had planned.

"How's it going?" he asked the circus bugs, who were back for a visit and busy practising their instruments just up the hill from the stream.

"Brilliant!" Slim replied. "Just brilliant. Don't worry about a thing. It's all under control. We'll have Atta's favourite song memorized by tomorrow night, no problem!"

"But our date is tonight," said Flik, with a hint of concern creeping into his voice.

"Oh," said Slim sheepishly.

"Told you so," said Francis.

"Don't worry," said Slim. "Remember, we're professional entertainers. You want an orchestra to dance to, and you'll have an orchestra to dance to."

"Are you sure you wouldn't like some magic instead?" Manny the Magician asked. "I have found that nothing inspires romance in a lady quite like cutting her in half."

"Um, I think I'll stick with the dancing," said Flik. But, speaking of inspiring romance, he'd almost forgotten all about the fireflies!

"Come on, guys!" he called to the dozen or so fireflies he'd hired for that evening. "I want some of you in the trees, some of you along the water and the rest of you over there by the picnic blanket ... perfect!" he said as their thoraxes lit up the quickly falling night. "Dinner is ready. Boat is ready. Music is ... almost ready. Everything is set to go!"

Suddenly, Flik looked down at his watch, and his heart skipped a beat. "Oh no! It's eight o'clock!" he yelled. "I've really got to go!"

Can you believe it? Flik was so busy getting everything ready, he'd almost forgotten to pick Atta up for their date!

THE
HUNCHBACK
OF NOTRE DAME

A Major Mess

High in the bell tower of Notre Dame cathedral, the gargoyles, Victor, Hugo and Laverne, began their 45th game of hide-and-seek that day.

"Ready or not, here I come!" called Victor. "And no one better be hiding in Quasimodo's underwear drawer! It's neither funny nor proper." And with that, he leaped over a pile of rumpled clothes and began searching among stacks of books and games and other scattered objects.

The tower, you see, was a mess! Quasimodo had only been away for a few days and still the tower looked like a hurricane had hit it. And why was that? Simply because the gargoyles were slobs!

Quasi had asked them to look after his things – particularly his carvings and precious bells – while he was away. "And of course," Quasi told them, "feel free to make yourselves at home." And, well, they had!

They had tried on his clothes and left them scattered all over the floor. They had leafed through his books and played all his games, without ever putting a single thing back. And they had even used his pillows for pillow fights!

And so it was with some shock and horror that Victor suddenly stopped their game and shrieked, "Do you know what day it is?"

"Excuse me?" said Hugo, peeking out from behind a pillar.

"It's Friday!" said Victor. "The day that Quasi returns home!"

"Oh!" Hugo gulped, gazing at the mess. "He's not going to be happy with us, is he?"

"Oh, but he is," said Victor, "because we're going to clean all this up. If we don't, he'll never trust us again."

"Maybe he shouldn't," muttered Hugo.

"Where is Laverne? Laverne!" Victor called. "Come out, come out, wherever you are. We have work to do!"

And work they did. They folded the clothes. They made the bed. They put the books back on the shelf. They washed the dishes and scrubbed the floor. They dusted Quasi's hand-carved models and carefully put them back. And they polished every one of Quasi's bells.

"You missed a spot on Big Marie!" Victor called to Hugo ... just as Quasimodo arrived.

"Guys! I'm home!" he shouted.

"Quasi! We missed you! How was your holiday?" the gargoyles asked.

"Great!" said Quasimodo. "You should try it sometime!"

And, after all the work the gargoyles had just done, a holiday is exactly what they needed!

Disney
101
DALMATIANS

A Helping Paw

The dairy barn was warm and cosy, and 99 exhausted, hungry pups were taking turns to drink warm milk from the motherly cows.

"We'd nearly given up hope that you would get here," the kindly collie said to Pongo and Perdita, who had just arrived with the puppies.

"We're so very grateful to you for your hospitality," Perdita murmured wearily.

"Would you just look at the little dears," said one of the cows. "I've never seen so many puppies in one place before!"

Pongo, Perdita and the puppies had just come in from a long and weary march in the cold. It was very late, and the pups waiting for a drink of milk could barely keep their eyes open. The puppies had recently managed to escape from the dreadful old house owned by Cruella De Vil. They had been held prisoner there, guarded by two villains named Horace and Jasper. Cruella was planning to make a fur coat out of their lovely spotted fur. Luckily Pongo and Perdita had rescued them all just in the nick of time.

The pups had their dinners and gathered around the collie, thanking him for his kind hospitality.

"Not at all, not at all," the collie replied.

"Do you have warm milk for supper every night out here in the country?" asked Rolly.

The collie chuckled. "No, but we do eat very simple country fare. I'm sure it's plainer than the food you eat in the city, but we eat big meals because of all the chores we do."

"And is it always this cold?" asked Patch.

"Well, now," replied the collie. "I suppose most of you come from the city. No, it isn't always this cold, but there are plenty of differences between living in the country and living in the city. Take leads, for instance. We don't keep our pets on leads here, the way you do in the city, since our pets have a lot of wide-open space to roam around in. There aren't as many dogs nearby, but there are certainly other sorts of animals that one doesn't see in the city. Take cows, for instance. And then there are sheep and horses and geese, and...."

Suddenly, the collie stopped talking. A tiny snore escaped one of the pups he had just been talking to. He looked around and realized that every one of the pups, as well as Pongo and Perdita, had fallen into a deep sleep.

"Poor little things," he said quietly, as he trotted outside to stand guard. "They've been through so much. I do hope they get home safely soon."

Hero of the Day

Radiator Springs was buzzing. It was the annual street race! Spectators lined the roads, cheering and waving flags in support. The whole town was there, as well as a flurry of tourists all bustling for a position to watch.

"What a perfect place, Ramone," said Flo. They were right by the finish line so they could get an excellent view of the winner in his final moments. "How exciting!"

"Not as exciting as being here with you," replied Ramone, with a wink.

Flo blushed. Ramone was ever the romantic. As she was about to return his kind, thoughtful words, there was a sudden *CLANG* sound to their right.

"Oops! Sorry!" came an apologetic cry.

"What's happening?" asked Flo.

Not far away, Mater was wandering through a group of angry cars with his tow rope swinging. Its hook kept clanging into tourists, who growled at him in disapproval.

"Watch where you put that thing!" one of them yelled.

Mater's heart sank in disappointment. "I guess I'll just leave," he murmured quietly, slipping away.

"Hey, look over there!" someone cried out. A cloud of dust suggested the racers were drawing nearer. "They're almost here!"

"I was really hoping to be in the front row," Mater sulked, with his back to the road. All he wanted was to be a part of the excitement. Not moaned at because he was rusty and clunky, with a hook that almost poked eyes out.

"Oh no!" a voice shrieked. "Someone's in the middle of the track!"

A small, young car zoomed into the road with wide eyes, oblivious to the danger he was in. The dust cloud created by the roaring racers got bigger and closer....

"No one will reach the little one in time," Mater realized. "But I can!"

He swung his tow rope above his head like a lasso and expertly launched it at the little car that was on the brink of being crushed. The hook latched on to the youngster's bumper and Mater quickly towed him back into the crowd.

"Wheeee! I'm flying!" the little one chirped as the racers shot over the finish line. They missed him by millimetres with not an inkling of the danger they had all been in.

The crowd cheered, but not for the winner. They cheered for Mater!

"Nice aim, friend," rejoiced Flo, as the cars surrounded him.

Mater couldn't believe his ears. He'd gone from getting in everyone's way to being the hero of the day!

DUMBO

Dumbo's Parade Pals

When Dumbo's circus came to town, the animals and circus folk marched in a big parade. The crowd loved seeing all the circus animals marching down the street.

Well, it may have been fun for the crowd, but it was no fun for Dumbo. His feet hurt, and he was *hungry*.

Then Dumbo noticed a peanut on the ground. He picked up the peanut and ate it. Then Dumbo saw another peanut, and another. Leaving the parade, Dumbo followed the trail of peanuts all the way to a playground.

"The peanuts worked!" cheered a little girl. "Now we have our own elephant to play with."

The girl and her friends gathered round Dumbo, patting his head. They marvelled at his long trunk and big ears. "What a wonderful little elephant!" they cried.

"Let's have our own circus," said a boy.

"I'll be the ringmaster!" cried the little girl. She led Dumbo to the middle of the playground. "Ladies and gentlemen! Presenting our star attraction – the Little Elephant!"

Dumbo knew just what to do. He stood up on his two back legs. Then he juggled some balls with his trunk. The children cheered.

Suddenly, Timothy Q. Mouse appeared. "Here you are!" he said to Dumbo. "We have to get back and get ready for the show!"

Dumbo nodded, and waved goodbye to his new friends. The children watched him go, looking disappointed.

"I wish I could see him in the circus tonight," one of them said. "But I don't have enough money for a ticket."

"Me neither," said the other children.

Dumbo was sorry that the nice children he had met would not be able to go to the circus. That night, he felt very blue as he put on his stage make-up and warmed up his ears. Finally, he tucked Timothy into the brim of his hat and climbed onto a tall platform.

"Ladies and gentlemen!" the Ringmaster cried. "I give you *Dumbo, the Flying Elephant!*"

Dumbo leaped off the platform, and his giant ears unfurled. The crowd cheered as Dumbo flew around the tent.

Suddenly, Dumbo spotted his playground friends. They were sitting in the first row! He swept by them, patting each child on the head with his trunk. The girl with pigtails waved at Dumbo. "Your mouse friend gave us free tickets!" she called.

Dumbo smiled and reached his trunk up to the brim of his hat, where Timothy was riding. He gave Timothy a pat on the head, too. He was the luckiest elephant in the world to have such wonderful friends!

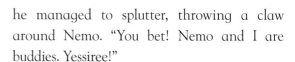

What a Crab!

Nemo was having trouble at school – and its name was Ruddy. The big crab was mean to Nemo and the other kids whenever he got the chance. The trouble was, he was crafty and he never did it when the teachers were looking.

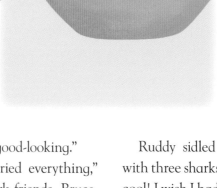

One day, he shoved Nemo into a tide pool and made him late for their coral lesson. Another time, he taunted Nemo by saying, "My dad's bigger and stronger than your dad!"

"Ignore him," Marlin told his son. "And just so you know, his dad *may* be bigger and stronger than I am, but he's certainly not as smart or good-looking."

"My friends and I have tried everything," Nemo complained to his shark friends, Bruce, Chum and Anchor. "But he won't leave us alone. What do you think we should do?"

"Just leave it to us!" said Bruce. "We're experts in behaviour modification."

The next day, three huge shadows fell over Nemo's classmates as they played in the school playground.

"Hello," Bruce said, putting a fin around the crab. "You must be Nemo's new little friend."

While Ruddy trembled, Bruce snarled, "We just wanted you to know that any friend of Nemo's is a friend of ours. You are a *friend* of Nemo's, aren't you?"

Everyone looked at Ruddy. "Oh, yeah!"

he managed to splutter, throwing a claw around Nemo. "You bet! Nemo and I are buddies. Yessiree!"

"Good!" Anchor said. "Because you don't want to know what happens to anyone who's not nice to our little pal here."

Chum cleaned a piece of seaweed from between his razor-sharp teeth with a spiny urchin. "You should stop by for lunch sometime," he said to Ruddy with a wink.

When Mrs Lobster arrived to pick up the class, the sharks said goodbye and swam away.

Ruddy sidled up to Nemo. "You're friends with three sharks?" he said. "Wow! That's pretty cool! I wish I had friends like that. In fact, I wish I had any friends at all."

"How do you expect to have friends when you're so, well, *crabby* all the time?" Nemo said.

Ruddy admitted that he hated being the new kid. He had decided to pick on everyone else before they had a chance to pick on him.

"If you promise to stop acting mean, I promise to be your friend," Nemo said.

"Deal," Ruddy agreed. "Besides, I guess I'd better be your friend if I don't want your shark pals to eat me."

Nemo didn't say a word. Bruce, Chum and Anchor were vegetarians, but Ruddy didn't need to know that – at least not today!

The Sensitive Hero

Chug and Sparky were visiting Dusty up at Piston Peak. They couldn't believe how beautiful the national park was.

Dusty told his friends to look around while he ran some errands. He reminded them how important it was to respect the wildlife.

"Remember the rules I gave you?" he said. Spark and Chug nodded to signal they did.

"Stay on the path, keep our engines idling, and don't make a noise," they said. "Piece of cake!"

While Dusty ran his errands, Chug and Sparky went for a spin around the forest to look for wildlife.

Soon, they came across a fallen tree blocking their path. Sparky thought he could use his forklift to move the tree out of the way, but Chug decided that was too much effort.

"It's quicker if we go around it," he said, revving his engine and powering off the path. Up ahead, there was a rustling in the trees and a dozen horned creatures ran off in fright.

"Dusty told us not to make a noise, Chug," Sparky scolded. "Now you've scared off the deer."

Chug felt bad. He returned to the path, but as he did so he knocked over a fence, making even more noise! As he bumped back down onto the track, the rocking set off his horn. It blasted loudly, scaring away even more animals.

"It's not my fault! I've got a sensitive horn!" Chug protested, but Sparky wasn't listening.

"You smell that?" said the forklift, sniffing the air. The friends turned to see smoke and flames curling up from some nearby trees. "A forest fire!" Sparky gasped.

He rolled backwards in shock, bumping into the fallen tree. His horn began to blast again. "Turn it off," said Sparky. "You'll frighten off every animal in the forest."

No matter how hard he tried, though, Chug couldn't shut off his blaring horn. A few miles away, Dusty and Blade heard the noise and swooped in to see what was going on. "I told him not to make a racket," Dusty groaned.

As they drew closer, though, they spotted the blaze. Dusty raced into action, dropping his containers of flame retardant over the fire – and over his friends, too!

The flame retardant stopped the blaze, and it also stopped Chug's horn, too!

Back at the base, Dusty thanked Chug for his quick-thinking. His horn made the animals run from danger, and alerted the fire crew.

Sparky giggled as he whispered to his friend, "We'd better not tell him it's all thanks to your sensitive horn!"

A Sleepless Sleepover

Bonnie was sleeping over at her mum's friend Betty's house and she had brought her toys to keep her company. "Oh, I love your nightcap, Sheriff!" she said, playing with her cowboy toys, Woody and Jessie.

Just then, Bonnie was called up to bed. "Let's go, Jessie! The others will sleep here," said Bonnie, carrying her cowgirl toy upstairs. She left Woody, Buzz, Mr Pricklepants the hedgehog and Trixie the triceratops downstairs.

After Bonnie had left, the toys came to life.

Mr Pricklepants began to yawn and stretch. "I think it's time to get some sleep," he said. Woody agreed, but Trixie wasn't ready to go to bed yet. "I can't sleep if I don't look at a computer," she complained.

"Betty doesn't have a computer," Buzz pointed out.

But Trixie already knew that. "I know!" she cried. "That means we can stay up and chat all night long!" The other toys grumbled – they wanted to go to sleep.

"Hmm, maybe we can find a way to make you feel sleepy, Trixie," wondered Woody.

"I'll read a nice book for you!" offered Mr Pricklepants. Unfortunately, the only book they could find was a recipe book and that made everyone feel hungry!

So Woody suggested another idea. "We can play a card game!" But Trixie thought that would be boring. "Exactly!" Woody laughed. "That's why it'd make you fall asleep. Let's get the cards out and see."

But the playing cards were on the top shelf of the bookshelf, out of reach of the toys. Luckily, brave Buzz and Woody were ready to accept the challenge.

"Don't worry," Buzz called down, when they had climbed halfway up. "We'll save your night's sleep!"

Finally, Buzz and Woody reached the top shelf. They pushed the playing cards towards the floor, where Mr Pricklepants had placed a cushion to catch them.

"Phew! That was a hard mission," said Buzz, climbing down from the final shelf and wiping his brow.

"*Shh!*" whispered Mr Pricklepants, pointing to where Trixie was curled up on the floor. "While you were climbing, Trixie was staring at the swaying pendulum and she fell asleep!"

Buzz couldn't believe it. "All that climbing for nothing!" he moaned.

"No," smiled the hedgehog. "Now we can go to sleep, too!"

But Woody and Buzz were too excited to sleep now – they wanted to explore! Mr Pricklepants sighed ... it was going to be a long night.

Timon and Pumbaa Tell It All

It was a very hot day on the savannah. Simba, Timon and Pumbaa were lying in the shade, barely moving. It was too hot for the three friends to do anything except talk. Pumbaa had just finished telling a story about the biggest insect he'd ever eaten (to hear him tell it, you'd think it was the size of an ostrich) and a silence fell over the little group.

"Hey, Timon," said Simba. "Why don't you tell me the story of how you and Pumbaa met each other?"

Timon looked at Pumbaa. "Do you think he's ready for it?" he asked.

"Knock him dead," said Pumbaa.

"It all started in a little meerkat village far, far away," began Timon.

"No," interrupted Pumbaa. "You've got it all wrong. It all started near a little warthog watering hole far, far away."

"If I recall correctly, Simba asked *me* to tell the story," said Timon. "And this is the story as told from *my* point of view."

"All right," said Pumbaa sulkily.

"And in that little meerkat village there was one meerkat who didn't fit in with the rest. All the others were content to dig, dig, dig all day long," said Timon. "*I* was that isolated meerkat. How I hated to dig! I knew I needed to go elsewhere, to find a home of my own, a place where I fitted in. So I left. Along the way I ran into a wise old baboon who told me what I was seeking – *hakuna matata* – and pointed me in the direction of Pride Rock. So I boldly set off towards this rock of which he spoke. And on my way there, I –"

"Met me!" Pumbaa rudely interrupted.

Timon gave him a dirty look and continued. "I heard a strange rustling in the bushes. I was scared. What could it be? A hyena? A lion? And then I found myself face to face with a big, ugly warthog!"

"Hey!" said Pumbaa, looking insulted.

"We soon realized we had a lot in common, like our love for bugs and our search for a home to call our own. So we set out for Pride Rock together. A lot of bad things happened along the way – hyenas, stampedes, you name it. But before long we managed to find the perfect place to live. And then we met you, Simba!"

"That's a nice story," Simba said with a yawn. "Now I think I'm going to take a nap...."

Pumbaa cleared his throat. "It all started near a little warthog watering hole far, far away," he began.

"You always have to have the last word, don't you?" said Timon.

"Not always," said Pumbaa. And then he continued with *his* side of the story.

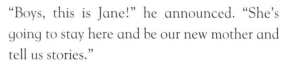

Return to Never Land

It had been a long time since Wendy's adventures in Never Land. But she never stopped believing. Years later, Wendy still loved to tell stories of Peter Pan, Tinker Bell and the Lost Boys to her own children. But her daughter, Jane, didn't have time for childish stories of pirates and pixie dust.

One night, Jane was fast asleep when a noise woke her. She gasped. Standing over her was Captain Hook!

"Hello, Wendy," Hook said, mistaking Jane for her mother.

Before Jane could say a word, the pirates stuffed her into a sack and jumped aboard Hook's flying pirate ship!

They set sail for the second star to the right and straight on till morning. When they arrived in Never Land, Hook tried to use Jane as bait to trap Peter Pan. He threw the sack with Jane inside into the sea!

Suddenly, something dived towards the water, catching the sack just in time. It was Peter Pan!

Peter flew to a nearby rock and freed Jane. "You're not Wendy," he said, confused.

Jane gasped. Peter Pan and Tinker Bell were right before her eyes! It seemed her mother's stories had been true after all!

When Jane explained she was Wendy's daughter, Peter took her to meet the Lost Boys.

"Boys, this is Jane!" he announced. "She's going to stay here and be our new mother and tell us stories."

Jane shook her head. "I'm not very good at telling stories," she said. "I have to go home."

The Lost Boys didn't understand why Jane wanted to leave. "What's the matter with her?" they asked Peter.

"I don't know," said Peter frowning. "She acts like ... a grown-up!"

Later that day, Peter found Jane building a raft. She wanted to sail home!

"The only way out of here is to fly," he told her. "All it takes is faith, trust –"

"And pixie dust?" finished Jane, sounding thoroughly unimpressed.

Peter took Jane back to the woods to see the Lost Boys and Tinker Bell. "Anyone can do it," said Peter excitedly. "Show her, Tink!"

Tinker Bell sprinkled pixie dust on the Lost Boys and they began to fly! The she scattered lots of pixie dust on Jane, too. But Jane still couldn't fly.

Jane became frustrated. She would never get home at this rate! "I don't believe in any of this!" she cried. "And I especially don't believe in fairies!"

Peter, Tink and the Lost Boys watched in shock as Jane stomped off to be alone.

Peter Pan
Return from Never Land

After Captain Hook had brought Wendy's daughter, Jane, to Never Land, she had met Peter Pan, Tink and the Lost Boys. Her mother's stories were true! But even though she'd seen them all with her own eyes, Jane still refused to believe in the magic. And she especially refused to believe in fairies.

"If Jane doesn't believe in fairies, Tink's light will go out forever!" said Peter, after Jane had stormed off.

Peter and the Lost Boys set out to find Jane, but Hook found her first.

"That pesky Pan stole my treasure. Help me get it back and I'll take you straight home," he said, handing Jane a whistle to blow when she found the treasure. Jane wanted to go home, so she agreed and headed back to find Peter.

The Lost Boys were happy to see Jane again. They took her on an exciting adventure through Never Land.

"Why don't we go on a treasure hunt?" Jane suggested. The others thought it was a good idea and Jane soon found herself in Dead Man's Cave with Hook's treasure! Peter was so impressed that he made Jane the very first Lost Girl. Jane was so honoured that she threw the whistle away and decided never to tell Hook about the treasure.

But one of the Lost Boys picked it up and gave it a good blow. Moments later, Hook and his pirates entered the cave and captured Peter and his gang.

Peter thought Jane had betrayed them. "Because you don't believe in fairies, Tink's light is going out!" he cried.

Jane felt terrible and left to find the fairy. When Jane found Tink, her light had faded to almost nothing. "I'm so sorry, Tink!" Jane sobbed.

Tinker Bell's light began to flicker back to life. Jane had started to believe!

On the pirate ship, Hook had tied the Lost Boys to the mast and was about to make Peter walk the plank.

"Not so fast!" someone shouted. It was Jane with Tinker Bell at her side! Hook was so surprised that Jane managed to snatch the key from him and free Peter and the Lost Boys, while Hook's crew stood gaping in shock.

An angry Captain Hook chased Jane up the mast. "Give up, girl!" he snarled.

"Never!" cried Jane. And thanks to a little pixie dust, she jumped off the mast and flew out of Hook's reach!

Before long, Peter and Tink flew Jane back home to London. When it was time for them to leave, Jane ran to the open window.

"I'll always believe in you," she promised Peter and Tink. And she kept her promise.

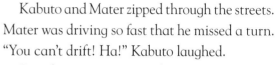

Tokyo Mater

One afternoon at Flo's V8 Café, three flashy modified cars roared past. "I used to be an import," Mater told Lightning McQueen. Mater described how he was driving through Carburetor County once and saw an older car....

Mater pulled up. "Looks like you could use a tow somewhere," he said.

"It is very far," replied the older car. His name was Ito-san.

"Well, no tow is too far for Tow Mater!" exclaimed Mater. Mater towed Ito-san all the way to Tokyo! Mater had never seen so many tall buildings. Then Mater accidentally bumped into Kabuto, the leader of a gang of ninja cars.

"You scratched my paint," Kabuto snarled. He circled around Mater. "*Dorifuto de shoubu da!*" he said in Japanese.

"He challenges you to a drift race." Ito-san explained that in a drift race a car drives fast and steers hard into turns, making the car slide.

"We will race at midnight," Kabuto said, then sped away.

"You need modification," Ito-san said. With help from some other cars, Mater soon got a slick blue paint job and a large rear spoiler. At midnight, he pulled up to the starting line.

"Race to the top of Tokyo Tower. First one to seize the flag will become King of All Drifters," Ito-san explained.

Kabuto and Mater zipped through the streets. Mater was driving so fast that he missed a turn. "You can't drift! Ha!" Kabuto laughed.

But then Mater went the wrong direction on a one-way street, and sped down an alley. He saw Kabuto up ahead, and drove up next to him.

"Good," said Kabuto. "But not good enough. Ninjas, attack!" A group of ninjas suddenly appeared. Mater was forced to slow down while Kabuto sped off laughing.

Back in Radiator Springs, Lightning asked, "What did you do?"

"Well, shoot. You oughta know," Mater replied. "You was there, too!"

Mater described how he was surrounded by ninjas. Suddenly, Dragon Lightning McQueen was there. "I'll take care of this – dragon style!" he said. With a kick of his rear tyre, Lightning sent each ninja flying.

Meanwhile, Kabuto was nearly at Tokyo Tower. But just then, Mater landed in front of him. "Well, hey!" Mater shouted. He took off down the highway, driving backwards. Kabuto chased after him. Then Kabuto pushed Mater over the railings. Mater quickly threw his tow hook onto the tower and pulled himself up to the top. He had finished the race first! "I win!" Mater said proudly.

Disney
THE EMPEROR'S
New Groove

Leaping Llamas!

"So Yzma and Kronk were out to get me the whole time! Some friends *they* were," Kuzco muttered as he trotted through the forest. Things had not been going very well for the Emperor-turned-llama. First, well, he had been turned into a llama. Then, while trying to get back to his palace, he had learned that his trusted adviser, Yzma, had really been trying to kill him!

Kuzco paused to scratch his ear with a hind hoof. And now he was all alone, without a friend in sight – not even that grubby peasant, Pacha. Actually, Pacha had probably been the closest thing Kuzco *had* to a friend. But now he was gone too.

Kuzco sighed. His best bet was still to get back to the palace. The problem was, Kuzco had spent his whole life having things done for him. Now that it was time to actually do things for himself, he wasn't sure if he could.

"Why me?" the llama whined to himself. He was pretty sure he was headed in the right direction, but the forest was so dense and dark. Why, there could be *anything* hiding in that tree ... under that fern ... behind that rock....

Behind that rock! Kuzco quickly leaped back as a panther lunged at him from behind a large rock. The panther's hungry jaws clicked shut just centimetres from Kuzco's snout.

"Help!" the llama bleated. Kuzco ran as fast as he could, but the panther was still gaining on him. *This is it*, thought Kuzco. *I'm doomed!*

Up ahead of him, Kuzco spotted a deep ravine. It was only about three metres wide wide.

"Okay," Kuzco said to himself. "Here's your chance. Llamas are nimble. Llamas are quick. Llamas can jump ... really ... faaar!"

THUMP!

Kuzco shook his head and looked around him. He had leaped across the ravine! And, back on the other side, snarling and pacing back and forth, was the angry panther.

Kuzco stuck his tongue out at the panther and trotted on his way. He had done it! He had escaped a panther, all by himself! "But I know," he said thoughtfully, "that I could do even better with a friend at my side. I wonder where Pacha went, anyway."

Just then, the forest opened up into a broad, sunny field. Kuzco heard a faint bleat. Llamas! There were llamas here, and Pacha was a llama herder. A broad smile appeared on Kuzco's furry face. He headed towards the herd, and, sure enough, there was Pacha. For the first time since the day he had woken up as a llama, far from home, Kuzco began to feel like he might really stand a chance. It was good to have friends.

A Nice Couple

It was a clear, sunny afternoon in Propwash Junction, and the post van had just made his deliveries.

Dusty had received a postcard. On the front were two smiling campervans, posing beside a bridge. Dusty smiled, too, when he saw the picture.

"Who are those nice campervans?" Dottie asked.

Dusty explained they were his friends, Harvey and Winnie, and that they were posing next to the recently rebuilt Augerin Canyon bridge.

Dottie and Chug wondered what was so important about the bridge. So Dusty told them the story of how he'd met the RV couple – and how it had turned into an exciting adventure for everyone!

The Fusel Lodge near Piston Peak had just been reopened after having lots of repairs done, and there was a big party to celebrate.

Winnie and Harvey were guests at the lodge, and were celebrating their 50th wedding anniversary.

The pair had honeymooned at the lodge all those years ago, and were trying to find the spot where they first kissed. They knew there was a waterfall and a bridge near the spot, but they hadn't been able to find it.

Dusty drew their attention to a map of Piston Peak. Together, they were able to work out where the couple's first kiss had taken place. "Augerin Canyon, by Upper Whitewall Falls!" Dusty announced.

Grateful for Dusty's help, they'd all spent a lovely evening getting to know one another, but the next day it was time to get serious again. Two wildfires had broken out in the park. Dusty and the other firefighters raced into action.

As Dusty and the others swooped around, spraying water and flame retardant on the fires, the Fusel Lodge guests were led to safety.

But poor Winnie and Harvey weren't at the lodge – they were off exploring Augerin Canyon, and found themselves in the path of one of the fires! Flames approached from both sides of the bridge. They were trapped!

Thinking fast, Dusty flew beneath the bridge and opened his pontoons. Filling them with water, he climbed sharply and doused the flames. Winnie and Harvey raced off the bridge, just before it collapsed completely.

Dusty had done it! He had saved the old RVs, and that had been the start of a friendship he knew would go on forever.

"What an amazing story," said Chug, when Dusty had finished.

Dottie agreed. "Yes, Dusty," she said. "You're a hero!"

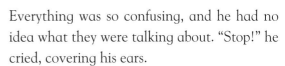

Computer Crazy

Up in Bonnie's bedroom, Woody ducked for cover as Rex came charging past. Rex was in a panic, as Trixie the triceratops came thundering after him.

"Cut it out, Trixie," Woody warned. "Good toys don't fight!"

"We're not fighting," Trixie said. "I'm just trying to help Rex."

Rex whimpered. "Trixie wants to teach me to use a c-c-computer."

Trixie loved the computer, and wanted her friends to enjoy it as much as she did. The problem was, Rex was terrified of trying new things.

"You don't want people to think that we dinosaurs are prehistoric, do you?" she asked. Rex had to admit that he didn't.

With a nudge from her horns, Trixie steered Rex in the direction of the computer room. "You'll soon see that computers are useful," she promised.

Woody watched on, shaking his head. "Trixie's right, but it's not right to make Rex do something he doesn't want to do."

Buzz disagreed. "He just needs our encouragement. Every toy should know how to use a computer. I think I'll help Trixie with the lesson," he said, hurrying after the dinosaurs.

With both Buzz and Trixie trying to explain how computers worked, Rex soon got in a flap.

Everything was so confusing, and he had no idea what they were talking about. "Stop!" he cried, covering his ears.

"Hmm," said Buzz, stroking his chin. "Maybe we should start off with something more fun."

"How about a game?" Trixie suggested. She tapped a few buttons and a space battle game loaded up on-screen.

Rex's eyes lit up with excitement as he watched the spaceships, aliens and laser blasts fill the screen. He took a step closer to the keyboard, watching Trixie pilot her rocket through an alien fleet.

"Hey, this is fun," he admitted. "Maybe computers aren't so bad after all!"

A little while later, Mrs Potato Head was looking for Buzz. "He went with Trixie and Rex," Woody told her. Their friends had been gone a while, though. Woody straightened his hat. "I'd better see what they're up to."

Through in the computer room, Woody could barely believe his eyes. Rex and Buzz were frantically bashing the keys. Explosions and laser blasts swooshed across the screen.

"What's going on, guys?" Woody asked.

Trixie slumped sadly at the side of the keyboard. "Rex loves computers now," she said, sighing. "The only problem is ... he won't stop playing!"

Disney

Lady and the TRAMP

A Rainy Night Out

"Yip!" Scamp barked at the squirrel nibbling on an acorn in the grass. His brother and sisters were taking a nap under the big oak tree, and there was nobody else around to have fun with.

"Yip!" Scamp barked again, and the squirrel darted across the lawn. Scamp chased it. The squirrel zipped up a lamp post and leaped onto a nearby tree branch. With a whimper, Scamp sat down and thumped his tail on the pavement. That was the problem with squirrels. They always got away too easily.

Disappointed, Scamp trotted along the pavement, stopping when he got to an open space. The grass here was tall, and butterflies flitted from wild flower to wild flower.

"Yip! Yip!" Scamp raced through the tall grass. He chased the butterflies to the end of the open space and back again.

It was getting dark. Scamp decided it was time to head home. He hadn't caught a single butterfly, but he'd had fun trying. He couldn't wait to get home and tell his brother and sisters about the new game he'd invented. They'd be so impressed!

Scamp trotted up to the front porch and tried to get through the doggy door. *THUNK!* His nose hit the wood, but it didn't move. The door was locked!

"Yip! Yip! I'm home!" he barked. "Let me in!" Scamp sat there for several minutes, barking. Nobody came to the door.

Suddenly – *BOOM!* – a clap of thunder echoed above him. Lightning flashed and rain began to fall.

Scamp bolted over to the big oak tree, sat down and covered his eyes with his paws. Thunderstorms were scary!

"I'm not going to cry," he told himself as his eyes started to mist over. He shivered. He'd probably catch a cold by morning!

Scamp let out a little whimper and moved even closer to the tree trunk. He buried his wet nose in his wet paws and closed his eyes.

Scamp was just falling asleep when a sound made him start. Somebody was coming up the drive!

By the time Jim Dear and Darling were out of the taxi, Scamp was dashing across the lawn as fast as he could go. He bolted through the door just as it opened.

"Scamp, you're soaking wet!" Darling declared as the puppy found his brother and sisters napping in front of the fire. And, as he lay down among them, Jim Dear came over with a warm towel to dry him off.

Home, sweet home, Scamp thought happily, as he drifted off to sleep.

Neon Racers

Lightning McQueen was in Japan for a race hosted by Shu Todoroki.

"*Buona sera!*" Francesco said. "Francesco is looking forward to beating you in Tokyo again."

"Then I'm afraid you will be very disappointed," Lightning taunted.

"You boys are so wrapped up in your rivalry, you won't even notice when I speed right past you," said Carla Veloso with a wink.

Before Lightning or Francesco could respond, a white car cruised up. "Welcome to Japan. Shu is waiting for you."

At his headquarters, Shu explained the race. "We'll be racing at night – an 85-mile trip from Mount Fuji to Ginza."

Shu motioned for several of his pit-crew members to darken his race shop. "Since we'll be racing in the dark, we'll all need special competition lighting." The other racers gasped. Shu was glowing!

The next evening, the racers – all lit up in bright neon – met halfway up Mount Fuji.

"When the flag drops, you may head straight down the mountain," Shu explained. "Or you may head up ... and sign the legendary climbers' book at the top!"

The racers gazed up at the summit.

"That climb looks intense," said Rip. "You can count me out."

"The choice is yours," said Shu. "Good luck!"

The flag dropped and the race began! Rip, Francesco and most of the other racers headed down the mountain. But Lightning, Shu, Carla, Lewis and Vitaly Petrov, the Russian racer, drove up. When they reached the summit, Shu called out, "There's the climbers' book!"

"Ka-chow!" Lightning said, signing the book. The other racers followed.

As they turned to head back down the mountain, Shu stopped them. "I forgot! There's another reward for reaching the peak – another road that leads straight down! Follow me!"

The five racers flew down the mountain. Suddenly, their road merged with another and they spotted the other racers just ahead of them. They had caught up!

"Where did you come from?" asked Francesco, when Lightning suddenly appeared beside him.

"You didn't think I'd make this easy on you, did you, Francesco?" asked Lightning. Smiling and revving his engine, he took the lead!

The two racers were so focused on passing each other, they didn't notice a car behind them. It was Carla Veloso! As promised, she slipped by the two competitors and won the race!

Bravest of the Bunch

"Come on, Nemo," said Gill, swimming through the fish tank. "You have to move faster, like this." He rapidly swished his black-and-white tail fin.

"Okay!" said Nemo. "Can I try again?"

"Of course you can! But let's see you put some more effort in this time," coached Gill.

Nemo wriggled his tail fin this way and that with all his might.

"That's better! You'll be in shape for my next escape plan in no time," Gill praised him.

The other fish swam over to find out what was happening. They watched in fascination.

"I'm in great shape already!" Nemo insisted, flexing both his big and little front-fins like a weightlifter with muscles.

"It's not all about strength, Nemo," Gill explained. "You must be brave! It's a dangerous world out there."

"Here we go again," said Gurgle, putting a purple fin to his eyes and shaking his head.

Bloat, on the other hand, was puffed up in excitement. He loved a survival story! Even if he'd heard it before.

"I was approaching the tank wall with my goal in sight," began Gill, his scarred face shimmering in the sunlight, "when a child's hand came and slammed me against the glass."

Nemo gasped. "Then what?"

"I didn't give up because nothing scares me," Gill said, with a proud smile. "I turned around suddenly and ... AAHHH!"

Nemo flinched.

Just as Gill had moved to demonstrate his story, a pirate skull appeared with a grisly expression and a patch over one eye. Gill had never screamed so loud before!

"Surprise!" cried Bloat, swimming out from behind the skull.

When Nemo got a closer look he realized the skull was just a plastic ornament. Gurgle and Bloat had dropped the skull behind Gill right at that crucial moment in the story ... having heard it so many times before they wanted to make it more exciting.

"So nothing scares you, huh, Gill?" laughed Bloat.

"Very funny, guys," Gill said, blushing with embarrassment.

The fish giggled and set the plastic skull back in its rightful place on the tank's bed.

"Of course, I knew it was them all along, Nemo," whispered Gill, in private. "I was just showing you what not to do."

Nemo smiled, secretlly happy to see that even Gill got scared sometimes. "Sure thing, Gill," he whispered back. "Whatever you say!"

GREAT MOUSE DETECTIVE

A Lesson in Confidence

"Oh dear!" Olivia, a very worried little mouse, sat with Dr Dawson next to the fireplace in Basil of Baker Street's home.

"What's the matter?" Dr Dawson asked.

"What's the matter?" Olivia repeated. "My father's been stolen by a peg-leg bat! Have you forgotten already?"

"No, no, dear," Dawson reassured her. "Of course not. I know you must be quite upset."

"Quite upset!" Olivia cried angrily. "I couldn't possibly *be* more upset!"

"But we're at Basil's now, and he's the best. You even said so yourself," Dawson said.

"But what if he doesn't want to help me?" Olivia asked.

"Why wouldn't he want to help you?" Dawson asked.

"You heard him," Olivia answered. "'I simply have no time for lost fathers,'" she said, quoting the detective.

"I'm sure he didn't mean it," Dawson said reassuringly. "He's just in the middle of something. Perhaps we caught him at a bad time. But, whatever the circumstances, my dear, you must try not to fret."

"I know you're trying to help me, Dr Dawson," Olivia said, as politely as she could. "But I don't know if I can really avoid fretting.

My father is out there somewhere, and I just *have* to find him!"

"You're right!" Dawson said. "You do have to find him. You have to help Basil track down your father and, in order to do that, you are going to need a clear mind. Now, can you have a clear mind while you're fretting?"

"It probably doesn't help," Olivia admitted.

"Can you think logically while you're upset?" Dawson asked.

"Well ... probably not," Olivia said.

"Can you work side-by-side with Basil of Baker Street, the Great Mouse Detective, to save your beloved father while you are *worried?*" Dawson asked.

"No!" Olivia paused as the truth sank in. "No, I can't. I owe it to my father to be level-headed. I can be sad and scared later – right now I have to be a detective, like Basil!"

"That, my young lady, is the smartest thing you could have said. And, if you can hold on to that attitude, your father will be found in no time." Dawson smiled at Olivia.

Just then, Basil came swooping back into the room. "Of course he will. I never miss my mark. Your father is as good as found, because I am just that good!"

Olivia smiled secretly. She knew *she* was just that good too.

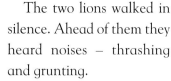

Hot on the Trail

"Over here!" Simba said, sniffing the trail. "It's going this way!"

"Yup, this way," Nala said with a nod, sniffing a stick. "And not long ago."

"I saw that stick first," Simba said. Nala was a good tracker, but Simba had learned from an expert – his mum. She was one of the best hunters in the pride.

"So what do you think we're following then, master tracker?" Nala asked. "Can you tell me that?"

Simba was silent.

They had seen some footprints, but they weren't clear enough to read. They'd also seen some dark wiry hair on a log, but that could belong to lots of animals.

"Something that isn't very graceful," Simba said. They had seen lots of crushed grass and broken sticks.

"Mmm-hmm." Nala nodded impatiently.

"A rhino!" Simba said confidently.

"A rhino?" Nala rolled onto her back, laughing. "Simba, you crack me up!"

"What?" Simba couldn't hide the hurt in his voice. "It *might* be a rhino!"

"The footprints aren't big enough," Nala said. "It's Rafiki, the baboon."

Now, it was Simba's turn to laugh. "Rafiki likes the trees, he doesn't use trails like a hyena!" The giggle died in Simba's throat and he felt the fur on the back of his neck stand up. Hyenas were clumsy and had dark wiry hair....

Nala didn't say anything, but her fur was standing up a little too.

The two lions walked in silence. Ahead of them they heard noises – thrashing and grunting.

"Simba," whispered Nala, "maybe we should turn back now."

"Just a little farther," Simba replied.

The young lions creeped through the grass on their bellies as quietly as they could. The grunting and thrashing grew louder. They could see a dust cloud rising. Simba stifled a growl. Something about the smell and the sound was familiar, but Simba could not put his paw on it.

As they creeped closer, two bodies came into view by the side of a termite mound. Simba pounced!

"Pumbaa! Timon!" he shouted, landing between his friends.

"Simba!" grinned the warthog. Termites dripped out of his muddy mouth. "Want some?"

Timon held a handful of wriggling insects towards Nala. "There are plenty to go around."

"Uh, no, thanks," Nala said as she came out of the grass, giggling. She shot a look at Simba. "I think I'll wait for the master tracker to hunt me up some lunch!"

New Recruits

The rebels of Radiator Springs were up to their old tricks again – taking over the roads with their wicked behaviour and disregard for the law. Sheriff was hot on their tails – he wouldn't tolerate this behaviour in his town.

"Sheriff doesn't quit," snarled the leader, Boost.

"Yeah, but he'll never catch us!" said his blue rebel friend.

"True, he won't, but I don't feel like spending all afternoon dodging him," Boost said and veered off-road unexpectedly.

His friends watched in surprise as Boost lifted the fencing that marked the border, shimmying underneath into unknown territory.

"We'll shake him if we go through here," Boost called to them.

His rebel companions followed, wriggling until they were safe on the other side.

"What's going on here?" the blue rebel wondered. There were tyres and bridges and and slippery oil patches and ditches and....

"Hello, recruits!" came a bark. Sarge approached with a scowl on his face. "You must be the new enlistments for my boot camp!"

The rebels realized exactly where they were. Sarge's assault course!

"Let's go then!" Sarge ordered. "Training starts right away."

"I don't feel like training, Boost," muttered his blue rebel friend.

"But Sheriff would never think of looking for us here, knucklehead," he snapped. "We'll just wait until things cool down!"

His friends grinned at his cunning plan.

"A little exercise with that old jeep will be a breeze anyway," said one.

But it seemed he'd spoken too soon. Sarge's course had them swinging over narrow bridges and wading through thick mud.

"I hope you don't dent yourself," Sarge warned as the rebels were forced to drive down a near-vertical rock face. It required every ounce of their strength not to topple and roll.

Hours later, they confessed. "We want out!" cried Boost. "We're not your recruits!"

"I know," said Sarge matter-of-factly. "Just figured a bit of training would do you good. A friend of mine asked to keep you out of trouble for a while."

With that, Sheriff appeared with a triumphant smile. "Enjoy yourselves?"

The rebels groaned, covered from bonnet to bumper in dirt.

"We should have let you bust us sooner," said an achy Boost.

It would have saved them the hard workout at least....

Disney Bambi

Winter Nap

Bambi nosed under the crunchy leaves, looking for fresh grass. There was none. He looked up at the trees, but there were no green leaves there either. Food was getting scarce in the forest.

"Don't worry, Bambi," Thumper said when he saw the confused look on Bambi's face. "We'll get through the autumn and winter. Dad says we always do. We find what we can when we can, and we always make it until spring."

Bambi sighed and nodded. Thumper's dad was smart. He knew lots of things about the forest.

"Besides, it's better to be awake than napping all winter," added Thumper.

"Napping?" Bambi didn't know that some animals slept through the winter months.

"Sure. You know, like Flower, and the squirrels, and the bears. They hole up for months. Haven't you noticed the chipmunks putting their acorns away the past couple of months?" Thumper pointed towards an oak tree.

Bambi nodded.

"That's their food for the winter. As soon as it gets cold enough, they'll just stay inside and sleep," Thumper explained.

"But how will they know when it's time to wake up?" Bambi couldn't imagine life in the forest without all the other animals.

Thumper tapped his foot to think. It was a good question. And, since he had never slept through the winter, he wasn't sure of the answer. "Let's go ask Flower." They headed for the young skunk's den.

"Hello," Flower said.

"Hello, Flower. You sleep all winter, right?" Thumper asked curiously.

"It's called hibernation." Flower yawned a big yawn. "Excuse me," he said, his cheeks blushing.

"So, Bambi wants to know who wakes you up in the spring," Thumper said.

"You'll be back, won't you, Flower?" Bambi wondered worriedly.

The little skunk giggled. "Oh, we always come back. Just like the grass and the flowers and the leaves," Flower explained. "I never thought about what wakes us up before. It must be the sun, I guess."

Bambi smiled. He didn't know the grass and leaves would come back in the spring too! He was feeling much better about the forest's winter nap.

Suddenly, Thumper started laughing. He rolled on his back and pumped his large hind feet in the air.

Bambi and Flower looked at each other in confusion. "What is it?" they asked together.

"You really are a flower, Flower!" Thumper giggled. "You even bloom in the spring!"

A Sunnyside Weekend

Mr Pricklepants was feeling upset after Bonnie had left him and Dolly at Sunnyside Daycare for the weekend.

"Why, oh why, did she leave us in this messy, crowded place?" Mr Pricklepants asked Dolly.

"Come on! It's not that bad!" said Dolly, trying to cheer him up.

"Yeah, we can do lots of things!" Stretch the octopus added, as the other Sunnyside toys gathered round to help.

But it wasn't working.

"I miss our cosy house," Mr Pricklepants sighed. "I miss my books, my poems, our cute tea-table with its little chairs...." He wandered away from the other toys, listing everything he missed.

Dolly knew she had to do something to make Mr Pricklepants feel better, so she came up with a plan and asked the other toys to give her a hand.

"Just give us some time!" she called after him. "We'll organize a special programme for you!" But Mr Pricklepants wasn't listening.

Later, Dolly found him sitting alone, reading a book. Mr Pricklepants looked happy to see her. "At last! You're back!"

"Please, follow me to the Caterpillar Gallery," she said, smiling and leading him to the Caterpillar Room. As they arrived, she announced, "Welcome to our art exhibition!"

"It's amazing!" Mr Pricklepants cheered.

"I'll be your guide!" said Stretch, showing him the children's colourful drawings of flowers and houses taped to the walls.

After a long visit to the gallery, Mr Pricklepants thanked Dolly for organizing it. "That was marvellous!" he praised.

But the fun wasn't over yet.... "The best is yet to come!" beamed Dolly. "As we prepare for the next event, you can enjoy a beauty treatment."

"Fantastic! This is just what actors like me love!" replied Mr Pricklepants, as he settled down, ready to be pampered.

When the beauty treatment was finished, Dolly led Mr Pricklepants to a posh tea party where Ken was waiting to greet them. "Please, be our guest!" he said, handing a toy teacup to Mr Pricklepants.

"Isn't this the poshest tea party you've ever had?" asked Dolly.

"It is indeed!" he cried.

After the tea party, the Sunnyside toys put on a play for Mr Pricklepants to enjoy. Dolly turned to him when it finished. "So ... have you changed your mind about Sunnyside?" she wondered.

"Definitely!" he said happily. "I can't wait to see what you've got in store for tomorrow!"

Bad Luck for the Best

Dusty was being interviewed on television about his amazing life story. As the camera rolled, he explained how he'd gone from racer to firefighter.

"I used to think of my racing days as a never-ending dream," he said, "but one day, on a training run with Skipper, my engine started to stutter."

Although Dusty recovered quickly, Skipper insisted he go and see Dottie for a check-up.

At the garage, Dottie discovered a problem – one of Dusty's mechanical components was failing! Dottie fitted Dusty with a warning light, and told him that if the warning light lit up, he had to slow down or risk doing some serious damage to himself.

"That night, I had to prove to myself I could still fly, and fly fast!" Dusty told the TV show's presenter. "But when I sped too fast, the warning light distracted me."

His concentration broken, Dusty had crashed into the filling station, triggering an explosion that threatened to burn the whole airfield to the ground!

Mayday the fire engine had done his best to put the fire out, but his old hose wasn't up to the job. The other vehicles had helped, and together they'd managed to save Propwash Junction – but only just.

It had been such a close call that the next day the airport was declared unsafe. Unless Mayday got refurbished and the base got a second firefighter, Propwash Junction could be closed down for good!

Dusty explained that later that evening he spotted a photograph of Mayday with what looked like a crop duster aeroplane. Mayday revealed that the crop duster had been converted, so instead of dusting the crops it dropped water to help fight fires.

"That gave me an idea," said Dusty. "I went straight to Piston Peak to start my training."

The show's presenter smiled, showing off his perfect teeth. "I bet it was an easy task for an expert racer like you, wasn't it?"

Dusty thought back. "Well, I wouldn't say it was easy!" he laughed, thinking of all the times he'd messed up. "But I met great friends, and in the end I did it!"

With Dusty becoming a certified firefighter, and Mayday receiving a full upgrade, Propwash Junction was declared safe once more.

"Everything started from a failing gearbox," said the presenter. "You do have a new one now, right?"

Dusty said he did. "But bad luck with my old gearbox was one of the best things that ever happened to me," he said.

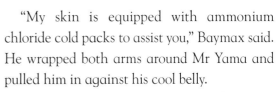

The Winning Robot

After Hiro destroyed his battle-bot, Little Yama, in the robot battle tournament, the gangster, Mr Yama, swore revenge.

One day, he cornered Hiro and Baymax and showed them his new creation, Big Yama. The robot barely came up to Mr Yama's knees, but the gangster insisted he was stronger and faster than the earlier model.

Big Yama was equipped with sharp saw blades and deadly knives. Hiro knew they would easily tear through Baymax's soft body, so while Mr Yama gloated, Hiro and Baymax turned and ran.

Furious, Mr Yama gave chase. "Come back here now," he panted, thudding along as fast as his pudgy legs would let him. With a groan, Mr Yama collapsed, gasping for breath.

Suddenly, Baymax stopped running. "Someone needs medical attention," he said, turning back towards the fallen gangster. Hiro tried to grab him, but Baymax's rubbery body slipped from his grasp.

Baymax waddled back to Mr Yama and scanned him. "I am Baymax, your personal healthcare companion," the robot said. "You are suffering from heat exhaustion. Your body temperature needs to cool down gradually."

Mr Yama tried to push Baymax away. "Keep away from me, you talking air balloon!"

"My skin is equipped with ammonium chloride cold packs to assist you," Baymax said. He wrapped both arms around Mr Yama and pulled him in against his cool belly.

"Let me go! You're not on my side!" Yama snapped.

Hiro laughed as Baymax hugged the villain tightly.

Just then, Hiro spotted Big Yama's remote control on the ground. While Mr Yama was occupied by Baymax's cooling hug, Hiro bent down and snatched the controller up.

When Mr Yama had cooled down, he wriggled free and shoved Baymax away.

"Are you satisfied with your care?" Baymax asked calmly.

"I'll be satisfied when you're in pieces!" Yama growled. He grabbed the remote and sneered at Hiro. "I'll destroy your useless robot."

Mr Yama pressed a button. With a loud bang, Big Yama exploded. Hiro grinned and handed him a circuit board he'd taken out of the controller. "You might need this!"

Yama roared with rage and shook his fists as Hiro and Baymax ran off. "I'm detecting high levels of stress, which are not good for your health, Mr Yama," the robot said, but this time he did stop. Even he could tell that the gangster had had quite enough medical attention for one day.

THE INCREDIBLES

Holiday Heroes

The Parr family was on holiday on a deserted tropical island. Their friend, Lucius – better known as the Frozone – was with them, and they were all looking forward to a few days in the sun.

While Dash and Violet explored, the others relaxed on the sand. Frozone used his ice powers to create refreshing, cold drinks.

Suddenly, there was a loud *BOOM!* from the mountain at the middle of the island. Bob lifted his sunglasses and frowned, trying to figure out what had caused the sound. When he realized what it was, his face fell. The mountain wasn't a mountain at all. It was a volcano, and it had just erupted!

Violet and Dash raced back to join the rest of the family, as hot lava began to ooze down the mountainside. As they watched, another explosion rocked the volcano, sending a huge chunk of rock hurtling towards them.

Dash dodged, but the others wouldn't be able to move in time. Bob reached out his arms and braced himself, catching the boulder before it could hurt his family.

That still left the lava to deal with. It sizzled and smoked as it sped towards them. Lucius raised his hands and hit the molten lava with his ice blast, but it barely slowed the liquid rock down.

"The heat is drying up the moisture in the air," he cried. "I won't be able to hold it back without more water!"

Bob grabbed his wife and son by their arms and dragged them towards the sea. If it was water his friend needed, it was water he was going to get.

Instructing Helen to form her elastic body into a bowl shape, Bob floated her into the tide. Taking Dash's hands, he ordered him to kick his legs at Super Speed. Dash's feet churned up a huge spray of water which Bob directed into Helen's bowl-shaped body.

Back onshore, Lucius was starting to go weak from the heat. His ice blast was now barely a cool breeze, and the lava was getting closer.

Bob ran up the beach, carrying Helen above his head. Halfway back to Lucius, he tripped. Helen was launched through the air. She flipped over, spilling the whole load of water over Lucius's head.

Recharged, Lucius's ice blast kicked in at full power. A thick wall of ice formed in front of them, freezing the lava and stopping it in its tracks.

Everyone was saved, but as they climbed back in the boat, Lucius said that next time the family went on holiday, he'd probably stay at home!

Rescuing Flo

Ramone paced frantically outside the Wheel Well Motel. He'd spent the entire afternoon getting ready, cleaning the mud from his grille, putting air in his tyres and even giving his flaming body-art a fresh coat of bright yellow paint. But where was Flo? He wondered if she was still pampering herself at home. Then again, she'd never been late in the past....

"We were supposed to meet here to celebrate my birthday. I guess she got lost!" Ramone grumbled. "I'd better go look for her."

He took off, swinging by Flo's V8 Café just to check she wasn't tangled up somewhere. But all was clear and the café was closed for the night.

Ramone continued through the streets of Radiator Springs and into the woods on the outskirts. Over the sound of rustling branches and chirping birds, he could just make out the faint sound of a voice.

"Help!"

Ramone's eyes widened. "That's Flo! Sounds like she's in trouble!" he gasped. "Keep talkin', Flo! I'm on my way!"

He followed her desperate cries – weaving through trees, spinning through the undergrowth and dodging big boulders. At the edge of a smelly swamp full of croaking frogs, his jaw gaped wide open.

"Flo!" he yelled.

Buried in the midst of the boggy water was his shimmering mint-green friend.

"Oh, Ramone! I've been so scared," she sobbed.

"I've come to rescue you," Ramone promised. He hated to see her so afraid.

"Watch out," warned Flo, as he was about to drive into the muck and grab her. "You might sink!"

Ramone paused. She was right. He looked around for something to help him.

"There's a rope in my boot," he realized, whipping it out as quickly as he could and attaching it to his bumper. He tossed the other end to Flo, who grabbed it in relief. With a few slips and slides on the muddy embankment, Ramone dragged Flo from the sludge.

"Safe and sound," he said, as her wheels met solid ground at last.

"I'm so sorry, Ramone," she apologized. "I had a lovely birthday present for you. It was a set of brushes, but I lost them in the mud."

"Don't worry, dear," said Ramone, cuddling up beside her. "The best birthday present I could have is being with you."

Flo blushed and smiled. She couldn't wait to get away from the horrid stench of the gloopy swamp and enjoy the evening with Ramone, her very own knight in flaming armour!

THE RESCUERS

A Purr-fect Night for a Stroll

Bernard was sweeping the floor of the Rescue Aid Society when Miss Bianca appeared.

"I'm going for a stroll," she said. "Would you like to join me?"

"Gosh, I don't know," Bernard said. "It's dark out. And it's raining too!"

"Yes," Miss Bianca said, smiling. "It's the *perfect* night for a stroll!"

Outside, Miss Bianca pulled her collar close to her neck. Bernard opened a big umbrella.

"Let's walk to Central Park," said Miss Bianca.

Bernard choked. "But that's 13 blocks away. Thirteen is unlucky!"

"Don't be silly," Miss Bianca said.

As they walked, it rained harder. Then, suddenly, Bernard stopped. "Listen!" he cried.

"Miaow!"

"It's a kitten," said Miss Bianca. "He sounds like he's in trouble."

"Stay back!" Bernard warned. "Cats are dangerous. They eat mice like us!"

"Over there!" cried Miss Bianca, pointing.

Under a postbox, a little orange kitten cowered from the rain. His fur was wet and he looked very sad.

"We've got to help!" Miss Bianca said.

"Let me go first!" Bernard insisted. He creeped up to the kitten. "Er ... hello," he stammered. "Are you lost?"

"I'm lost and very hungry!" the cat cried.

"I was afraid of that," said Bernard, eyeing the kitten's sharp teeth and claws nervously.

Miss Bianca leaned in. "Where are your parents?" she asked.

"I'm an orphan," the kitten replied.

"We must help him!" said Miss Bianca.

"I have an idea," said Bernard. "Follow us!"

He took Miss Bianca's arm and they walked to Morningside Orphanage. They knocked, and old Rufus the cat answered.

"Nice to see you two again," Rufus said. "And who's your friend?" he asked.

"He's Young Mister Kitten, and he's an orphan," Miss Bianca replied.

"He's hungry," said Bernard nervously.

"Here's a nice bowl of milk," said Rufus. The kitten lapped it up.

"You know," Rufus said. "I could use a helper around here. Would you like to be adopted?"

The kitten threw his paws around Rufus's neck and purred with joy.

It was late, so Miss Bianca and Bernard said good night, and left Rufus and the kitten to get to know each other. Out on the street, Bianca took Bernard's arm.

"See," she said, smiling at Bernard. "I told you it was the purr-fect night for a stroll!"

Manners, Mowgli!

A strange but delicious smell drifted past Mowgli's nose. Turning around, he spied several platters of food. A moment later, people filed in and sat in a circle around the food. Mowgli was excited. He had just come to live in the Man-village, and he was about to have his first meal!

Mowgli lunged forward and grabbed a piece of meat. He shoved it in his mouth and chewed. He had never tasted cooked meat before, and it was delicious! As the juice dribbled down his chin, he grinned at the humans surrounding him.

They did not grin back. In fact, they were looking at him in disgust. Surprised, Mowgli's mouth dropped open. A piece of half-chewed meat fell out. Why was everyone staring?

"Disgusting!" said an elderly woman.

"Why, he eats like an animal!" said a girl.

Mowgli didn't understand a single word they said. But it suddenly dawned on him that he didn't live in the jungle any more. Humans did things differently from the jungle creatures. Mowgli sighed. Would he ever fit in here?

Smiling sheepishly, Mowgli finished chewing and wiped his mouth with his arm. Then he sat back and watched the others eat.

They used strange, sharp sticks to cut with and flattened, paddle-like ones to scoop the food into their mouths. They took small bites and chewed with their mouths closed. Why, they didn't even seem to enjoy the meal at all!

Mowgli tried to copy them, with little success. The sharpened stick didn't cut nearly as well as his teeth, and half the food fell off the paddle.

"He's as clumsy as a baby," someone said.

"Maybe he really is an animal," said a girl.

At the next meal, Mowgli watched for a long time before he began to eat. The food was strange to him – warm liquid with soft vegetables. Holding his bowl in one hand, he tried to scoop the soup into his mouth with the paddle. But it kept slipping off, leaving him with almost nothing.

Mowgli put his bowl and paddle down with a frustrated sigh. Then, ever so slowly, he picked up the bowl a second time and lifted it right to his lips. Then he took a big gulp of soup, swallowing and smacking his lips.

The others stopped and stared yet again. Then the village elder nodded and lifted his bowl to his mouth and took a long sip, finishing with a lip-smack of his own. He smiled at Mowgli. Soon everyone was gulping the soup, slurping and smacking away.

Mowgli grinned. It looked as though he might fit in after all!

HERCULES

The New Neigh-bour

Pegasus grazed peacefully outside the house where Hercules and Meg lived. Now that Hercules was a mortal and not a god, life was a little quieter than it used to be. This morning, however, there was some excitement in the village. Some new neighbours were moving in.

"Let's go over and make them feel at home," Hercules told Meg. They gathered some flowers and headed over to meet them.

A little while later, Pegasus heard a soft whinnying. He turned to discover a beautiful mare approaching him. His heart soared. But then Pegasus remembered the time that Pain and Panic had disguised themselves as a filly and captured him. He was determined not to fall for their trick a second time. He spread his wings and charged, shooing the horse down the hill.

The mare raced past Meg and Herc as they returned home. "Pegasus, what are you doing?" asked Meg. "That's no way to make our neighbours' horse feel welcome." Pegasus gulped. The beautiful horse who had tried to meet him really *was* a beautiful horse!

"If I were you, I'd get over there and try and make it up to her," suggested Hercules.

Within minutes, Pegasus pranced across the neighbours' field, stopped in front of the mare and struck a noble pose. He doubted any filly would be able to resist a stallion as handsome as himself. The lovely horse was unimpressed. She turned so that her tail swished right in Pegasus's face! Herc's horse knew he would have to do something amazing to impress this beauty. He flapped his wings and rose into the air. Then he swooped and somersaulted across the sky. When the filly started to walk away, he flew alongside her – and crashed right into a tree!

Hercules was watching from the hillside. *Pegasus certainly does need some help*, he thought.

Meg had an idea. "The right gift might convince that mare to forgive him," she said. She piled a basket high with apples and oats and tied a huge red ribbon around it.

But, when Pegasus went over to deliver the gift, holding the basket handle in his teeth, the female horse kicked it over. Then the mare whinnied and stomped, letting Pegasus know exactly what she thought of him.

Finally, Pegasus realized what he had to do. He walked over to the filly with his head bowed and gently nudged her. She neighed and nuzzled him back. All she had wanted was for Pegasus to say he was sorry. Now she understood that even though he was a bit of a birdbrain, her new friend had a good heart.

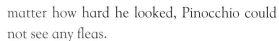

Imagine That!

The carnival was in town. Pinocchio grabbed his friend Jiminy Cricket and off they went. Pinocchio was amazed at all the marvellous sights. There were jugglers to see and games to play. He even saw an elephant doing tricks!

"That elephant is amazing!" Pinocchio cried.

"I suppose," said Jiminy.

Next they came to a lion's cage. The big cat opened his mouth and roared.

"Look at those teeth!" Pinocchio marvelled.

Jiminy Cricket nodded. "They're pretty big, that's for sure."

Then they saw a giraffe.

"What a long neck!" Pinocchio exclaimed.

"Giraffes are all right, I guess," said Jiminy with a shrug. Pinocchio was confused.

"If you don't like elephants, lions or giraffes, what kind of carnival animals do you like?" Pinocchio asked.

"Fleas," said Jiminy.

"Fleas?" Pinocchio said, even more confused.

"Come on! I'll show you," said Jiminy.

Jiminy led Pinocchio to a tent with a sign that read 'Flea Circus'.

Inside, Pinocchio saw a tiny merry-go-round and little swings. There were small animal cages and a little trapeze. There was even a tiny big top with three miniature rings. But no matter how hard he looked, Pinocchio could not see any fleas.

"That's because there *aren't* any fleas," Jiminy explained.

"What's the point, then?" Pinocchio asked.

"The point is to use your imagination," said Jiminy. "Why, you can do anything with your imagination. You can even see the fleas at the Flea Circus."

"But I don't see them," said Pinocchio, confused.

"You have to pretend to see the fleas, and pretty soon you can," said Jiminy. "Like that juggling flea over there. Oops, he dropped his juggling pins."

Pinocchio laughed and joined in the game.

"That flea is going to jump through a ring of fire," Pinocchio said. "I hope he makes it!"

"Now the fleas are doing acrobatics," Jiminy declared.

"They've made a flea pyramid And the flea on top is standing on his hands," said Pinocchio.

Finally, it was time to go home.

"What did you think of the Flea Circus?" asked Jiminy Cricket.

"It was the most amazing circus I ever saw, and I didn't really see it at all," Pinocchio replied, laughing.

"Yes, indeed. You imagined it," said Jiminy Cricket. "Imagine that!"

Buzz Off!

The toys were excited. Bonnie was going to the park with Woody, Jessie and Dolly. The others were looking forward to a day of fun, too. But Jessie was worried. "Keep an eye on Buzz," she told her friends. "I think he may have a loose wire."

Bonnie rushed in and grabbed her bag. "Buzz, you're in charge now," she said as she left.

The Peas-in-a-Pod started bouncing excitedly on their shelf. "Wait! This looks dangerous," said Buzz.

Just then, Slinky slipped from the shelf, causing the Aliens and peas to fall, too! They tumbled down on top of Buzz. He stood up and looked around. "*Donde esta mi nave?*" Buzz asked.

"Oh, great," Hamm sighed. "He's switched into Spanish mode again."

Rex tried to look in Buzz's back panel, but the space ranger dodged him! The toys tried to catch him, but Buzz grabbed a curtain from the doll's house and held it up like a bullfighter's cape. Hamm ran to tackle his friend, but he skidded and – *CRASH!* – Hamm slid right into the bookshelf and a book fell onto Buzz's head! After a moment, Buzz pushed the book away.

"Buzz, are you okay?" Rex cried.

"Buzz, are you okay?" Buzz repeated.

Hamm whispered to Buttercup, "He must have got knocked into Repeat Mode!"

The toys were worried. Jessie had asked them to take care of Buzz! They had to fix Buzz before Jessie and Bonnie returned.

"We're gonna have to jiggle his wires," Hamm sighed.

The toys pulled Buzz onto the bed, then Rex jumped. *Boing!* Buzz flew right off the bed and landed on the floor! Then the toys heard the car pull into the driveway.

"Hurry!" Hamm cried.

Rex undid Buzz's back panel and stared at the wires. He didn't know which one to fix!

There was a noise outside and the toys went limp just as Bonnie's mother walked in, put down Bonnie's bag and left again. Jessie climbed out. "Buzz, are you okay?" she asked.

"Oh, he's fine," Trixie propped Buzz into a sitting position. But he fell over with a *thunk*.

"It's not my fault!" Rex wailed. "There are too many wires!"

Jessie laughed, then she whacked Buzz on the back. Buzz blinked and looked at his friends. "Do I have something on my face?" he asked. The other toys sighed with relief – Buzz was back to normal!

Minutes later, Bonnie arrived. Everything was the way she had left it. "Thanks for looking after everyone, Buzz. I knew this place would be okay with you in charge!"

The Lazy Bulldozer

In the dead of night, when the tractors were snoozing in their field, Mater and Lightning McQueen creeped stealthily towards them.

"C'mon, Lightning," whispered Mater.

Lightning McQueen sighed. "Why do you always tease the tractors?"

"Because they're not bulldozers," Mater replied with a chuckle.

"What would you know about bulldozers?" Lightning wondered.

"All there is to know, pal," Mater insisted. "I used to be known as El Materdor, you know."

"Are you serious?" said Lightning, in awe.

Mater thought back to one of his fights, wearing his black matador hat. At the time, he wasn't so rusty and his paint shined with intricate patterns. "I was losing the crowd at a big event. They were booing me loudly."

"Tough crowd," said Lightning.

"Yup. They started demanding their money back and all because my bulldozer was half asleep in the arena ... even with that racket going on!"

"So what happened?" asked Lightning McQueen, curious.

"I stormed up to my bulldozer and told him to get a move on. Next thing I know, I'm choking on the exhaust fumes he's blasted in my face!"

Lightning laughed. "This is one funny story! At least I have nothing to do with it for once." Mater had a habit of including Lightning McQueen in his stories. As far as memories go, Mater had interesting ones ... but Lightning could never recall being a part of them, as much as Mater insisted they were true!

"I almost gave up, half asleep in the arena, until you showed up to help me!"

"Oh, right, of course," Lightning sighed.

"You performed an incredible handbrake turn that kicked a load of dust into the bulldozer's face, even though I warned you not to!" Mater said. "You see, bulldozers get cranky when roused all of a sudden."

"But we made a lucky escape, right?" Lightning McQueen pressed.

"Barely! It almost tore our bumpers off!" replied Mater. "That's why I like tractors. They're calmer."

"So why don't you do more exciting things like that now?" Lightning McQueen wondered.

"Oh ... this is exciting," Mater grinned.

Like a beast in the dark, Frank the combine flashed his headlights in the car's faces and kick-started his engine with a roar.

"See!" cried Mater.

But Lightning McQueen couldn't hear him. He was already racing for the hills.

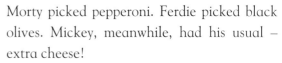

An Uncle Mickey Day

Morty and Ferdie Mouse were oh-so-very excited. Today was their number one favourite kind of day. It was an Uncle Mickey day! That meant their Uncle Mickey was going to take them out to do all kinds of special, surprising things.

"Uncle Mickey!" the twins called when he came to pick them up. "What are we doing today?"

"What *aren't* we doing today, you mean," said Mickey. "I thought we'd start with bowling."

"Hooray!" cheered Morty and Ferdie.

At the bowling alley, Morty and Ferdie discovered that if they rolled the bowling ball together, they could knock at least four or five pins down every time.

Then it was off to the park for some hide-and-seek and a game of catch. Uncle Mickey didn't mind being the finder in hide-and-seek every time. And he didn't mind chasing the balls that Ferdie sometimes threw way, way over his head.

"I'm hungry," said Morty when at last they stopped to rest.

"Me, too," said Ferdie.

"How about some pizza?" suggested Mickey.

"Okay!" the twins shouted together.

At the pizza parlour, Mickey let Morty and Ferdie choose their favourite toppings.

Morty picked pepperoni. Ferdie picked black olives. Mickey, meanwhile, had his usual – extra cheese!

"All finished?" asked Mickey. "We'll have to hurry if we're going to go to the carnival."

"All right!" the boys shouted eagerly.

After the carnival, where they each won a prize, the boys told Mickey what a great day it had been.

"Well, it's not over yet," Mickey told them.

"Really?" said Morty.

"What's next?" asked Ferdie excitedly.

That's when Mickey held up three tickets – and a mitt. A baseball game! Oh, wow!

There was nothing in the whole wide world that Mickey's nephews liked better than baseball games ... and popcorn ... and peanuts ... and ice cream. And to make things even better, Uncle Mickey caught a foul ball, and their favourite team won. They even watched fireworks at the end of the game.

"Wow, Uncle Mickey! Thank you so much!" said the twins when they finally returned home, tired and full and very, very happy. "This has been one of the best Uncle Mickey days ever!"

"Oh, this was nothing," said Uncle Mickey. "Just wait until next time!"

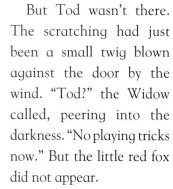

The Fox and the Hound

Late for Supper

Widow Tweed filled the large baking pan with meat and vegetables, then rolled out a flaky crust and set it on top. After crimping the pie's edges, she slipped the pan into the oven. "Chicken pie," she said. "Tod's favourite!"

Humming to herself, she washed the dishes in the sink and tidied up the cottage. Then, she set the table with her best tablecloth and dishes. She added a special milk saucer for Tod.

Widow Tweed looked out of the window and noticed that the sun was setting. "I wonder where that clever little devil has got to," she said.

She watched the sun sink behind the rolling forest hills, then sat down and picked up her knitting. She had a project to finish. Besides, the pie should be ready soon, and Tod was never late for supper.

"Knit one, purl two, knit one, purl two," the Widow said quietly as she put the finishing touches on a soft blanket she was knitting for Tod's bed. She knew the little fox had a fur coat of his own, but everybody liked something cosy to lie on when they curled up to go to sleep.

The smell of chicken pie drifted past her nose, and the Widow got up to take it out of the oven. The crust was golden brown, and the creamy sauce was bubbling around the edges.

She set it on the counter just as she heard a scratching at the door.

"Right on time, as usual," she said as she opened the door. "Dinner's ready, Tod."

But Tod wasn't there. The scratching had just been a small twig blown against the door by the wind. "Tod?" the Widow called, peering into the darkness. "No playing tricks now." But the little red fox did not appear.

The sky was dark now. A few clouds drifted across the moon. "Oh, Tod," she said. "Where are you?"

Stepping back into the house, she pulled on her shoes and a jumper. She'd just have to go out to look for him. After lighting an old kerosene lantern, she opened the door for a second time – and nearly tripped over the red fox on her front porch. He sat there quietly, a colourful bouquet of wild flowers at his feet.

"Oh, Tod!" she cried. She picked up the bouquet and scooped him into her arms. "You sweetie pie."

Tod nuzzled the Widow's neck as she carried him into the house and deposited him on his chair at the kitchen table. Soon, the two were sharing a delicious feast of chicken pie. And, after supper, the Widow admired her bouquet above the mantel while Tod curled up in his bed with his cosy new blanket.

Blackout's Blackout

Dusty was hanging out with his friends, the Smokejumpers. Blackout rolled past, looking for a can of oil he'd lost.

"Same ol' scatterbrain Blackout," Dusty chuckled to himself.

"Do you know how he got his nickname?" asked Dynamite.

Dusty had no idea, so Dynamite told him the full shocking story.

"An alarm had come in, worse than usual," Dynamite began. She explained a fire was raging through an area filled with electrical power lines. If the flames hit those cables it would be a disaster.

With no time to lose, the fire and rescue crew had raced into action. Little did they know, at the time, that there was an emergency at Fusel Lodge, too. The electricity supply was short-circuiting, and the fuse box was spraying sparks in all directions.

The lodge could go up in flames at any minute, but it was too dangerous for anyone to touch the fuses. They needed an expert, but they were all off tackling the blaze. There was nothing the staff could do but wait ... and hope.

Dusty listened intently as Dynamite continued her story. She told him how the Smokejumpers had made their jump and landed at the edge of the fire. The heat was intense, but they ignored it as they set about clearing the area.

"The fire mustn't reach the power lines," Dynamite told the team.

That was when Blackout spotted the flames edging closer to some bushes surrounding an electricity post. If the bushes caught fire, the wooden pole holding the wires up could quickly follow, which would bring down the whole area's electricity supply.

Blackout started cutting the bushes with his circular saw, but the flames closing in distracted him. His saw slipped, slicing through the electrical post. The pole toppled like a falling tree, and as it fell the tangled wires touched Blackout's metal frame.

He cried out in shock as a surge of power zapped through him. The jolt hurt, but worse than that, it made Blackout completely lose his memory!

That moment, over at Fusel Lodge, the fuse box stopped sparking. By bringing down the power lines, Blackout had cut the lodge's electricity, preventing a fire breaking out.

"Whoa! He's lucky to be alive," said Dusty, when Dynamite finished her story. "And at least he got his memory back."

They looked at their friend, still searching for his lost can of oil. "Sort of!" Dusty laughed.

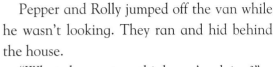

Special Delivery

Now that their family had grown so large, Roger, Anita, Nanny and the Dalmatians had moved to the country, or to the "Dalmatian Plantation", as Roger liked to call it. A weekly delivery of dog food came from the city. It arrived every Thursday at 3pm, and Rolly looked forward to it with eager anticipation.

One Thursday, Rolly and Pepper noticed that the back of the van had accidentally been left open. "Are you thinking what I'm thinking?" Pepper asked Rolly.

Rolly nodded. "Snack time!" Rolly and Pepper made a dash for the van and leaped into the back. Pepper clambered up onto the pile of bags and sniffed around. There had to be some loose food somewhere....

"Bingo!" Pepper cried. "Rolly, up here!"

Rolly was there in an instant.

Slurp, slurp, crunch! The two puppies were so busy eating that they didn't see the van driver come out of the house.

SLAM! He closed up the back of the van. A second later it was rumbling down the drive.

"Uh-oh," Rolly whispered.

Finally, after what seemed like a very long time, the vehicle lurched to a halt. The back door opened, and the driver began unloading bags of food.

Pepper and Rolly jumped off the van while he wasn't looking. They ran and hid behind the house.

"What do you two think you're doing?" a gruff voice asked.

The puppies spun round. A big bulldog was looking down at them. "This is my property," the dog said. "It is time for you to scram."

The two puppies stared at him.

"Now!" he barked.

"You don't scare me," Pepper said boldly. "You're not half as bad as Cruella."

The bulldog's mouth fell open. "Do you mean Cruella De Vil?" he asked. "You must be Pongo and Perdita's puppies! I heard about your adventures over the Twilight Bark! You live on the Dalmatian Plantation, right?"

"Yes!" cried Rolly. "Can you take us there?"

"You bet!" the bulldog said. "Let's go!"

Luckily, Pongo and Perdita were out that day and didn't realize what a pickle Rolly and Pepper had got themselves into. But there were 97 puppies waiting in the garden as Rolly and Pepper arrived with their escort.

"Wow," said Lucky, after Pepper and Rolly had told everyone their tale. "Were you scared of that big mean bulldog?"

"No way!" Pepper spoke up. "That bulldog was all bark and no bite!"

Piston Peak Party Time

The party for the reopening of the Fusel Lodge in Piston Peak National Park was in full swing. Dusty Crophopper and Lil' Dipper were called over by two elderly campervans who were guests at the lodge. They introduced themselves as Harvey and Winnie, and they said they needed a little help.

"We honeymooned here 50 years ago," Winnie told them. "And Harvey is trying to find the spot where we had our first kiss."

Harvey looked at a map of the park. "I'm telling you, there was a bridge and a magnificent waterfall," he said.

"That sounds like Augerin Canyon...." Dusty said. He'd been there training a few days before.

"That's right! Anger Canyon!" Harvey said, excitedly.

"It's over by Upper Whitewall Falls," Dusty continued.

"By Whitewash Falls!" Harvey exclaimed. "See? I told you I knew where it was!" His memory was clearly every bit as good as his hearing.

Later in the evening, Dusty and his new friends sat round a firepit outside, talking about their jobs.

"Maybe this firefighting thing will be a second career for you," Harvey said.

"Oh yeah," said Dipper, "this is a second career for all of us. Windlifter was a lumberjack, Cabbie was in the military and I hauled cargo."

When Dusty thought about it, he didn't think it was such a bad idea, but he wasn't ready to give up on his racing career.

The next morning, Dusty's old friend Skipper called him on the radio, waking him up. His friends back home in Propwash Junction had some disappointing news. The new gearbox they had found had arrived – but it was the wrong one.

"We've called every parts supplier, repair shop and junkyard in the country," said Chug sadly. "Nobody has your gearbox."

Dusty was overwhelmed with sadness. Maybe his racing career really was over.

But Dusty didn't have time to be upset for long. Moments later, Maru, the mechanic, burst into Dusty's hangar. There were two new wildfires burning in the park.

Blade gave the order to scramble the vehicles and, within minutes, Dusty and the rest of the air-attack firefighting team were airborne. Blade directed Windlifter and Dipper to the blaze to the west, while he and Dusty went east. That's when they saw that the fires were moving towards the Fusel Lodge!

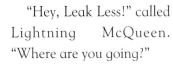

On Track Fun

The stadium boomed with applause and anticipation, as the crowd waited to see who would win and take the trophy?

"Lightning McQueen and Leak Less are engaged in a brilliant neck-and-neck duel!" the commentator's voice rang out. "Down the final stretch, it's still too close to call!"

The crowd were on the edge of their seats.

"Oh wait!" cried the commentator. Leak Less was having a spot of bother at the last minute. His wheel buckled at a jaunty angle, throwing him off-course. "Leak Less blows it big time and Lightning speeds on to victory!"

The crowd erupted in excitement and confetti fell from the sky. Lightning McQueen grinned from his first place podium with another beautiful, shiny trophy at his wheels.

"I was so close," groaned Leak Less from his second place stand. When the award ceremony ended, he wandered off, feeling embarrassed about what had happened on the track.

"Great race!" insisted his friend. "You almost beat Lightning McQueen."

"Huh?" said Leak Less. "Oh, right ... yeah."

"You said it, dude!" came a malicious bark. Chick Hicks rolled towards Leak Less. "You *almost* beat Lightning McQueen, but you're nowhere near as good." He laughed wickedly.

"There he is now. He'll want to come and tease you. He does that."

Leak Less panicked and started to drive away in a hurry.

"Hey, Leak Less!" called Lightning McQueen. "Where are you going?"

Leak Less wove between the cars in the car park, trying desperately to lose Lightning McQueen among them, but Lightning was just too quick and agile around corners.

"Hold on!" Lightning McQueen begged. "What's the matter?"

Leak Less turned to face him. "Now you're gonna tease me!"

Lightning McQueen was shocked. "Never!"

"But Chick Hick said –" Leak Less mumbled.

"Chick Hicks!" interrupted Lightning McQueen. "Now I know why you ran away. Chick's just jealous because he wanted to be on the podium! I haven't had that much fun in a long time," he told Leak Less, with a smile. "I came to invite you to celebrate with my friends."

Leak Less bloomed with happiness. "Wow!"

They celebrated together deep into the night, laughing and sharing oil-shakes and retelling their favourite races ... and all the while Chick Hicks skulked in the shadows. If he wasn't always so mean, he could have been having fun, too!

Disney
DUMBO
Dumbo's Daring Rescue

Dumbo stood on his platform high above the floor of the circus Big Top. Below him, the clowns looked the same size as peanuts. He could hear them calling for him to jump.

"All right, kid. You're on," Timothy said, from the brim of Dumbo's hat.

Dumbo was ready. He knew what he had to do because he did the same thing every night. When the firefighter clowns called, Dumbo would leap from the platform and plummet towards the ground. Then, at the last possible moment, Dumbo would spread his

tremendous ears and fly. The audience would cheer. And the show would be over.

"Hey, kid, that's your cue!" Timothy squeaked in Dumbo's ear.

Taking a step forward, Dumbo began to fall. He sped faster and faster towards the floor of the tent. The audience swam into view. They were screaming and laughing. Then, all of a sudden, Dumbo saw something else.

There, in the first row, was a little girl sitting all by herself. She was crying and holding on to a stick of candyfloss.

In an instant, the little elephant forgot all about the act. Spreading his ears, he swooped away from the shouting clowns. He scanned the seats intently. Why was the girl all alone? Where were her parents?

"Dumbo! What are you doing?" Timothy clung to Dumbo's hat as he soared towards the peanut and popcorn sellers. "We don't have time for a snack now!"

Dumbo ignored his friend. The little girl needed their help!

At last, Dumbo spotted what he was looking for.

There, standing next to the candyfloss stall, were two very worried-looking parents.

"Clara, where are you?" the father called. His voice was lost in the noise of the crowd – his daughter would never hear him calling!

Dumbo circled the tent again, turning back towards the bench where the little girl sat sobbing. How could he tell her that her parents were looking for her? He had to bring them together. Swooping low, Dumbo stretched out his trunk and scooped up the little girl.

"Dumbo, what are you doing?" Timothy cried again.

Dumbo sailed back and placed the girl gently beside her parents.

Immediately, the little girl's tears were dried. She was safe in her parents' arms!

The crowd went wild as Dumbo soared high over the arena. Even the clowns were smiling.

"Nice work, kid," Timothy said, patting Dumbo's head. "Good show."

A Whale of a Tale

"Hop aboard, explorers!" called Mr Ray. Nemo, Tad and the rest of the class jumped on the back of the big manta ray. It was 'special guest' week and they were going to the Drop-off.

When they reached the reef's edge, a royal-blue tang fish swam up to meet them.

"And here is today's special guest," Mr Ray announced.

"Hello, everyone," said the blue tang. "I'm Dory ... um ... am I? Yes! Just kidding! I'm Dory, and I'm very happy to be here!"

"Dory, can you teach us something about whales today?" asked Mr Ray.

"Well, let's see ... whales are very big, but they eat little creatures called krill. And I should know. One whale I met *almost* ate me –"

"So it's not true!" blurted Tad.

"What's not true?" Dory asked.

"Sandy Plankton said Nemo made up that story about how you and Nemo's dad got eaten by a whale!" said Tad.

"I did not make it up!" cried Nemo.

"Well," said Dory, "technically, Sandy Plankton is right. We weren't actually *eaten* by the whale –"

Tad smirked, until Dory added, "We were just in the whale's mouth for a mighty long time!"

"Whoa!" said the class. They were quite impressed. Tad frowned.

"You see, the whale was just giving us a ride to Sydney. I find if you talk to a whale beforehand, it clears up most ingestion issues," Dory explained.

"Excellent lesson!" said Mr Ray. "Now teach us a few words in whale."

"Oh, okay," said Dory. "Now repeat after me. Haaaaavve aaaaaaaaaa nnnniiiiiice daaaaayyyy!"

"Haaaavve aaaaaa nnnniiiiice daaaayy!" the class repeated.

"Very good!" said Dory.

"This is stupid," said Tad. "You didn't...."

Suddenly, Tad stopped talking. Everyone just stared at Dory in horror.

Slowly, Dory turned around. A blue whale was right behind her!

Dory simply shrugged and told the whale, "Weeeee weerrrrre juuuuuuuuusssst praaaaactisinnnng!"

With a loud bellow, the whale wished her a nice day anyway, then swam off.

"So, Tad, do you believe Dory now?" asked Nemo.

"Wow, that was *so* cool!" cried Tad. "I can't wait to tell Sandy Plankton how I was almost eaten by a whale!"

Nemo and Dory just sighed.

A Silo Scare

Flik took a step back and gazed up at the giant silo he and a troop of ants had just finished building. Now that the colony was using his harvester, they had a lot of wheat. The silo would store the wheat safely.

"Nice job, Flik," Queen Atta said.

Flik blushed bright red. A compliment from Atta always made his face feel warm. Atta was the smartest and prettiest ant in the colony. She was also its new queen.

"Thanks, Atta," Flik said, trying to sound casual. "It should keep our wheat dry all winter."

Suddenly, a voice called down from the top of the silo. "Hellooooo," it said.

Flik and Atta looked up. It was Dot, Atta's little sister. She and her Blueberry friends were sitting on top of the silo.

"The view up here is amazing!" Dot called.

"Dot! Be careful!" Atta said worriedly.

Dot grinned down at her sister. "We will!"

"Don't worry," said Flik reassuringly. "I built in several safety –"

Atta interrupted him. "I have a meeting," she told Flik. "Stay out of trouble," she added in a louder voice. For a second Flik thought Atta was talking to him. Then he realized that she was talking to the Blueberries.

"I'll keep an eye on them," Flik said.

"Come on up, Flik," Dot called as Atta hurried away. "You just have to see the view!"

"Coming!" Flik replied. He did want to see the view, and he also wanted to keep a close eye on the Blueberries.

But, just as Flik got to the top, one of the Blueberries leaped into the silo.

"Wheee!" she cried as she zoomed down towards the pile of wheat.

"The silo is not a playground," Flik told the other girls. "It's for storing wheat, and I built in all these extra safety devices –"

"Come on, Flik," Dot interrupted. "We don't need any safety devices!"

Grinning, she jumped into the silo and slid to the pile of wheat at the bottom. Two other Blueberries followed. But then – *whoops!* – another Blueberry accidentally pushed down a lever. A big pile of wheat tumbled into the silo, heading straight for the Blueberries below!

Panicked, Flik hit a switch. The falling wheat was caught halfway down by a handy-dandy wheat stopper – one of the safety devices he'd built into the silo.

The Blueberries stared at Flik. Just then, Atta walked by. "Dot, what are you doing?" she asked.

"Uh, Flik was just showing us his great safety devices," Dot said sheepishly.

"And they really work," said Flik, relieved.

Disney
THE
LION KING

Hakuna Matata

"Why are you so sad?" Pumbaa asked Nala.

"I'm not sad," Nala said. "I'm just a little more on the serious side than the two of you."

"I think you could use a little *hakuna matata*," Pumbaa said.

"A whona mawhatta?" Nala asked.

"You really think she can handle it?" Timon whispered to Pumbaa out of the side of his mouth.

"Of course I can handle it!" Nala said, raising her voice. "I just need to know what it is first."

"Ahhhh, *hakuna matata*," Pumbaa said dreamily. "It's the problem-free way of dealing with all of life's inconveniences."

"It means, 'No worries'," Timon explained.

"Oh, I get it," Nala said. "Instead of dealing with your problems, you just ignore them and pretend they don't exist."

"*Hakuna matata* helps you relax," Pumbaa tried to point out.

"It sounds like your *hakuna matata* is just another way of saying 'uninspired and lazy'," Nala continued.

"I think she might have just insulted us," Timon whispered to Pumbaa.

"There you are," Simba called as he came walking towards them. "What are the three of you up to?"

"I was just learning about a strange little notion called *hakuna matata*," Nala explained.

"Isn't it great!" Simba said with a grin.

"Well, sure," Nala said. "If you don't ever want to get anything done."

Simba frowned. "It's not like that. *Hakuna matata* will help you get through things."

"Sure," Nala continued. "*Hakuna matata* – I don't have to worry. I don't have to try."

"I guess you could look at it that way," Simba said. "But, for me, it means, 'Don't worry about it right now. It's okay.' It gives me the strength to get through the bad times."

"Wow, I hadn't thought about it like that," Nala said.

"So, are you ready to join us now?" Timon asked.

"Absolutely!" Nala smiled.

"Then bring on the crunchy beetles!" shouted Pumbaa.

"And let's go tease some elephants!" cried Timon.

"Everyone to the mud hole for a mud fight!" Simba yelled, and the three of them started off.

"Oh, dear," murmured Nala, "this isn't exactly what I had in mind." But she smiled, and ran after her carefree friends. "Last one to the mud hole is a rotten egg!" she cried.

Disney · PIXAR

TOY STORY

A Pea Problem

The Peas-in-a-Pod were having fun bouncing around Bonnie's room, chasing after each other and laughing.

Buzz and Woody were having almost as much fun watching them, when Woody noticed one of the peas was missing! Then something suddenly landed on Woody's head.

BOING!

"There she is," laughed Buzz, as the pea landed in front of them.

Woody turned to the pea. "You should be more careful about where you bounce, Peatrice," he said, rubbing his head. The pea looked upset.

"I'm Peanelope!" she corrected him. The other peas landed either side of Peanelope, looking equally upset.

"You keep getting our names wrong!" one of them complained.

"Yeah! It's so annoying," added another.

"Huh? I'm sorry," Woody apologized. "But you look so similar...."

"It's not fair!" said one pea, turning to another. "I can't help looking exactly like you."

Buzz overheard the peas talking and wanted to help. "Can I tell you a story?" he asked.

The peas were happy to have something to distract them, but Woody wasn't sure it was the best thing to do. "Maybe we should apologize," he suggested.

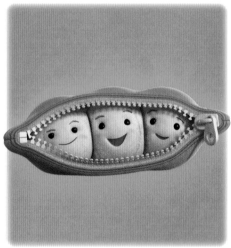

"Don't worry!" replied Buzz. "I've got a plan."

When the peas were settled in front of him, Buzz began his story. "I was exploring the dangerous planet Zurg. It seemed to be deserted ... But suddenly I heard a strange humming. In a minute, I found myself surrounded by Emperor Zurg's army of robots!" The peas gasped!

Buzz continued. "They kept humming and closing in around me – they wanted to capture me! But then I heard a different noise ... it sounded like singing! The Zurgrobots didn't like the sound of that so they ran away. I realized it was another Zurgrobot making that noise. It turned out that this zurgrobot, who was called Zenny, didn't like humming and so he saved me! You see, even though Zenny looked exactly like the other zurgrobots –"

"– he was different from them!" finished Woody, with a cheer.

"You, too!" Buzz said to the Peas-in-a-Pod. "You look the same, but each of you is unique!"

"And we know it even though we get your names wrong!" Woody added.

The peas looked pleased. "Wow! You're great guys," they smiled.

Happy in the knowledge that even though they all looked the same, each pea was different, they bounced off to play some more.

THE INCREDIBLES

Supers to the Rescue

Bob Parr – aka Mr Incredible – had become bored of pretending to be normal, and had secretly taken up superhero work again. He'd kept this secret from his wife, Helen, and had ended up as a prisoner on the island of Nomanisan – owned by Syndrome, who was Mr Incredible's ex-number-one fan, Buddy.

Buddy had turned himself into a Super by building machines and an Omnidroid robot, which only he could defeat. Helen had discovered where her husband was, and she knew the only way to help him was to become Elastigirl once more.

Elastigirl followed the homing signal on Mr Incredible's suit in a borrowed jet. She soon found that her Super children, Violet and Dash, had left Jack-Jack at home with a babysitter and stowed away on the jet! They had found the Super suits that Edna Mode had made for them!

As they approached the island, missiles attacked the jet. Elastigirl told Violet to create a force field around the plane. But Violet didn't think she could make one that big.

In his prison cell, Mr Incredible listened to the attack on his family with horror. "Target destroyed," came a voice from a speaker.

"You'll get over it," Syndrome sneered.

A desperate Mr Incredible grabbed hold of Syndrome's assistant, Mirage. "Release me now, or I'll crush her!" he said.

"Go ahead," said Syndrome. He knew that Mr Incredible could never do such a thing. Defeated, the hero let Mirage go.

But Mr Incredible's family was still alive. Elastigirl had stretched herself around Violet and Dash to protect them, just as the missile blew the jet out of the sky. Then she had made herself into a parachute and floated, with her children, down to the water below.

Elastigirl stretched into the shape of a boat, while Dash pushed her and Violet to shore by kicking his speedy legs. They soon found safety in a cave.

"I'm going to look for your father," Elastigirl told her children. "If anything goes wrong, use your powers ... when the time comes, you'll know what to do."

After Helen left, the cave suddenly filled with a huge ball of fire. Dash and Violet fled – they only just escaped! The fire was the rocket exhaust from Syndrome's base. He had launched the Omnidroid towards the city!

The Parr family were going to have to use all their Super strength to save the city, and each other, from Syndrome.

Mater Private Eye

Lightning McQueen drove up to the air pump. "My tyres are going flat."

Just then, Mater popped out of nowhere. "Flat tyres, ya say? I thought I solved that crime. I was a private eye," Mater explained. Then he told his friend about his detective days. "It was a Friday night...." he began.

Mater sat behind the desk in his office reading an article about accidents caused by tyres blowing out. "I was on to something big," Mater explained. "There was a counterfeit tyre ring."

A car named Tia drove in. "I need you to find my sister, Mia," cried Tia. "She's been carnapped! She was last seen working at Big D's club, The Carpacabana."

Big D was a sedan who had recently opened a nightclub. That night, Mater went to the club. A singer was performing. After her song, she came to Mater's table. "I'm looking for Mia. Have you seen her?" Mater asked.

"I saw her a couple of days ago with Big D. She smelled salty, like the ocean," the singer said. But before he could find out any more, Mater was thrown out of the club.

Luckily, a friendly rubbish truck gave Mater a clue that led him to the docks. There, he saw Mia on the deck of a huge cargo ship! Mater tried to sneak onto the boat to rescue her, but he was spotted! Then Big D rolled out. A crane grabbed Mater and hoisted him up.

Just then, Tia rushed forwards. She had told Big D that Mater would be coming to the docks. Tia explained it was the only way to save her sister. The crane held Mater over the water.

Back in Radiator Springs, Lightning was on the edge of his bumper. "What did you do?"

Mater laughed aloud. "Like you don't know, Lieutenant McQueen!"

Then Mater continued his tale. Police Lieutenant Lightning McQueen drove onto the docks with a group of squad cars. "Looks like we caught you, Big D," he said. But Big D's workers pushed barrels down a ramp to keep the police away. Meanwhile, Tia hit a switch on the crane and it lowered Mater to the ground. Mater threw his tow hook at another crane, which dropped its crate – right on Big D! The crate split open, and tyres spilled all over Big D.

"Aha! Just what I thought – counterfeit tyres," Mater said. Big D had been swapping good tyres for fake ones. It was his fault there had been so many car accidents lately. Now that Mater had uncovered Big D's scam, the police stepped in.

"You led us right to him, Mater," Lightning announced gratefully. "Take him away, boys!"

Disney
Lady and the TRAMP

Like Father, Like Son

Tramp had a whole new life. He had gone from being a stray to becoming a member of the Dear household. And now, he and Lady were proud parents.

But Tramp was finding it difficult to change some of his old ways.

"Tramp," Lady said gently, "you need to set an example for the puppies – especially Scamp."

Scamp had an adventurous side, just like his dad. So, it wasn't surprising that father and son often got carried away when they played together. They couldn't resist the urge to roll in a puddle of mud – and then chase each other across the clean kitchen floor.

Soon, Aunt Sarah and her two troublesome cats, Si and Am, were going to be visiting. Lady was worried.

"Don't worry. I promise to keep Scamp away from those troublemakers," Tramp said.

"And?" replied Lady.

"And I promise to stay away from them, too," Tramp added.

When the big day came, Lady and Tramp herded their pups into a bedroom and told them to stay put. But Scamp was curious. He slipped out of the room and hid behind the living room settee. Then he sneaked up behind the cats and swiped at their tails as they flicked back and forth. The cats turned and chased Scamp over the settee, under a table and into a cupboard.

Well, Tramp thought, *I suppose I'm going to have to chase those nasty old cats whether I want to or not!*

He enthusiastically dived into the cupboard. Seconds later, Tramp and Scamp emerged. Much to Aunt Sarah's horror, Si and Am were later found inside, tied together with a scarf. When no one was looking, Tramp and Scamp shared a victory wink.

Tramp and Scamp were banished to the garden for their antics. When Lady came out that evening, she found that they had dug up the entire garden looking for bones. Father and son saw the look on Lady's face and knew that they were about to get a lecture.

Tramp looked at Lady innocently. "You want him to get exercise, don't you?" he asked.

"Try it, Mum!" Scamp cried. "It's fun."

"What am I going to do with you two?" Lady said, laughing.

Tramp and Scamp dragged a huge bone out from behind the kennel.

"Join us for dinner?" Tramp replied.

"Well, all right," Lady said. "But, as soon as we're done, we're cleaning up this yard."

"Yes, ma'am!" chorused Tramp and Scamp, looking very pleased with themselves.

Disney · PIXAR
THE INCREDIBLES

Trick or Treat

It was Halloween, and Dash was dressed up as a terrifying sea creature, complete with scary mask. He paced the floor impatiently. He wasn't allowed to go out trick or treating until his dad got home, and his dad was working late.

"Can't you take me?" he asked his mum, but she had her hands full with Jack-Jack. Helen did know someone else who could take Dash out, though.

Violet grumbled as she trudged along behind Dash. He was halfway through warning her for the tenth time not to try stealing any of his sweets, when they heard a gentle sobbing.

Looking around, they soon saw three younger children sitting on the kerb, crying over their empty sacks. The boys were all in costume, and took off their masks as Dash and Violet approached.

The boys explained that two ghosts had swooped past them and stolen all their sweets. Dash began to bounce around excitedly. He'd never seen a real ghost before, and wanted to race off to find them.

"Ghost don't exist," Violet said, but after children said the spooks had floated off towards the park, she decided to go and investigate.

In the park, Dash and Violet heard the sound of cackling, and ducked behind a bush. They peeked through the leaves and saw two much bigger boys wearing scary ghost costumes. They were eating sweets, and laughing about how they'd stolen them from the little kids.

"They're just a couple of bullies," Dash whispered.

Violet nodded in agreement. The bullies had to be taught a lesson, and she knew just how to do it. She leaned closer to Dash and began to whisper, "I've got an idea...."

Moments later, Dash ran out of the bushes, wearing his normal clothes. "Help, help!" he cried, being careful not to run at Super speed as he darted past the bullies. "There's a monster after me!"

The bullies frowned. Someone was copying their idea of scaring the little kids, and they were not happy about it.

Marching into the trees, the bullies spotted the sea creature costume approaching. "Take off the mask!" they growled. "We aren't afraid of you."

Slowly, the monster lifted up the mask. The bullies gripped each other with fear when they saw there was no head underneath! Crying, they ran off, just as Violet turned visible again. She and Dash picked up the sweets and returned them to the little boys.

Violet smiled. Halloween had turned out to be super, after all.

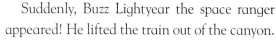

Wild West Showdown

A train rumbled across the desert. Suddenly, the roof exploded and the outlaw One-Eyed Bart climbed out, carrying bags of stolen money. Luckily, Sheriff Woody was there to stop him!

"You've got a date with justice, One-Eyed Bart!" cried the sheriff.

"Ai-ai-yah!" came a cry from behind Woody. It was One-Eyed Betty, One-Eyed Bart's karate-chopping wife! She knocked Woody right off the train.

Suddenly, Jessie the cowgirl came speeding up on her trusty steed, Bullseye. They saved Woody just in time!

But One-Eyed Bart wouldn't be stopped that easily. He pulled out a detonator and blew up a bridge across a giant canyon. Bart and Betty jumped into their getaway car.

"It's me or the kiddies!" yelled One-Eyed Bart. "Take your pick!"

As the outlaws sped away, Jessie saw that the train was filled with orphans – and it was heading right towards the broken bridge! Woody had to save the orphans before going after One-Eyed Bart.

Woody rode Bullseye and leaped onto the engine. He quickly found the brake. The train came to a screeching halt – but not soon enough. It plunged into the canyon with Woody and the orphans still on board!

Suddenly, Buzz Lightyear the space ranger appeared! He lifted the train out of the canyon.

"Glad you could catch the train, Buzz!" shouted Woody.

Jessie cheered as Buzz carried the train to safety. Next, Buzz used his laser to slice One-Eyed Bart's getaway car in two. Suddenly, a giant dog with a metal coil for a body surrounded the outlaws.

"You can't touch me, Sheriff!" shouted One-Eyed Bart. Suddenly, a giant shadow appeared overhead. A pig-shaped spaceship beamed One-Eyed Bart, One-Eyed Betty and their sidekicks to safety.

"Evil Dr Porkchop!" cried Woody.

"That's *Mister* evil Dr Porkchop to you!" yelled the villain. With a wicked laugh, Dr Porkchop dropped an army of vicious monkeys onto Woody, Jessie and Buzz.

"Buzz!" shouted Woody. "Shoot your laser at my badge!"

Buzz aimed his laser beam at Woody's badge and fired. The beam bounced off the badge and hit Dr Porkchop's spaceship.

BOOM!

Soon the villains were all tied up and ready to go to jail.

"Good job, deputies!" Woody shouted. The sheriff and his friends had saved the day again!

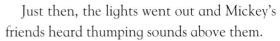

Mickey's Spooky Night

Mickey glanced at the clock. "Oh, gosh! I need to get ready for my Halloween party. Where did I put that old pirate costume?"

As Mickey went upstairs to the dark attic, lightning flashed and thunder crashed outside.

He went over to an old trunk. He brushed off the dust, turned the key in the lock, opened the trunk ... and a skeleton popped out!

"Agh!" Mickey jumped back. Then he realized it was just a plastic party decoration. "Phew!"

Mickey rummaged around. "This is a lot of cool Halloween stuff! I'll take it all downstairs."

Meanwhile, Pluto was chasing a ball in the garden. As he charged under the clothesline, one of the sheets came loose and fell on him. It covered him from head to tail and he couldn't see to find his doggy door!

Suddenly, it started raining and the wet sheet stuck to Pluto like glue. He ran all over the garden, but he couldn't shake it off.

At the front of the house, Donald, Goofy, Minnie and Daisy pulled up in their car.

"Look at the lightning!" said Goofy.

Daisy giggled nervously. "It's very spooky."

Mickey's friends hurried inside. "Mickey, we're here!"

But there was no answer. Mickey was still upstairs and couldn't hear them.

Just then, the lights went out and Mickey's friends heard thumping sounds above them.

Minnie gasped. "What was that?" It sounded like a big, heavy object was being dragged across the floor upstairs.

Suddenly something white ran past the window. Mickey's friends were too scared even to scream!

By now, Mickey was heading downstairs in his costume, carrying the skeleton. His friends looked up to see a horrible monster coming towards them.

Suddenly, the lights came back on. "Gosh, hiya, gang," said Mickey.

Minnie smiled. "Mickey! You scared us!"

Daisy sighed and said, "Mickey, this is the scariest, most exciting Halloween ever!"

"Yeah, Mickey, it's the best haunted house I've ever been in," Donald agreed.

"Uh – haunted house?" A puzzled Mickey looked around.

Just then, Pluto found his way in through the doggy door. He ran into the living room. Mickey and his friends looked up and saw – a ghost!

Then Mickey looked again. "Oh, Pluto! It's just you! Let's get you dried off!"

Mickey dried Pluto with a towel and smiled at his friends. "With all of these ghosts, shadows and noises, this is the scariest Halloween ever!"

Disney
The Fox and the Hound
Wild Life

Tod the fox had just arrived at the nature reserve, a vast, beautiful forest where wild animals were protected from hunters. Widow Tweed had brought him there to keep him safe, since her next-door neighbour, Amos Slade, had vowed to hunt him. Amos was angry with the fox because his beloved dog, Chief, had been injured while chasing after him.

At first, Tod didn't understand why his kind owner, Widow Tweed, had left him in the middle of this strange forest, alone and afraid. But she had seemed to be as sad about leaving him as he was about being abandoned.

The first night was dreadful. It had poured with rain and, although he tried to find shelter in different hollows and caves, they were always inhabited by other animals. There was no room for the poor, wet little fox. But the next morning, things began to look up. Tod met a pretty young fox named Vixey. She showed him around the forest, which had many beautiful waterfalls and streams full of fish.

"I think I'm going to like it here, Vixey," said Tod. Having lived his whole life with the Widow Tweed, he had never met another fox before, least of all one as lovely as Vixey.

But Vixey had lived the life of a wild fox, and she knew more about the world than Tod.

"You must be very careful, Tod," she warned. "Remember, we're foxes, and we have many enemies. You must always be on the alert for danger!"

"Come on, Vixey," scoffed Tod. "We're in a game reserve! I heard the Widow Tweed say that there's no hunting allowed in this forest. What could possibly happen to us here? We don't have a care in the world!"

Suddenly, a huge shadow fell over the two foxes. A look of great fear crossed Vixey's face. Turning around slowly and cautiously, Tod saw why. A huge bear was standing up on its hind legs. And it was staring straight at them!

"*Grrrr!*" the bear growled.

"Run!" yelled Vixey.

Tod didn't need to be told twice. The two foxes dashed away from the bear, scampering over hills, racing through a hollow tree and jumping over a narrow stream. When they were well away from the bear, they stopped and leaned against a rock, panting hard.

"Okay," Tod said, when he had caught his breath a bit. "I see what you mean about the dangers, Vixey. From now on, I'll be a lot more careful."

"Mmm-hmm," she replied. Then she smiled. "Come on," she said to Tod. "Let's go fishing!"

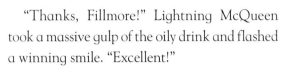

Secret Fuel

Lightning McQueen was feeling glum.

"How's it goin', soldier?" asked Sarge.

Lightning McQueen glanced at the crowd nearby. They were inching closer, matching every move their hero made.

"These fans won't give me any rest, Sarge," he sighed. "They all want to learn my secret for success."

"What did you tell them?" asked Fillmore. "I think they should consider yoga!"

His friends smiled warmly but Lightning McQueen remained sad.

"Or," Fillmore added, "they could try a sip of my home-made organic motor oil?"

Lightning McQueen thought deeply. "Actually ... what about the new bio-fuel you've been working on?"

"The new fuel ... well ... it has its drawbacks," Fillmore warned.

Lightning McQueen looked at his fans. "Really?" he said mischievously. "Interesting...."

With a staggering burst of speed, he took off. "Let's go! I want to try the new bio-fuel!"

His friends quickly followed in pursuit.

"I still have to make a few adjustments to the bio-fuel...." Fillmore explained.

"Don't worry!" Lightning McQueen insisted. "I'm a race car. I can handle anything!"

When they arrived, Fillmore nudged an oilcan over. "Here it is, Lightning. Drink up!"

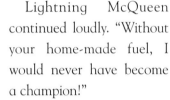

"Thanks, Fillmore!" Lightning McQueen took a massive gulp of the oily drink and flashed a winning smile. "Excellent!"

Fillmore was surprised.

Lightning McQueen continued loudly. "Without your home-made fuel, I would never have become a champion!"

"You're joking, right? You usually don't even drink –" Fillmore began to say, but was interrupted.

"Hear that!" yelled the fans in the distance. "That's McQueen's secret!" They rushed over on eager wheels.

"I want a sip of your new bio-fuel!" said one.

"Me, too!" cried another.

The fuel was guzzled down.

"Now we can be as fast as Lightning McQueen!" they shouted.

But then the thirsty fans started groaning. Smoke puffed from their pipes in black bursts.

"We need a mechanic!" they bellowed.

The cars sped off in a cloud of dust, with their poorly engines growling.

"They'll be happy now!" Lightning McQueen laughed. "They're racing like real champions!"

"It's odd though...." said Sally suspiciously. "Why didn't the bio-fuel bother you?"

"Because I only pretended to drink it!" he confessed, chuckling.

At last, he got some peace and quiet.

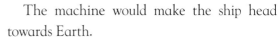

DISNEP · PIXAR
WALL·E
Finally Home

On the Axiom, the ship where all the humans now lived, little robot EVE delivered a special plant from Earth to the Captain. EVE had found it among the treasures of a robot called WALL·E.

The Captain was overjoyed, because this plant meant that he and all the humans could return to Earth. But the Captain's robot, AUTO, wouldn't let them. Quickly, it snatched the plant and dumped it down the rubbish chute.

The plant hit WALL·E. The little bot was climbing up to get to EVE! Happily he delivered the plant right back to her. But AUTO electrocuted WALL·E and sent him back down the chute with EVE.

WALL·E and EVE ended up in the ship's rubbish bay. EVE rescued the injured little bot while WALL·E tried to give her the plant. He still thought she wanted it more than anything else. But WALL·E was wrong. EVE just wanted to help WALL·E now.

Soon EVE flew them up and out of the rubbish bay, with the plant in hand. She wanted to get WALL·E home to Earth so she could find the right parts to fix him.

The Captain was fighting AUTO for control of the ship by now. He sent a message to EVE, telling her to take the plant to a large machine called the holo-detector.

The machine would make the ship head towards Earth.

The Captain finally managed to turn off the bad robot's power. EVE fought to reach the holo-detector. At last she put the plant inside the machine. Finally they could return to Earth.

But all was not well. WALL·E had been crushed by the giant machine! Heartbroken and more determined than before, EVE wanted to take WALL·E home to his truck, where she could find the right parts to bring him back to life. As soon as the Axiom landed on Earth, EVE headed straight for WALL·E's home and repaired him. At last, he powered up ... and began cubing trash. Something was wrong. He was just another trash-cubing robot. All the love was gone. He didn't even recognize EVE!

Sadly, EVE held WALL·E's hand and leaned towards him. An electric arc passed between their heads – the robot kiss. She was saying goodbye. Then ... WALL·E's hand began to move. EVE looked into his eyes. He was coming back to life! He recognized her!

"EVE?" he said. After following EVE across the universe, WALL·E had ended up right where he had started – home. But this time he had the one thing he truly wanted – EVE's hand clasped in his own.

The Four-legged Festival

Quasimodo was a kind young man who was always quick to offer help to anyone in need. He was especially drawn to those who were alone in the world. After spending years confined to the bell tower of the cathedral, Quasimodo knew just how terrible loneliness could feel.

It wasn't surprising, then, that Quasimodo had a growing collection of orphaned animals. First he had taken in a stray kitten, and then an abandoned puppy. Next he adopted a lamb, an old donkey, a baby bird and an ox. Esmeralda and Phoebus helped him build a pen to keep them in. But they weren't sure how he could afford to continue feeding so many pets.

"I'll find a way – somehow," Quasimodo told the couple, trying to reassure them. "They're counting on me!"

The Festival of Fools was coming up, and Quasimodo was a little worried about how his pets would react to all the noise and excitement. "While you're helping Clopin with his puppet show at the festival," said Esmeralda, "why don't we have Djali keep an eye on the animals?" Djali was Esmeralda's clever little goat. He was used to crowds, and often danced with Esmeralda in the village square.

"Why, thank you, Esmeralda!" replied Quasimodo. "That's a wonderful idea."

The day of the festival arrived. Esmeralda brought Djali and put him inside the pen with the other animals. The square quickly filled with people wearing costumes and masks. Delicious smells drifted through the air from the sellers' stands. The animals pushed at the sides of the pen, wanting to investigate the new smells and sounds. Djali also wanted to join in the fun. He nibbled at the latch of the pen and the gate flew open.

Djali heard the tinkling of Esmeralda's tambourine on the far side of the square and ran towards the sound. The other animals followed – even as the goat crashed through a stall full of masks for sale!

Everyone turned to see the animals, which were now disguised as jesters and kings, songbirds and queens. The masked animals danced right past Clopin's puppet wagon and onto Esmeralda's stage. Quasimodo watched in amazement as Djali and the others joined in the gypsy's merry dance. The crowds cheered and showered the performers with coins.

When the show ended, Esmeralda climbed down from the stage and delivered the money to Quasimodo. "This should take care of whatever food you need to buy," she said happily.

Quasimodo felt like dancing for joy – but he decided to leave that to the animals!

Bambi

First Frost

Slowly, Bambi opened his eyes. Curled up next to his mother, he was toasty-warm in the thicket. Bambi blinked sleepily, peering past the brambles. Something was different. The forest did not look the same. The air was crisp and cold, and everything he could see was frosted and sparkling.

"Jack Frost has been," his mother explained. "He's painted the whole forest with ice crystals."

Bambi was about to ask his mother who Jack Frost was, and how he painted with ice, when he heard another voice, an impatient one.

"Get up! Get up! Come look at the frost!" It was Thumper. He tapped his foot impatiently. "We haven't got all day!"

Bambi stood and looked at his mother. When she nodded approvingly, he scampered out of the thicket. Bambi looked closely at the colourful leaves on the ground. Each one was covered in an icy-white pattern. He touched his nose to a big orange oak leaf. "Ooh, it's cold!" he cried.

"Of course it is!" Thumper laughed.

"I think it's beautiful," said Faline, as she stepped into the clearing.

"Me too," Bambi agreed.

"Come look at this!" Thumper hopped away and the two young deer followed, admiring the way the sun sparkled on the frost-covered trees and grass.

Thumper disappeared under a bush. Then Bambi heard a new noise. *CREAK, CRACK.*

Faline pushed through the bushes with Bambi right behind her. There was Thumper, cracking the thin ice on a puddle with his feet.

Bambi had never seen ice before. He pushed on the thin layer of ice covering the puddle with his hoof. It seemed to bend. Then it suddenly shattered!

Soon the three friends were stomping on the ice-covered puddles. When all the ice was broken, Faline had an idea. "Let's go to the meadow!"

Bambi thought that was a great idea. The grass would be sparkling! They set out at a run, bounding and racing each other through the forest. But when they got to the meadow's edge, they all stopped.

They looked, sniffed and listened quietly. They did not sense danger – no, the trouble was that in the meadow, nothing was different. There was no frost.

"What happened?" Bambi asked.

"Frost never lasts long," Thumper explained. "It melts as soon as the sun hits it. But don't worry. Winter is coming, and soon we'll have something even better than frost. We'll have snow!"

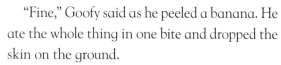

A Wonderful/Terrible Day

"What a wonderful day!" Mickey Mouse said to himself. He hummed as he strolled through the outdoor market. The air was crisp. The leaves were pretty shades of red, yellow and orange. And the perfect hunk of cheese was right in front of him.

"I'll take that cheese and a loaf of bread," he told the market seller.

"You're just in time," the seller replied. "I'm about to close up shop."

Meanwhile, Donald Duck was just leaving his house. "What a terrible day!" he grumbled. He had overslept and woken up with a crick in his neck.

Donald hurried to cross the street, but had to stop for a red light.

When the light turned green, he stepped into the street.

HONNNK! A big truck roared past, just missing Donald.

"Watch where you're going!" Donald shouted. He raced ahead to the market.

"I'll take a loaf of bread, please," he said to the seller.

"Sorry," the seller replied. "I'm sold out."

"Sold out?" Donald's eyes bulged in his head. "Sold out?"

Down the block, Mickey Mouse was having a friendly chat with Goofy. "How have you been, Goofy?" he asked.

"Fine," Goofy said as he peeled a banana. He ate the whole thing in one bite and dropped the skin on the ground.

In the market, Donald sulked. He was hungry!

"This is so unfair!" he huffed. Donald started off towards the park, but a second later he slipped on a banana skin.

"Ooof!" Donald fell to the ground with a thud. Scowling, he got to his feet.

Not far away, Mickey was spreading out his picnic blanket in the park. All around him, children were laughing and playing.

"Hey, kids!" he called with a friendly wave. He took a big bite of his cheese sandwich and chewed happily. "What a wonderful day," he said again.

Donald kicked a pebble along the pavement while his tummy growled. And then, all of a sudden – thunk! – a ball hit him on the head.

"Watch it, kids!" Donald shouted. He rubbed his sore head. "What a terrible day!"

Just then, Donald heard a familiar voice call out, "Hey, Donald! Come and have a cheese sandwich with me!"

Donald saw Mickey waving to him from under a tree. Donald wanted to stay mad. But the truth is that no duck can resist a cheese sandwich. He smiled and ambled over. Maybe it wasn't such a bad day after all!

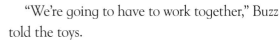

Sunnyside Boot Camp

Early one morning, Buzz and Rex arrived at Sunnyside Daycare. As soon as it was safe, they popped out of Bonnie's backpack. Even though they lived with Bonnie now, Buzz and Rex liked to come and visit the toys at Sunnyside.

Buzz greeted Sarge. When Andy went to college, Sarge and his last two cadets found a new home at Sunnyside. Sarge told Buzz he wished he had more soldiers.

"There are recruits all around you," Buzz said. "Let's have a boot camp."

"I have lots of boots!" Ken cried. He ran off to get them before anyone could explain what a boot camp really was!

During the children's naptime, the toys sneaked outside and started training.

Ken reappeared wearing some cowboy boots. When Sarge told him to run laps of the garden, Ken was horrified!

Meanwhile, the others were working hard. Sarge ordered everyone onto the bouncy trucks in the playground. Rex hopped on one and started rocking it slowly. But then Big Baby joined Rex and rocked it faster!

"Too fast!" cried Rex. "Stop!"

But when Big Baby stopped rocking, Rex went flying! He landed on top of the climbing frame! Sarge and Buzz came up with a mission – to rescue Rex.

"We're going to have to work together," Buzz told the toys.

All the toys agreed to help – except Ken. "These are vintage," he said, pointing to his cowboy boots.

The other toys made themselves into a tower, but it was too short to reach Rex! They told Ken they needed his help.

Ken thought for a moment then nodded. "Fashion has never held me back before!" he shouted.

He quickly removed his cowboy boots and climbed to the top of the tower. But he still couldn't reach Rex!

Then Ken had an idea. "Stretch," he called, "hand me my 1972 cherry-red striped platform boots!" He put them on and reached out to Rex. "Gotcha!" said Ken.

"We did it!" cheered the toys.

"Good work, troops," Sarge congratulated them. "Mission accomplished."

Then it was time for Buzz and Rex to go. They said goodbye to all the toys. But Buzz couldn't find Ken....

Finally Buzz found him.

"Thanks for your help today," said Buzz. "You're a great soldier!"

"Thanks, Buzz. But, great just doesn't cut it," said Ken. "Once I finish designing our new army boots – we'll be fabulous!"

DISNEY
THE EMPEROR'S
NEW GROOVE

Kronk's Feast

"One more time!" Kronk cried. The Junior Chipmunks looked at their leader, took deep breaths and launched into "We're Not Woodchucks" for the fourth time. "We're the ch-ch-chipmunks. We're not w-w-woodchucks," the kids sang, half-heartedly puffing out their cheeks.

The tired troop sagged on their log.

Next to them, Bucky the squirrel and three of his friends sang along too – in Squirrel. "*SQUEAK. SQ-SQ-SQ-SQUEAK. SQ-SQUEAK SQUEAK, SQUEAKER, SQUEAK.*" The furry animals' tails drooped.

"I'm really hungry," Tipo whispered to his sister Chaca.

"Keep singing," Chaca said behind her hand. "He's got to be done soon."

While the children began another verse, Kronk stood at the fire. He mixed, flipped and seasoned in a frenzy. He had been cooking for hours, and the smells drifting towards the tired troop were delicious.

"I'm ... almost ... ready." Kronk struggled to balance several plates on his arm before spinning around to present them to the troop. "*Voilà!*" The big man grinned. "*Bon appétit!*"

The troop leaned forward and smiled. The food looked as good as it smelled. They began to help themselves.

Kronk stood back modestly. "I do pride myself on being a bit of a gourmet," he said.

Everyone was pleased. Everyone, that is, but Bucky and the squirrels. Where was *their* food?

"*Squeak! Squeaker, squeaker, squeak,*" Bucky mumbled behind his paw. He gave a quick nod, and all of them ran off towards Kronk's tent. This was an outrage! The squirrels were Junior Chipmunks, too!

Bucky held open the tent flap as the squirrels ducked inside. "*Squeak,*" Bucky commanded as he pointed at Kronk's sleeping bag. The other squirrels nodded. They knew what they were supposed to do – chew holes in Kronk's bedding! Just as the squirrels were about to get to work, they were interrupted.

"Oh, *squeeeaak,*" Kronk's deep voice crooned from outside. "*Squeaker squeeeaak!*"

The squirrels peeked outside the tent.

There was Kronk, holding a new plate. Balanced upon it were a golden-brown acorn soufflé and a bowl of steaming wild-berry sauce.

Bucky shrugged sheepishly at the leader.

"Thought I forgot you, huh? Would Kronk do that?" The leader set the tray down. "How about a hug?"

The four squirrels grasped the large man's legs and squeezed. All was forgiven. Together all the Junior Chipmunks enjoyed their meal.

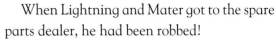

Mater in Paris

One lazy afternoon, Mater was listening to music. Suddenly the music stopped and a voice spoke to Mater through the radio. It was British secret agent, Holley Shiftwell!

"Hello, Mater!" she said. "Sorry to startle you. I'm contacting you because Finn and I need your help. We're in Paris tracking several Lemons who escaped from the World Grand Prix. Will you help?"

"Sure thing!" Mater said. "Love to!"

Suddenly, Siddeley the spy plane landed in the middle of Main Street! Mater's best friend, Lightning McQueen, drove up. "Mater, what's going on?" he asked.

"I'm going on a secret mission to Paris," whispered Mater. "You wanna come, too?"

"Paris? Um ... well ... sure," said Lightning.

Once in Paris, Mater and Lightning met up with Holley and Finn.

"We've been tailing these Lemons for a while, but they keep getting away," said Finn.

"Them Lemons are tricky," said Mater. "You just gotta learn how to think like them. If I was a Lemon, I'd make sure I had plenty of spare parts."

"Brilliant," said Finn. "You and Lightning can visit the spare parts dealer at the marketplace. Holley and I will head to the markets on the west side of Paris."

When Lightning and Mater got to the spare parts dealer, he had been robbed!

"Them Lemons was here already," said Mater. Then he spotted a trail of spare parts on the ground. The pair followed the trail all the way to a nearby café where Mater noticed two odd-looking cars. One of them backfired and his grille fell off. It was a disguise!

"Lemons!" cried Mater. "Their old exhausts make 'em backfire!"

The Lemons quickly fled the café. Lightning and Mater followed them through the city. But suddenly, there were not two, but six Lemons surrounding them!

"We're gonna get rid of you once and for all, tow truck, and your race car friend, too!" yelled one of the Lemons. Then he sprayed knock-out gas at Mater and Lightning.

But Mater quickly spun his tow hook! It blew the gas back at the Lemons. The thugs instantly passed out.

Some more Lemons arrived, but Mater had an idea....

Lightning and Mater led the Lemons on a chase, all the way to the top of the Eiffel Tower. The Lemons were so exhausted, they tipped over. Finn and Holley arrived just in time to capture them. Another great mission completed by secret agent Mater!

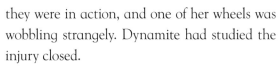

Sweet Dynamite

usty was chatting with Pinecone and Blackout, two of the Smokejumpers. They were talking about the crew's leader, whose nickname was Dynamite.

"At one point we were going to call her something else," Blackout said.

"And what was that?" Dusty asked curiously.

After glancing around to make sure Dynamite wasn't in earshot, Blackout started to tell the story.

"It all goes back to when she'd just arrived to take over as team leader," Blackout began.

He explained how on her very first fire, Dynamite had proved how efficient she was at being leader. She'd raced into action without a moment's hesitation, barking orders to the other Smokejumpers before they'd even hit the ground.

Dynamite had known exactly what to do to stop the blaze spreading. She'd zipped around the clearings, shouting commands at the other Smokejumpers as they worked to halt the fire's progress.

It had taken a lot of hard work and effort, but under Dynamite's command the crew had stopped the fire taking hold, allowing the air crew to swoop in and put out the flames.

When they'd all returned to HQ, though, Pinecone had a problem. She'd hit a rock while they were in action, and one of her wheels was wobbling strangely. Dynamite had studied the injury closed.

"You may have sprained a semi-axle," she said. "You'd better let Maru have a look at you."

It was clear that Pinecone couldn't drive over to Maru herself, so Dynamite had kindly carried her there on her back. Before they left, she took a few moments to make sure the rest of the crew were all safe and unhurt, too.

When Dynamite had dropped Pinecone off, she returned to find the others giggling. "We may have come up with the perfect call sign for you," said Blackout.

"You're so mindful and caring we think something like Sugar or Sweetie would be just right," laughed Drip.

Dynamite had looked furious. She raised up on her wheels as she bellowed, "How dare you make fun of me?" at the top of her voice.

The other Smokejumpers leaped back in fright, quickly realizing that while their new boss was caring, she was anything but sugary-sweet! In fact, her personality was a little on the explosive side, and so a new name was quickly settled on.

The new boss would be named Dynamite, and from that day on the rest of the crew were always careful not to set her off!

THE JUNGLE Book

Dawn Patrol

One day, Mowgli went to the jungle to visit his old friend Baloo the bear.

"Why so sad, Mowgli?" asked Baloo.

"It's the dry season, and the river is getting low," said Mowgli. "My friends in the village are worried about running out of water."

"Oh," said Baloo. He scratched his head. "But what about the spring in the jungle? It never goes dry."

Mowgli shook his head. "The spring is much too far inside the jungle. It would take all day to get there from the village."

Just then, Bagheera the panther padded over. "Mowgli, I might have a solution for you – Dawn Patrol."

The next morning, Bagheera, Baloo and Mowgli all waited by the spring. Before long, the ground shook with the approach of Colonel Hathi and his elephants.

"Hup, two, three, four. Hup, two, three, four," chanted the Colonel as the herd marched behind him.

"Here they come," announced Bagheera. "Dawn Patrol."

Quickly, Bagheera, Baloo and Mowgli hid in the bushes. They waited for the elephants to stop at the spring and take a long drink.

"Ready to try my plan?" Bagheera asked Mowgli. The boy nodded, then the two sprang

from the bushes crying, "To the river! Quick! Everyone, as fast as you can!"

The elephants looked up in alarm. "What's the meaning of this?" asked the Colonel.

"Shere Khan is coming! Run for the river!" Mowgli shouted in reply.

"Company ... RUN!" cried the Colonel, and the elephants stampeded through the jungle.

Bagheera and Mowgli watched the herd knock down every tree between the spring and the river. When Mowgli reached the river, he turned around and saw a clear, easy path straight to the big spring!

Now it was time for Baloo to play his part.

"Hey, whoa!" cried Baloo, running up to the herd. "False alarm!"

"What's that?" asked Colonel Hathi.

"Shere Khan isn't coming after all," said Baloo. "Human hunters are after him, so he's heading far away. We're all safe!"

The Dawn Patrol sighed with relief. Then Colonel Hathi called, "Forward, march!"

As the elephants marched off, Mowgli grinned. "With this new path to the spring, my friends will never run out of water."

Bagheera nodded. "Good work," he said.

"Yes, it was," said Baloo with a laugh. "And you know what was good about it? Somebody else did the work for us!"

Disney Pinocchio

Slugger

Pinocchio, as you know, was not always a real boy. Once, he was a puppet. And before that, he was a log. And before that, he was the trunk of a tall, shady tree. But that's of no great importance to our story ... it's simply to remind you that Pinocchio was not always a boy – and that to him, being a real boy was indeed a dream come true.

Our story, in fact, takes place some time later, when Pinocchio was walking home from school one day. He had just been thinking to himself of what real-boy play he would enjoy that afternoon – climbing trees, or skimming stones, or maybe just stomping in the mud – when suddenly he spied a whole group of real boys gathered in a field just down the road.

"What are you doing?" asked Pinocchio.

"Playing baseball," said a red-haired boy.

"Baseball?" Pinocchio hadn't heard of that game before. But it sounded like fun.

"Can I play?" he asked.

The boys nodded.

"Did you bring a glove?" one boy asked.

"A glove?" said Pinocchio.

"That's okay," said the boy. "You can use mine while I bat." He tossed a big, brown leather glove into Pinocchio's hands. "You can play first base."

Pinocchio grinned. First base! That sounded important! This game was going to be fun. Now, if he could just work out which base was first....

Luckily, the other boys ran off to their bases, leaving just one empty. Pinocchio trotted out to the dusty square. Then he waited to see what came next.

"Batter up!"

It didn't take long. One fast pitch, and before Pinocchio knew it, a ball was sailing over his head, and a tall boy was running full speed at him!

"*Ahhhhh!*" Pinocchio screamed, covering his face with his big glove. The boy was safe. And Pinocchio moved to right field. But on the very next pitch, where should the ball fly, but up ... up ... up ... and down to right field. This time, Pinocchio tried to catch it – but it landed with a *plop* on the grass behind him.

But Pinocchio never gave up and, when it was finally his turn to bat, he stepped into the batter's box and held his head high. To Pinocchio's surprise, the bat felt strangely natural in his hands ... almost like a part of his old, wooden self. He watched the pitcher carefully ... and on the first pitch – *CRACK!* – he sent the ball high and away, into the sky.

"Hooray!" the boys cheered. A slugger had been born! And a real boy had learned a new game.

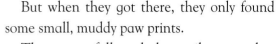

The Kitten Sitters

"We're going to look after Minnie's kitten, Figaro, tonight," Mickey Mouse said to his nephews, Morty and Ferdie.

As Minnie and Figaro arrived at Mickey's house, Pluto came racing across the lawn, an angry chicken behind him!

"Pluto! Have you been chasing chickens again? Maybe Figaro can teach you some manners!" Minnie said as she stomped off, leaving Figaro sitting in Mickey's arms.

Minnie was hardly out of sight when Figaro leaped down and scampered into the kitchen. He jumped onto the table, knocking over a jug of milk.

Pluto growled, but Mickey just cleaned up the mess. "Be nice, Pluto," he said.

Later, Pluto ate all his food. But Figaro refused to touch the food Minnie had left.

At bedtime, Morty called out, "Uncle Mickey, did you close the kitchen window?"

"Oh, no!" cried Mickey. The window was open and Figaro was nowhere to be seen.

Mickey and the boys searched the house but couldn't find Figaro. So they went to Minnie's house, but Figaro wasn't there either.

"Have you seen a little black-and-white kitten?" Mickey asked a policeman in the street.

"I certainly have!" he answered. "He was teasing the ducks by the pond!"

But when they got there, they only found some small, muddy paw prints.

The group followed the trail to another street, where they met a lorry driver.

"Have you seen a kitten?" Mickey asked.

"Yes!" cried the driver. "He knocked over my eggs!"

Mickey groaned as he paid for the broken eggs.

They searched the whole town, but there was no sign of the kitten. When they returned home, the sun was starting to rise.

Soon, Minnie drove up. "Where's Figaro?" she asked.

Just then, there was a loud clucking. A dozen hens came flapping over the garden fence, with Figaro close behind.

"There's your sweet kitten!" exclaimed Mickey. "He ran away, teased the ducks by the pond. Then he broke the eggs and –"

"I had hoped Figaro would teach Pluto some manners," Minnie said. "Instead, Pluto has been teaching him to misbehave!" She picked up Figaro and drove away.

"We'll tell her the whole story later, when she's not so upset," said Mickey to the boys.

"Don't tell her too soon," begged Morty. "As long as Aunt Minnie thinks Pluto is a bad dog, we won't have to kitten-sit Figaro."

Mickey smiled. "Maybe you're right. We could all use some peace and quiet."

FINDING NEMO

Bubble Trouble

At the foot of Mount Wannahockaloogie, Bloat rallied his friends to come and watch his attempt to cross the stream of bubbles bursting from its top.

"Watch closely, Nemo," Bloat said. "I'm going to show you my secret move for crossing the volcano's famous ring of fire."

Nemo giggled. "But isn't it just a stream of bubbles?"

"This is the most powerful stream of bubbles in the whole tank," Bloat informed him. "And it will not stop me!"

Bloat dived in.

"See my approach?" he called. "It's about the angle of entry! Now it gets really hard...."

But as he was about to expertly force his way against the current, the bubbles vanished!

"What happened?" Nemo wondered.

"It lost oomph," Bloat said, confused.

"Let's investigate!" suggested Nemo.

Nemo and Bloat found Peach stuck to the side of the tank. She peeled her pointy pink head from the glass as they explained what had happened.

"It could be an electrical issue," Peach said.

Jacques overheard them. "If the problem is down here, I'll find it," he said, scurrying along the tank bed. Following the tube that carried the bubbles to the volcano, all seemed fine, until he discovered a great big knot.

"*Voilà!*" said Jacques.

The culprit was Bubbles the fish. He had tied a knot in the tube so he could watch the bubbles gather in a mass.

"Let those bubbles free at once," demanded Gill, swimming slowly towards them all.

The pressure in the tube was rising, making it expand. Quickly, they gathered to straighten the tube, but the knot exploded!

Nemo got caught in the blast and landed in the spray of bubbles shooting towards the volcano.

"Help!" he screamed, as he was sucked into the volcano. Moments later, he came out of the top inside a giant bubble!

"Stay still, Nemo!" instructed Gill. "Ride it to safety!"

Nemo gulped as the bubble went higher and higher. It broke the surface of the water and he could see the ocean outside the window.

"I'm free!" he cheered.

But the bubble burst ... and Nemo plopped back into the tank.

"Sorry, kid," said Gill.

"All bubbles pop," added Bloat.

Nemo didn't mind. He knew his Dad would come for him one day. For now, he just enjoyed the crazy, unpredictable adventures he had with his new friends.

Buzz's Space Adventure

One day, after a long playtime, the Peas-in-a-Pod were feeling tired. They asked Buzz to tell them a story about space!

"Once upon a time," Buzz began, "the evil Emperor Zurg stole a top-secret Space Ranger Turbo Suit. Star Command knew I was the only one who could get it back!"

"Wow," said Woody. "I wonder how it feels to be a space hero."

"Me too," said Rex. "Hey, Buzz! Can I be in your story? But with big arms?"

"Sure, why not?" said Buzz, as he continued.

"I was heading into dangerous space, so I brought a special crew – First Lieutenant Woody and Second Lieutenant Rex!

"As we touched down on Planet Zurg, a loud humming noise filled the air. We needed to investigate.

"Suddenly, we spotted an army. There were hundreds of Emperor Zurg's loyal Zurgbots, and all of them were humming. Woody and Rex had it covered, so I went off to find Zurg's headquarters ... and that Turbo Suit!

"But I hadn't gone far when I saw one Zurgbot standing on his own. It was strange. Usually, they never travelled alone. His humming sounded odd, almost like a melody.

'Hold your fire!' the Zurgbot cried. 'I'm not like the others! My name is Zenny, and I don't want to hum – I want to sing. But the emperor will not allow it.'

"Apparently this Zurgbot also opposed Zurg! But with the entire galaxy at stake, how could I trust him?

'I will take you to the Turbo Suit,' Zenny promised.

"True to his word, Zenny quickly led me into the heart of Zurg's lair – and to the Turbo Suit.

"But as I reached for the suit, a band of Zurgbots attacked. And they had my lieutenants! Then Zurg appeared and our doom seemed near....

'Not so fast, Zurg,' a voice called out.

"It was Zenny!

'Quiet, Zurgbot!' ordered the emperor.

'No,' said Zenny. 'I may look like other Zurgbots, but I don't have to act like them!'

"And with that, he began to sing!

"As Zenny's voice grew louder, stalactites fell from the cave's ceiling. They dropped to the floor, trapping Zurg. Zenny untied our bonds and set us free! Quickly, I climbed into the Turbo Suit and, with the help of my lieutenants, defeated the Zurgbot army! Zenny helped too!

"As we headed home, we could see Zenny below, teaching the other Zurgbots to sing. Planet Zurg would be a happier place from then onwards. The end."

Thunderbolt Patch

Every evening, Pongo, Perdita and their 15 Dalmatian puppies would gather around the television to watch the heroic adventures of Thunderbolt the dog. The puppies would stare wide-eyed as Thunderbolt saved the day from all sorts of thieves and villains. Patch wanted to be just like Thunderbolt!

After the programme, it was time for the puppies to go to sleep so Pongo and Perdita could go for a walk with their humans.

But one night, Patch had other ideas. "Can't we stay up longer?" he pleaded.

"It's time for sleep now," Perdita replied, as she and Pongo left for their walk.

But Patch didn't want to go to sleep. He wanted to go on a great adventure, just like Thunderbolt! And when the puppies heard a strange scurrying sound, Patch saw his chance.

"Look!" whispered Patch, pointing to a small mouse sitting near the puppies' basket. "It's a big bad bandit! We've got to catch him!"

The puppies all wanted to play pretend, so they scampered out of bed and sneaked upstairs after the fearsome outlaw.

"Follow me," Patch whispered, pretending to be Thunderbolt. "That nasty scoundrel is heading towards the music room."

Before the puppies could catch the bandit, they heard someone coming up the stairs.

It was Nanny! If she caught the pups, they would be in big trouble.

"Hide," whispered Patch. The pups quickly scampered into the music room and found hiding places.

"Now, what's all this noise?" Nanny wondered, looking around the apparently empty room.

As the pups held their breath, Patch spotted the scoundrel slipping back downstairs. When the coast was clear, the puppies resumed their chase.

"That burglar must be in here somewhere," said Patch as the puppies searched the empty kitchen.

"There he is!" shouted Rolly, suddenly.

Rolly darted towards the bandit ... but he knocked over a bag of flour. The flour covered Rolly, turning him white!

"That pup doesn't have any spots," Patch said, pointing to his brother. "He must be the *real* intruder!" Patch pretended.

The puppies all pounced on Rolly, but soon Pepper saw Pongo and Perdita outside.

"Mother and Father are coming!" Pepper exclaimed. "Everyone back to bed!"

"Come along, chaps!" shouted the leader of the pack. "Thunderbolt Patch will save the day!"

When Pongo and Perdita peeked in on their precious puppies, they found them ... curled up in bed, just as they had left them!

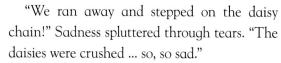

Sadly Ever After

Anger, Disgust, Fear, Sadness and Joy all worked together in Headquarters and watched over their girl, Riley.

"Sadness, cheer up! We're ice-skating! We love ice-skating!" Joy said.

"I'm too sad to skate," Sadness whimpered.

"You know what you need? A happy memory! Pick one," Joy replied.

"Maybe that time we went to the park and had a picnic?" Sadness suggested.

"That's a great memory," Joy cheered. "We did lots of things that day. Mum and Dad surprised us with a cupcake! Riley was about to take a bite when –"

"A ladybird landed on the icing and got stuck," Sadness continued. "Poor ladybird."

"Sadness!" Joy pleaded.

"That picnic was just peachy until that dog ran in and ruined everything!" shouted Anger. "That must make you angry, right, Sadness?"

"Mum and Dad wouldn't let us take the dog home," Sadness moaned.

"You left out the most gruesome part of that day," said Disgust. "We slipped in the mud and disgusting gloop went everywhere. Doesn't that completely gross you out?"

Sadness sighed. "No, it's sad. That jumper was our favourite. We ruined it."

"Um, remember when we made a daisy chain?" said Fear. "A giant bee nearly stung us!"

"We ran away and stepped on the daisy chain!" Sadness spluttered through tears. "The daisies were crushed ... so, so sad."

"This clearly isn't working. Choose a sad memory," suggested Joy.

"There was that time we missed the school bus," Sadness began.

"That was sad, but how does it make the three of you feel?" Joy asked the team.

"Furious!" screamed Anger. "That bus driver left three seconds early!"

"And we nearly choked on the exhaust fumes! Beyond gross," Disgust added.

"And we were going to get in trouble for being late for school!" Fear explained.

"Do you want to know how I remember that day?" Joy asked. "It was the best day ever! Mum ended up driving us to school. We sang out loud to the radio and stopped for a delicious hot chocolate!"

"You're right, Joy," Anger said calmly. "Maybe that wasn't so bad."

"Nothing gross about that," said Disgust.

"I feel all warm and safe now," Fear said.

Sadness thought for a moment. "I feel...."

"Great, right? You're happy! We're all happy," said Joy. But then....

"I feel sad!" Sadness cried. "When we took a sip of the hot chocolate, we burned our tongue."

Anger, Disgust, Fear and Joy just sighed.

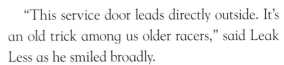

Fans Old and New

In a blur of red, Lightning McQueen zoomed across the finish line! The crowd cheered as he took a victory lap around the stadium.

"Once again, Lightning wins the race!" Doc Hudson boomed over the speakers.

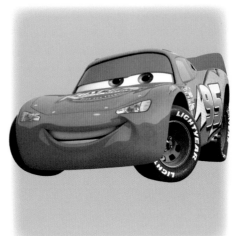

Not only had Lightning won the Piston Cup, but he'd also beaten his best time!

News of Lightning's new record spread quickly and Chuki the reporter was eager to get an interview with everyone's favourite race car.

"Where's the champ?" Chuki asked excitedly.

Doc rolled his eyes. He knew Lightning would want a rest after his big race.

"He's busy training," Doc said sternly.

"Stay on the track, kid!" Doc warned over the speakers.

On no, thought Lightning. *Chuki must be after me for another story!*

As Lightning slowed down, Leak Less drove up beside him.

"What's the matter, buddy?" asked Leak Less.

"I'm being hounded by a reporter, Leak Less! I don't know how to get away!" Lightning answered glumly.

"Is that all?" Leak Less laughed. "Follow me!"

Lightning felt confused as Leak Less turned off the track and drove down an entrance he hadn't noticed before.

"This service door leads directly outside. It's an old trick among us older racers," said Leak Less as he smiled broadly.

Lightning smiled back. "Thanks for the tip! I'm sorry that I interrupted your own training session."

"That's okay! I'm on my way to a fans' rally. Do you want to tag along?" asked Leak Less.

"You bet!" Lightning answered excitedly. "It's always a pleasure to meet new fans."

"Ha-ha! They're not exactly what I'd call 'new'," chuckled Leak Less.

Leak Less and Lightning arrived at the rally. It was decorated with yellow and black flags, and vintage posters of Leak Less.

The small crowd cheered as their hero rolled into the garage. Leak Less led the way proudly. "Like I was telling you, I'm a racing veteran and my fans are getting on in years."

Lightning looked around the crowd of fans. There were some old models he didn't know were still driving around!

The fans were all very excited to meet the young racer and share stories about their hero. They had lots of questions about Lightning's recent race in the Piston Cup and how he'd beaten his own record.

Oops, thought Lightning. *I bet Chuki wouldn't have asked me so many questions!*

Pinecone Passion

Another blaze had been safely put out in Piston Peak. Dusty and some of the Smokejumpers were catching their breath before heading back to base.

The friends discussed their names and call signs. Dusty explained his name didn't really have any meaning behind it, while the Smokejumpers said there was a reason behind all of their nicknames.

Dusty realized he had no idea how Pinecone had come to get her name, so he settled back as Drip began the story.

Back when Pinecone had joined the team, the others had noticed she liked to slip away into the forest whenever she had any free time.

One day, Drip had spotted her wandering mysteriously among the trees, her eyes fixed on the forest floor. Every so often, she'd stop and pick something up off the ground. It was very strange behaviour indeed.

When Drip told the other Smokejumpers about the newbie's odd behaviour, they'd all wondered what she could possibly have been collecting. Drip had explained that he couldn't see what it was, but he had seen the newcomer stash whatever she'd collected in a nearby locker.

Curious, the crew had gone to look inside, but the locker was shut tight. Maru the mechanic had overheard everything, and was just as intrigued as the Smokejumpers. They had to know what was hidden in that locker!

Hooking his forklift fork under the handle, Maru heaved. At last, the latch turned and the locker doors flew open. Hundreds of pine cones rolled out, completely burying poor Maru.

"Why would she be hoarding pine cones?" Blackout wondered. He jumped as Pinecone rolled up demanding to know what they were doing.

"We were just curious!" said Drip. They asked her if she was a pine cone collector, and she giggled.

"No! I'm a botany enthusiast," she said. She told them how she loved studying plants, but pine cones most of all.

She explained that once she'd studied them, she was always careful to put them back exactly where she'd found them. But the locker door springing open had mixed up all her samples.

Dusty laughed as the Smokejumpers told him that Pinecone had loomed over them as she'd made them put the samples back in order one by one.

After spending hours putting the cones back in the locker, Avalanche and the others agreed there couldn't be a more perfect nickname for their botanist friend than Pinecone!

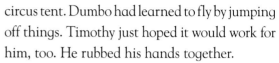

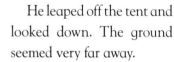

A Talented Mouse

"Look, Dumbo," Timothy Mouse said, pointing to the newspaper. "There's another article about us in here!"

That wasn't unusual. Ever since Dumbo had become famous for being able to fly, everyone was interested in him.

Mrs Jumbo, Dumbo's mother, peered over Timothy's shoulder. "What a nice story," she cooed. "Too bad the picture isn't better – why, I can hardly see you, Timothy!"

Timothy peered at the paper. "Hey," he said, scanning the story, "this article doesn't mention me at all!"

"It's all right," Mrs Jumbo said soothingly. "Everyone knows how important you are."

Timothy puffed out his chest proudly. After all, he had taught Dumbo to fly!

Then he sagged again. "Am I really that important?" he said. "It's Dumbo who has the talent – not me."

Mrs Jumbo and Dumbo tried to comfort him, but he wandered away sadly. He was so smart, so talented – he should be famous too!

"I have to figure out a way to get famous on my own," he muttered. "But how?"

Suddenly he snapped his fingers. "I've got it!" he cried. "I'll learn to fly, too! That way Dumbo and I can be famous together!"

He quickly climbed to the top of the tallest circus tent. Dumbo had learned to fly by jumping off things. Timothy just hoped it would work for him, too. He rubbed his hands together.

"Here goes nothing...." he muttered.

He leaped off the tent and looked down. The ground seemed very far away.

"Uh-oh!" Timothy said with a gulp. What had he done? The ground got closer and closer. Timothy squeezed his eyes shut....

Suddenly, Timothy felt himself being whisked upwards. Opening his eyes, he saw that he was clutched in Dumbo's trunk.

"Whew!" he gasped. "Thanks, chum!"

Dumbo smiled at his little friend. He set Timothy in his cap.

Timothy settled into the familiar spot. Flying was much more fun when Dumbo's ears did all the work!

Soon they landed beside Mrs Jumbo.

"Oh, Timothy!" she cried. "You're safe! When I saw you fall, I was so worried. Dumbo and I don't know what we'd do without you."

Timothy blinked. "Never thought of it that way," he mused. "Maybe I'm not front-page news every day. But who cares? I know I'm important, and my friends know it, too. That's what matters!"

He smiled. He had plenty of his own talent, and that was good enough for him!

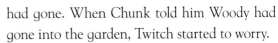

Garden Guardians

Bonnie had brought Woody with her to Sunnyside, but when it was time to go home she had accidentally left him behind.

Woody stared sadly out of the window. It was Friday, so Bonnie wouldn't be back at the daycare centre until Monday.

"Bonnie hasn't left you on purpose, Woody," said Chunk the rock-like action figure.

Woody smiled. "I know, Chunk," he said, brightening up. "It'll just be like a little holiday."

It was a beautiful day, so Woody decided to head outside to take a relaxing stroll in the garden. The place sure was quiet without any kids around, but as Woody passed the climbing frame he heard something rustle in the long grass nearby.

"Hey!" he said. "Is anybody there?"

When no one replied, Woody stepped into the grass. "Come out, friend," he began, pushing aside the long blades. Before he could say any more, a piece of string went tight around his foot. He gasped as he was pulled up into the air.

"Hands up!" shouted a voice from the grass, as Woody dangled helplessly from a tree branch above.

Meanwhile, back inside, the bug-like action figure, Twitch, was wondering where Woody had gone. When Chunk told him Woody had gone into the garden, Twitch started to worry.

"What? Didn't you warn him that *they* are out there?" he gulped. "He might fall into one of the traps they built to stop intruders."

Chunk's face fell. "Oops!" he said.

Along with Stretch, the rubbery purple octopus, Chunk and Twitch raced out of the daycare centre and into the garden. They searched the sandpit and crawled under the picnic tables, searching for the missing sheriff.

"Woody! Woody!" cried Stretch.

"Where are you?" yelled Chunk. He was feeling guilty. He should have warned Woody what was in the garden.

The toys were about to call for help when Twitch spotted something. "Look!" he said, pointing to a spot near the climbing frame.

Chunk and Stretch sighed with relief. Woody was standing in the grass, laughing and chatting happily with a group of tiny green army men. "It was a pleasure to meet you again, sir!" said the sarge, saluting.

"We got worried for nothing," said Twitch.

Woody smiled. It was nice to catch up with Andy's old toys, the army men, again, but he had to admit that dangling from that trap had got him a little worried, too!

A Real Sleeper!

"Time for bed, Nemo," said Marlin. "It's a school day tomorrow," he added. "You need to get your rest."

"Okay," said Nemo. "But can you tell me a story? How about one from when you were younger?"

"Well, just one then," said Marlin, swimming back over to his only child. He thought for a moment, then smiled broadly. "Did you know that when I was younger – much younger, actually – did you know I wanted to be a comedian?"

Nemo's eyes widened with surprise. "*You?* A comedian? Aren't comedians supposed to be, umm, funny?"

"Well, you see, son," said Marlin, "life is not easy for a clownfish. You may as well realize that now. See, when you're a clownfish, everyone you meet assumes that you're funny. It's a common mistake. Anyway, years ago, I figured that as long as everyone expected me to be funny, I would try being funny for a living."

"But, Dad," said Nemo, "you aren't funny at all."

"Hey, now! Wait just a minute!" Marlin said, a bit huffily. "In my day, I was known as quite the crack-up! Let me see. I'm sure I can remember some of my old routine, if I just think about it for a minute." He thought for a moment. "All right, it's all coming back!"

He cleared his throat. "Good evening, ladies and jellyfish! The ocean sure is looking *swell* tonight. Would you like me to give you a coral report about the latest happenings on the reef? Get it?" he said, looking down at Nemo. "You see, there's something called an oral report, and the words 'coral' and 'oral' sound quite a bit alike."

Nemo gave his father a pained look.

"So, the other day my appendix nearly burst," Marlin carried on happily. "So I decided I'd better go to a sturgeon!"

Nemo blinked. "Dad, these really aren't that funny," he said with a yawn.

"A *sturgeon*. Get it? Rather than a surgeon?" Marlin sighed and continued his routine. "A funny thing happened on the way to the show tonight. I met a guy, nice fish and all, but he seemed to be a bit down on his luck. He told me he was living on squid row."

Nemo's eyes were starting to droop sleepily.

"Do you know why the whale crossed the ocean?" Marlin continued. "Now, don't try to guess. I'll tell you – the whale crossed the ocean to get to the other tide. The other *tide*."

Nemo's eyes were now completely closed, and a tiny snore escaped from him. Marlin smiled at his sleeping son.

"Works every time," he said with a chuckle.

Mater's Jukebox

"Ye-ha! Ready or not, Radiator Springs ... my jukebox is ready!" Mater hollered. He had made a fantastic jukebox and he couldn't wait to show all of his friends.

He hooked it up to his tow rope and off he went. The first car he saw was Ramone, but Ramone didn't have time to listen to the jukebox. Little tractors were messing up his body paint shop!

"I've got to clean up this place!" Ramone cried.

"Gee, I see what you mean," Mater said.

Next, Mater passed by his best friend, Lightning.

"Sorry, Mater!" Lightning called. "I've got to round up these little tractors." Lightning zoomed after another little tractor as it darted away.

Dadgum! Them little tractors sure is fast. I can help, but it's hard to move fast with my brand-new jukebox, Mater thought.

At Casa Della Tyres, Luigi had no time to hear Mater's junkyard jukebox either.

"No-no-no-no!" Luigi cried. "Look at Luigi's Leaning Tower of Tyres! Now she is just Luigi's Pile of Tyres!"

Mater knew he had to help, but how?

In front of the fire station, Red was sobbing over his trampled flowers!

"Did the little tractors do this?" asked Mater.

"Hey, you know what? Maybe a little music would –" But Red was too sad to listen.

Mater rounded the corner and found Sheriff. "Hey, Sheriff, you'll never guess what I made...."

"Mater! I've got no time to stand around. I need to round up these little rascals." Sheriff turned on his siren and drove away after the tractors.

For such cute little fellas, these tractors sure are causing a load of trouble! Mater thought. *I gotta put away my jukebox so I can help my friends.*

As Mater continued on his way back to the scrapyard to return his jukebox, he cranked the music up loud and began to sing along. One tractor followed him shyly.

Soon, other tractors started following Mater and his jukebox! To his surprise, Mater noticed the music was attracting all of the little tractors. He turned up the volume even more and started a little tractor round-up.

"Well, lookee here!" Mater shouted. "These little fellas like my music!"

"Mater rounded up the tractors!" cried Sally.

The whole town cheered. "Hip, hip, hooray for Mater!"

"That's music to my ears!" Sheriff sighed.

Everyone was happy. The tractors were out of trouble, the music was great and Mater had finally been able to show off his jukebox!

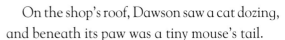

Dawson Takes the Case

"My little boy is missing!" a sobbing Mrs Mousington cried to Basil the Great Mouse Detective. "Can you help me find him?"

"I'm terribly sorry," said Basil. He was examining a brick wall very closely, looking for clues. "But I'm working on an important case for the Queen. I don't have time."

"No, wait!" cried Dr Dawson, Basil's partner, as Mrs Mousington turned to leave. "Madam, if the Great Mouse Detective is too busy, then perhaps I can offer you my services."

"Splendid!" said Basil.

Before Dawson left with Mrs Mousington, Basil stopped him. "Don't forget this," he said, handing Dawson an umbrella.

"But it's a sunny day," said Dawson, puzzled. "Why would I need an umbrella?"

"A sunny day can turn dark quicker than you think," advised Basil. "Remember that, Dawson, and you'll do fine."

Dawson shrugged and took the umbrella. Then he turned to Mrs Mousington and said, "Show me where you last saw your son."

Mrs Mousington took him to a shop. Dawson searched the area and found a long, white hair. But a closer look told him this was not just any hair. It was a cat's whisker!

Calling to a bird in a nearby tree, Dawson asked for a lift up.

On the shop's roof, Dawson saw a cat dozing, and beneath its paw was a tiny mouse's tail.

The bird set Dawson down on the roof, and he wondered how he was going to lift the cat's heavy paw. Then he remembered the umbrella!

Using one end as a lever, he heaved. Beneath the cat's paw he found Mrs Mousington's terrified son.

"The cat was saving me for dinner!" the little boy mouse cried.

Dawson pulled the little mouse free. With relief, he waved at the boy's mother, who was waiting on the pavement below. But before Dawson could signal another bird for a ride down, the cat woke up.

Dawson saw only one possible escape – he opened his umbrella and jumped with the little boy mouse in his arms.

Mrs Mousington let out a terrified scream. But the umbrella filled with air and slowed their fall until they landed gently on the pavement.

Mrs Mousington hugged her little boy close. "Oh, Dr Dawson, thank you!" she cried.

Back at the Great Mouse Detective's house, Basil was delighted to hear how Dawson had saved the little boy.

"It was easy," Dawson told Basil, smiling. "Thanks to your umbrella, I'd call it an open-and-shut case!"

Toys on Ice

Poor Bonnie was stuck in bed, recovering from a nasty case of the flu. She was feeling a little better, but still needed lots of rest.

"I'm sorry, honey, you can't go and see *Songs on Ice*," said her mum, stroking Bonnie's head.

"But my whole school is going," whimpered Bonnie. "It's a musical!"

Bonnie's mum told her that getting some rest was more important. She needn't have worried – Bonnie had already fallen back asleep.

"Poor Bonnie," said Woody, when her mum had left. "She looks so sad. We must do something for her."

"Do you have a plan, Woody?" asked Buzz. Woody smiled. He always had a plan! The sheriff set about explaining it to the others, then they all swung into action.

The snow was falling as the toys all sneaked out into the garden, carrying a large plastic tub. Mr Pricklepants the hedgehog shook his head. "Get a lot of snow and take it inside?" he said. "It's absurd."

"Trust me," said Woody. "Bonnie will play the musical 'Toys on Ice' with us, and she'll be happy again."

Rex thought it was a great plan, but before he could tell Woody, his feet slipped on the ice. Rex spun in a circle, his tail sending the other toys flying in all directions. They crash-landed into the snow, face first! This was going to be harder than Woody thought.

Buzz sat up, looking around. The aliens were nowhere to be seen. Where could they have gone?

"Surprise!" cheered one of the little three-eyed creatures. The other two popped up beside him. "Let's have a snowball fight!"

Woody shook his head firmly. "Guys, we have no time to play," he began, but then a snowball hit his face and he remembered that toys always had time to play. "So, it's war, huh?" he said, reaching for the powdery snow. "My snowballs are the fastest in the west!"

After a fun snowball fight, the toys filled the tub and carried it back into the living room. They were about to celebrate another successful mission when something terrible happened. The snow began to melt!

Woody's shoulders sagged. There was no way Bonnie would be able to play 'Toys on Ice' now. Buzz patted him on the back. "I'm sure Bonnie will find a way to play with us anyway, Woody."

And Buzz was right! When Bonnie woke up she felt much better, and the big tub of melted snow was just the thing she needed to create her very own version of the musical – 'Toys on Water'!

Raiders of the Lost House

The trek across to Paradise Falls was long and difficult. After hours of walking, Carl and Russell stopped for a rest. Carl tied the house to a large rock to stop it floating away, but when they returned to it, the house had disappeared!

They searched around, but there was no sign of the house anywhere. Carl started to panic. Everything he owned was in that house. Had his whole life really just vanished when he wasn't looking?

"Don't worry, Mr Fredricksen. Dug will help us," said Russell. "Dug, find the house!"

The golden retriever sniffed around the clearing, letting his nose lead the way. Russell and Carl followed as Dug dived into the bushes, catching up with him at the foot of a tall tree.

"Point!" said Dug, raising one paw and using his nose to point up at the branches. Carl looked up, hoping to see his house. Instead, though, he saw a squirrel munching on some nuts, minding its own business.

Carl clutched at his hair. "What if it floated away?" he groaned.

Suddenly, Russell spotted something colourful through a gap in the trees. They looked a lot like the balloons that had been tied to Mr Fredricksen's house.

When they climbed the tree to see more clearly, however, they realized the mass of colour wasn't balloons – it was butterflies. Hundreds of brightly coloured butterflies flapped and fluttered in a cloud above them.

As they watched, the butterflies seemed to form into the shape of an arrow. Could they be pointing the way to Carl's house? Russell decided to investigate. After all, Wilderness Explorers always tried to help wildlife, so it made sense that wildlife would help a Wilderness Explorer in return.

They followed the direction of the arrow, and Carl couldn't believe it when they stumbled out of a dense clump of trees and saw his house floating right ahead of them. The old man whooped and laughed and cheered as he and Russell ran towards it.

When they got there, Carl was shocked to see the house was still attached to the same rock he'd tied it to earlier. He knew it was the same one, because of the stone's distinctive pattern. But if it was still tied to the rock, how could it have moved?

The answer became clear when a little green head and four stubby legs emerged. It wasn't a rock at all, it was a giant tortoise. The tortoise always carried its own house around on its back, but for a little while, it had been carrying two of them!

The Rust Bucket Derby

"Ye-ha!" hollered Mater as he and Lightning McQueen pulled into the Rust Bucket Stadium. Mater owned the stadium and he loved it.

Bubba, a big tow truck twice the size of Mater, drove up with two smaller tow trucks close behind.

"You were right, Bubba!" said one. "This is perfect for our headquarters!"

Mater and Lightning stared in surprise.

"You heard right," said Bubba. "Tater and Tater Jr here own the Po' Tater Towing Company. And they're gonna set up an office right here in Rust Bucket Stadium. You challenged me to a racing derby, Mater. Remember? The winner gets your stadium!" Bubba sneered.

"Well, if you say so, Bubba," said Mater. "You know how I forget things!"

"Tater and Tater Jr will be the judges," Bubba declared.

"That's not fair!" Lightning exclaimed.

"Go, Bubba!" shouted Tater and Tater Jr as they took the judges' seats. "Let the tyre snaggin' begin!"

Guido threw tyres into the air. Both tow trucks sent their hooks whipping up and caught four tyres, but Bubba knocked one out of Mater's grip.

"Whoo-oo, I win!" Bubba shouted.

"Bubba didn't play fair," Tater Jr whispered to Tater.

"What does it matter?" Tater replied.

The next event was cone dodging. Mater raced backwards and Bubba couldn't keep up. Mater won! Now it was the last event, a one-lap race. Whoever won would be champion!

"Say goodbye to your stadium," Bubba snarled as he roared into the lead. Mater was catching up when Bubba dropped his tow hook onto the track!

"Bubba, stop, that's dangerous!" Lightning yelled. Bubba sneered, but then his hook snagged in the road!

"Help!" Bubba cried, flipping onto his side. Mater screeched to a stop. Whipping his tow cable in the air like a cowboy, he hooked on to Bubba's window.

"You want to help Bubba even though he's trying to take your stadium?" asked Tater.

"He's in trouble," said Mater. "C'mon! We can pull him up if we work together!"

They pulled with all their might and Bubba was saved. After this, Bubba decided that Mater could keep his stadium.

"Mr Mater, will you teach us how to snag tyres?" asked Tater Jr.

"Sure thing, Taters," Mater said. "Always glad to help friends."

Disney
Aladdin

Monkey See, Monkey Do

"Come on, Abu!" Aladdin called across the busy Agrabah marketplace.

From his perch on top of the basket seller's cart, Abu barely heard the call. He was captivated by the monkey he had just spotted peeking out at him from behind the fruit seller's cart. Abu jumped off the basket cart and darted over to say hello.

But the other monkey ran away and hid behind a wheel. From his new hiding place, he peeked out at Abu.

Abu looked around, trying to think of a way to draw out the monkey. The fruit seller was distracted, talking to a customer, so Abu hopped up onto the cart and picked up an apple. He balanced it on top of his head, then scurried over to the edge of the cart and peered down, hoping to attract the monkey's attention.

But he was gone.

Abu heard monkey chatter behind him. He turned around to find the monkey standing at the other end of the fruit cart, balancing an apple on *his* head, just like Abu.

Abu laughed and picked up a pear and an orange. He began juggling them in the air, hoping to amuse the other monkey.

But the other monkey didn't look amused. He looked annoyed! He thought Abu was trying to show him up. Not to be outdone, the monkey also picked up a pear and an orange and began to juggle them, just like Abu.

Abu put the fruit down. He did a handstand on the cart railing.

The other monkey did a handstand too.

Abu grabbed hold of the cart awning, then flipped over and swung from the awning by his tail.

The other monkey did the same.

Abu laughed again. He thought this game was fun. But now he wanted to find a stunt that the other monkey couldn't copy. Abu looked around. He spotted Aladdin coming his way. Abu had an idea! He jumped off the fruit cart, darted over to Aladdin and scrambled up the length of his friend's body until he was sitting comfortably on top of Aladdin's head.

The other monkey stared in amazement. He didn't know that Aladdin was Abu's friend. How could he copy that stunt? He looked around. The closest human was the fruit seller. Throwing caution to the wind, the other monkey scurried over to him – but he'd only climbed as high as the fruit seller's shoulder before the man chased him away.

Then, from behind the basket cart, the other monkey crossed his arms, pouted and watched that sneaky Abu laugh and wave goodbye as he was carried away on top of Aladdin's head.

Deputy Mater

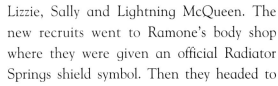

The cool morning air in Radiator Springs felt wonderful as Sally looked out from her motel. Suddenly, a noisy blur whizzed by. It was Boost, Wingo and DJ playing loud, thumpy music.

"Slow down!" Sally cried out, but the speeding pranksters were long gone. Sally rolled over to Flo's V8 Café for breakfast, where she saw Fillmore talking with Sheriff.

"Good morning, fellas," said Sally. She told Sheriff about the speeders.

"I know, Sally," said Sheriff, "but I'm having a hard time keeping up with them."

"Why don't we get you some help, man?" Fillmore suggested.

"What a terrific idea!" exclaimed Sally. Just then, Mater came down Main Street. There was something different about him.

"Hi there, Mater. What did you do with your door? It's painted white!" exclaimed Sally.

"Oh shoot, I was asking Ramone if he could cover my rustiest spot and he had the wrong colour paint in the sprayer thing."

Sally looked thoughtfully at Mater's white door. "How do you feel about helping Sheriff out – and all of us?" she asked.

That afternoon, Sheriff proclaimed Mater an honorary Radiator Springs deputy! Mater read out a list of helpers. He chose Sarge, Lizzie, Sally and Lightning McQueen. The new recruits went to Ramone's body shop where they were given an official Radiator Springs shield symbol. Then they headed to Main Street.

Lizzie heard something in the distance. "Heads up, deputies!" she cried out.

Mater rolled into the middle of the road just as a familiar, noisy blur came to a halt centimetres away.

"Hello, pranksters," said Mater sternly. Facing him were Boost, Wingo, DJ and Snot Rod, all puffing from racing so fast. "We're glad you like our town. But would you please respect our rules? The speed limit here is much lower than you're goin'."

"We saw a sign that said 66, sir, and we thought we were going the right speed," Wingo explained. Mater gestured to a blinking yellow light hanging over the intersection.

"What's that for?" asked DJ.

"I'm deciding here 'n' now to make it the slow-down light," said Mater. "When you see it you keep it cool on the accelerator. Okay?"

The pranksters all nodded.

"I bet you guys could use some oil," said Flo as she passed around fresh cans.

So all the cars, from the slowest cars in town to the rushing visitors, all settled down to enjoy the beautiful day in Radiator Springs.

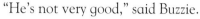

"Hey, Hey, We're the Vultures!"

"Nothing exciting ever happens around here," Buzzie complained to his vulture singing buddies.

"That's not true," said Flaps. "What about that fight we had with the tiger Shere Khan the other week?"

"Blimey, you're right," said Ziggy. "That was pretty exciting."

"But what are we gonna do now?" asked Buzzie.

"Why don't we sing?" suggested Ziggy.

"Hey, good idea!" said the other three vultures.

"Only one problem," said Dizzy. "We need a tenor."

"Aww, you're right," said Ziggy. "That little Man-cub fellow, Mowgli, would have been a great tenor. Too bad he left the jungle."

"So, what are we gonna do?" asked Buzzie.

"How about we hold an audition?" suggested Ziggy.

"Good thinking," said Flaps.

So the vultures put the word out in the jungle and, a week later, there was a line of animals ready to try out for the group.

"Name?" Buzzie asked the first applicant.

"Coconut," the monkey replied.

"All right, Coconut, let's hear ya sing," said Flaps.

Coconut shrieked for a few minutes, and the four vultures huddled together.

"He's not very good," said Buzzie.

"And he's a monkey," added Flaps.

"Next!" said Dizzy.

The vultures auditioned a lemur, two sloths, a wolf, a hippo, a toad and an elephant. None seemed like the right fit. Finally, the last animal stepped up.

"Name?" asked Buzzie.

"The name's Lucky," answered the vulture. "Hey, aren't you the four fellows that helped that little Man-cub scare away that tiger Shere Khan?"

"Yeah," said Buzzie. "We are."

"Then I guess you four might be called 'lucky' yourselves!" cried Lucky. He began to laugh at his own joke.

"Go ahead and sing," said Ziggy, rolling his eyes.

Lucky sang for a few minutes and the four vultures huddled together.

"He's not bad," said Dizzy.

"Plus, he's a vulture," said Ziggy.

"And he's the last one left," pointed out Flaps. That settled it.

"You're hired!" the vultures sang.

"See, told you I was Lucky!" said the vulture.

"But only with auditions," said Dizzy.

"Yeah," Buzzie chimed in. "When we meet Shere Khan again, we'll see how lucky you really are!"

Becoming a Legend

Dusty was waiting on the runway at JFK International Airport. The Wings Around the Globe rally was about to begin, but as Dusty looked around at the other competitors he started to feel very nervous. The other racers were all famous, and Dusty felt way out of his league.

"Hey, *amigo!* What's up?" asked El Chupacabra. El Chu was a Mexican racing legend and one of the fastest planes around. He was the Mexican champion, and considered himself to be one of the greatest racers in history.

Dusty told El Chu that he felt out of place among the famous racing champs, but the Mexican was quick to set his mind at rest. "No one's manufactured as a champion, you know?" he said. "The others all started from scratch, too."

Little King, a friendly Irish plane, trundled across the runway. "Your friend's right," he said. "Just try to do your best."

He explained that while he was now the number one racer in Ireland, it wasn't always the case. Little King had flown the County Cork mail route for years, battling heavy rain, driving winds and powerful thunderstorms.

"That's why I decided to try racing. I figured it couldn't be that much more demanding than delivering mail!" he laughed.

Another racer, Gunnar Viking, overheard their conversation and wanted to share his story. He said that back before he'd started racing he was an ambulance plane in Norway, flying much-needed spare parts all over the country. He'd had to learn to fly at high speeds, and that had given him the confidence to give racing a try.

"My story isn't quite so thrilling," said a little pink plane, who rolled over to join them. "I used to fly from city to city delivering small packages. That's why they call me Pack Rat!"

"And now you're a famous racer," said Dusty. He smiled, feeling much happier. All the other racers had come from humble beginnings, just like he had. Maybe he did belong at the rally, after all.

"What about you, Señor El Chu? Do you have a story to tell?" asked Little King.

El Chu puffed up his propeller. "*Si!* I wasn't always the greatest racer in Mexico," he told them. "I'm also a famous singer, and actor adored by audiences everywhere, a great *luchador* and...."

The other planes groaned and rolled their eyes. Dusty giggled. He and the others may all have come from modest beginnings, but there was certainly nothing humble about the legendary El Chupacabra!

Disney·PIXAR

MONSTERS UNIVERSITY

The Glove Challenge

One morning at Monsters University, Mike Wazowski was leaving his room to go to his first lesson of the day when suddenly something stopped him in his tracks. Right there, on the floor in front of him, was a bright pink human glove!

Mike screamed in fright. Monsters were not supposed to touch anything that belonged to a human because they were told it could contaminate them. If any item from the human world entered the monster world, the Child Detection Agency had to destroy the item and decontaminate any monster that touched it.

Hearing Mike's scream, the other monsters rushed out of their rooms.

They all gathered round the glove, staring at the strange object. It wasn't very often they got to see a real human belonging! Everyone started to wonder what would actually happen if they touched it....

The monsters began nudging each other, wondering if anyone would be brave enough to take on the glove challenge.

"I can touch it ... I'm not afraid!" shouted Mike, trying to sound confident.

"Easy there, little guy," grunted Sulley, moving to the front of the crowd. "Let a monster with real scare potential take care of this!"

Mike brought himself face to face with Sulley. "So touch it," he said. "I dare you!"

"And I double-dare you!" replied Sulley.

"Gentlemen," called a voice from the crowd. "Are you not up to the challenge?" It was Mike's rival, Johnny "The Jaw" Worthington. Johnny was the leader of the top fraternity at Monsters University, Roar Omega Roar, and had refused to let Mike join because he didn't think he was scary enough.

Mike was not going to let Johnny tease him in front of all the other monsters. He was determined to prove that he was brave enough to touch the glove. "Okay then," Mike said. "I'm gonna do it."

But Sulley wasn't going to let Mike take on the challenge on his own. "Let's do it together."

Slowly, they approached the glove. But just as they were reaching out their hands to touch it ... a voice calling out made them stop. "You've found it!" it shouted.

Mike and Sulley froze. Who could that be?

Suddenly a small, green monster with five eye stalks, like the shape of a hand, ran across the floor.

"My hat!" the monster said. "I was looking for that everywhere!" Then it picked the glove up, put it over its head and left – leaving behind a very confused bunch of monsters.

Bambi

The Winter Trail

One winter morning, Bambi was dozing in the wood when he heard a thumping sound nearby. "C'mon, Bambi!" his bunny friend Thumper called out. "It's a perfect day for playing."

Bambi followed Thumper through the forest. The sky was blue and the ground was covered in a blanket of new snow.

"Look at these tracks!" Thumper said excitedly. He pointed to a line of footprints in the snow. "Who do you suppose they belong to?" Bambi didn't know, so they decided to follow the trail. They soon came to a tree.

"Wake up, Friend Owl!" called Thumper.

"Have you been out walking?" Bambi asked.

"Now why would I do that?" Friend Owl replied. "My wings take me everywhere."

Bambi and Thumper continued on. Next, they spotted a raccoon sitting next to a tree, his mouth full of red berries.

"Hello, Mr Raccoon," Bambi said shyly. "Did you happen to see who made these tracks in the snow?"

The raccoon shook his head and began tapping the tree. "I know!" Thumper cried. "He thinks we should ask the woodpeckers."

Soon, Bambi and Thumper found the woodpecker family. "Did you make the tracks in the snow?" Thumper called up to the birds.

"No, we've been here all day," the mother bird answered.

"If the tracks don't belong to Friend Owl or the racoon and they don't belong to the woodpeckers, then whose can they be?" Bambi asked.

"I don't know," replied Thumper, curiously.

They soon reached the end of the trail, and the tracks led all the way to a snowy bush, where a family of quail was resting.

"Did you make these tracks?" Thumper asked.

"Why, yes," Mrs Quail answered. "Friend Owl told me about this wonderful bush. So this morning, my babies and I walked all the way over here."

Thumper and Bambi happily joined the quail family for a snack.

Soon, it was time for the friends to go home. They'd spent all day following the trail. When they turned to leave, a big surprise was waiting for them – their mothers! Bambi bounded over to his mother and stretched his nose up for a kiss.

"How'd ya find us?" Thumper asked.

Thumper's mother looked down at the tracks in the snow.

"You followed our trail!" Bambi cried. His mother nodded.

"Now, let's follow it back home," Bambi's mother said. So that's just what they did.

Small Fry

One evening, at Poultry Palace, Bonnie was excited to see which toy would come with her Fun Meal. She looked over at the display case, where she saw a mini Buzz Lightyear. "Can I have a Buzz Lightyear?" she asked.

The cashier shook his head. "I'm sorry. Those are for display only."

"Come on, Bonnie," said her mum.

Mini Buzz watched Bonnie playing in the ball pit with the real Buzz Lightyear and Rex. Then he leaped out of the display case and ran over to them.

When Bonnie wasn't looking, he pulled the real Buzz deep beneath the colourful balls. Then Mini Buzz popped up next to Rex.

Soon, Bonnie's mum put them in Bonnie's backpack. Mini Buzz was thrilled. Bonnie's mum hadn't noticed he wasn't the real Buzz!

Later that night, the real Buzz Lightyear crawled out of the ball pit. He was trapped inside Poultry Palace! As he tried to escape, he met some strange toys.

"Well, hello!" called a friendly mermaid toy. "Welcome to the support group for discarded Fun Meal toys."

The group of toys looked nice but Buzz knew he needed to get back to his friends. He just needed to work out how to escape....

In Bonnie's bedroom, Mini Buzz hopped out of the backpack. He greeted the other toys. "I'm Buzz Lightyear. I come in peace!"

"He says the plastic in the ball pit made him shrink," Rex told the others.

"No way. Where's the real Buzz?" Woody asked.

But Mini Buzz was having too much fun! He grabbed Woody's hat and ran around the room!

"It's playtime! I'll be the cowboy!" he yelled.

That was the last straw. The toys tackled Mini Buzz and tied him up. The little toy confessed that he had left Buzz in the ball pit!

The toys started planning a rescue mission. Hamm suggested picking the lock of Poultry Palace. One of the toys wanted to drive a truck through the front door!

"Or you could use the drive-through," came a new voice.

It was Buzz! He was back!

Buzz glared at Mini Buzz. "So, what do you have to say for yourself, Space Ranger?"

Mini Buzz just gulped.

Later at Poultry Palace, Mini Buzz apologized to Buzz with the help of the unwanted toys. "Sorry, Buzz. I just wanted to belong somewhere, but now I know I belong right here!"

The other toys applauded. It looked like Mini Buzz had found a place where he would fit in and be loved.

Disney
ROBIN
hood

Robin Lends a Hand

It was a hot day in Sherwood Forest – a very hot day! So hot that the Sheriff of Nottingham had decided not to collect taxes, for fear the coins would burn his greedy hands!

As for himself, Robin Hood was trying to keep cool in the shade of Sherwood's oaks. Taking off his hat, he stretched out under the tallest, broadest tree, closed his eyes and waited for a breeze.

"Halt! Who goes there?" he shouted suddenly. "Oh!" His eyes rested on a startled little bunny with a load of twigs scattered about his feet. "Skippy, my good man. Forgive me. I didn't mean to scare you."

Quickly, Robin helped to load up Skippy's arms once again. "Now, then," he said, patting the bunny on the shoulder. "That's better." But Skippy didn't seem to agree. Robin didn't think he had ever seen him look so unhappy.

"Why so glum, old chum?" Robin couldn't help but ask.

"Oh, Robin," Skippy sighed. "It's so very hot, and all the other children have gone to the swimming hole. But Mother has so many chores for me to do, I don't think I'll ever be able to join them."

"I see," said Robin, nodding. "That could get a fellow down, now, couldn't it?"

"I'll say," said Skippy.

"Unless ..." Robin went on with a big grin, "... a fellow had a friend to help him out!"

Skippy's sorrowful face grew brighter. "Do you mean...?"

"Indeed!" replied Robin, bending to pick up some sticks. "I have no other pressing engagements this sultry day. Allow me to assist you, my boy, and I dare say we shall have your chores done in half the time, at least."

"Hooray for Robin Hood!" Skippy cheered, nearly dropping his sticks once again.

And so, working together, Robin Hood and Skippy gathered firewood. They wrung out the laundry and hung it out to dry. They picked some juicy plums and a basketful of lettuce, weeded the garden and built a scarecrow. By lunchtime, in fact, not only was every one of Skippy's chores done, but he and Robin had washed all the windows and swept Skippy's cottage floor.

"Robin Hood, how can I ever thank you? I'd still be hard at work if it wasn't for you!" Skippy asked when they were through.

Robin scratched his head and thought for a moment. "I have it!" he declared at last. "Take me swimming with you!"

"Okay!" Skippy said happily. "C'mon, let's go! Last one in is a rotten sheriff!"

DISNEY · PIXAR

WALL·E

M-O's Luck

After hundreds of years cleaning up Earth on his own, one day everything changed for WALL•E. He met EVE and fell in love.

WALL•E followed EVE on an amazing journey to the Axiom spaceship, discovering all the wonders of space as they went. On the rings of Saturn he used his laser to carve EVE's name into a rock as a sign of his love. Then he sent it flying far, far away....

Following the discovery of plant life, the humans and robots of the Axiom spaceship had returned to Earth to clean up the planet and rebuild their home. But when they arrived they discovered there was still a lot of cleaning to do.

The landscape was every shade of brown imaginable with a few green plants growing defiantly out of the dry ground. In the distance, the sun shone behind mountains of rubbish.

Although taking down the giant tower of rubbish proved to be hard work, the clean-up operation was a success. It even left space to build houses for the worker-bots who had helped, including WALL•E and EVE's friend M-O. Now M-O finally had a place he could call home. M-O liked to keep his new house shiny and clean, but that wasn't always easy!

One day M-O was happily sprucing up his house, when he suddenly spotted a dust cloud approaching fast ... it was the other worker-bots on their way to visit him. M-O loved his friends but they always made such a mess!

M-O quickly zoomed towards his friends and called for them to stop. M-O was lucky – this time he managed to stop his friends from making his clean house all dirty. M-O turned and admired his house sparkling in the sunshine.

All of a sudden, a huge shadow fell across the ground covering M-O and his house in darkness. There was a deep rumbling sound coming from above and the ground began to shake. M-O looked up and saw a huge comet falling from the sky. It was heading straight towards his house!

M-O wheeled around frantically but there was nothing he could do. The comet hit the Earth with a great *KABOOM!* causing a huge pile of dirt and rubbish to fly up in the air.

M-O's little head popped up from beneath a mountain of dust that now completely covered him and his house. Maybe M-O wasn't so lucky after all!

M-O took a closer look at the rock that was now smoking in a crater by his house. With a start, he noticed EVE's name was engraved on the rock and surrounded by a big heart. His friends WALL•E and EVE would have some explaining to do when they returned!

Scrooge's Nature

"Would you look at that!" Huey pointed to a picture of a Junior Woodchuck relaxing in a hammock, while another camper fished in a nearby lake.

"And that!" Dewey's eyes widened. He pointed at a picture of a star-filled sky in the same brochure.

"Camping at Faraway Lake sure looks fun," Louie agreed. "Do you think Unca Scrooge would...?"

"You never know. He might pay for us to go," Huey said. The three boys looked at one another.

"Nah!" they said in unison. Uncle Scrooge may have been the richest duck in the world, but he did not part with his money easily.

"Let's show him, anyway," Huey said. "It's worth a shot."

The other boys followed Huey into their uncle's study.

Dewey nudged Huey forward. "Look at this, Unca Scrooge." Huey thrust the brochure into his uncle's lap.

"*Humph.*" Uncle Scrooge scowled at the glossy photos. "What have we got here, lads?"

"It's a camp. It's educational," Huey replied.

"Looks like a waste of my hard-earned money," the old duck said.

"But ... but we could camp out under the stars," Dewey said.

"And cook over a fire," Louie put in.

"And see nature," Huey added.

Uncle Scrooge's eyes narrowed. He looked from the brochure to his nephews' hopeful faces and back to the brochure. So, they wanted to learn about nature, did they?

"Here you are, boys," said Uncle Scrooge a short time later. He smiled from the safety of the screened-in back porch. "You have tents...." He indicated the three small leaky tents set up in the garden. "You can see the stars...." In fact, only one or two stars were visible. "And you're cooking over a fire," Scrooge finished, pointing at the tiny, smoky little flame.

Huey slapped at a mosquito on his arm. Dewey shook his head to chase away a cloud of gnats. Louie yelped as he was dive-bombed by a bat. Who knew the garden had so much nature in it!

"This is much better than that Junior Woodchuck nonsense, isn't it, boys?" Uncle Scrooge asked, with the smile of a duck who has saved himself a penny.

"Yes, Unca Scrooge," Huey, Dewey and Louie said. Then they turned back to the fire.

"I think ..." said Huey.

"... next time ..." continued Dewey.

"... we ask Unca Donald!" finished Louie.

Red Emergency

Radiator Springs was covered in a shimmering blanket of frost and snow.

"Hey, Ramone!" called Lightning McQueen as he glided across the ice. "It's the winter holidays. I thought you were going to paint yourself in special, festive colours?"

"I would like to," he said, with a sigh. "But I need some red paint and can't remember where I put it!"

Red paint was essential with Christmas coming up. It's the most festive colour you could possibly have!

"Out on the motorway there are trucks full of all sorts of supplies," Lightning pointed out. "Let's take a look."

On the roadside, they watched an army of busy cars racing to get to their families for the Christmas season.

"I don't see any paint trucks, do you?" Ramone asked glumly.

Lightning shook his head. "Sorry, Ramone!" he apologized.

Back in Radiator Springs, Ramone headed home, disheartened. "Looks like I will have to stay purple this year," he said.

As he was about to wish Lightning farewell, a colourful, painted tyre bounced in his path, causing him to brake sharply. There was only one place a new tyre could have escaped from....

Quickly, they drove over to Guido and Luigi's shop.

"Hi there, friends!" Guido greeted them.

Ramone stared at the tyres on the floor. They were painted a mixture of blues and greens. "So that's why you wanted to borrow my paints!" he said. "I'm desperate for some red! Do you have any left?"

Guido shook his head. "No! I only took the green and blue." Then he added hastily, "But I remember, Flo needed the red paint!"

Ramone's eyes widened in realization. "That's true! She's decorating the café for the holidays."

Ramone and Lightning took off, and found Flo outside her café full of fairy lights and tinsel.

"Of course I've got it!" she told Ramone, after he'd explained his predicament. "Had you forgotten?"

Ramone looked away embarrassed as Flo fetched his red paint can.

"Here it is, featherbrain!" she giggled.

Ramone smiled at her. "What would I do without you?" he said.

With a quick spritz, Ramone created a new winter coat of the brightest, cheeriest red for all to admire.

Now Ramone was the most festive car in all of Radiator Springs!

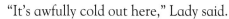

Sledging

Lady stood on the porch and watched as Jim Dear and Darling walked up the front path. Jim pulled a sledge and Darling held their son. They were all covered in snow, rosy-cheeked and smiling from ear to ear.

"That was fun! Wasn't it Darling?" Jim asked.

"I don't know the last time I had so much fun," Darling agreed, patting Lady on the head.

"But we should get out of these wet clothes before one of us catches a cold," Jim said, leaning the sledge against the side of the house.

"I agree," Darling said. And the three of them hurried inside.

Just then, Tramp came walking up the front path. "Hey, Pidge," he said to Lady. "What do you say we take this old thing for a spin?" He pointed a paw towards the sledge.

"What is it, anyway?" Lady asked him curiously, walking up to inspect the strange object more closely.

"A sledge!" Tramp told her.

"What do you do with it?" she said.

"You use it to ride down hills, Pidge," Tramp explained.

Lady looked worried. "That sounds dangerous," she said hesitantly.

"Nah, it's fun!" Tramp cried. "So, what do you say?"

"It's awfully cold out here," Lady said.

"Oh, come on," Tramp said. "It'll be great! You saw how much fun Jim Dear and Darling had." Tramp grabbed the rope in his teeth and pulled the sledge across the porch and down the steps.

Lady took off after him. "Wait for me!" she cried.

"Come on, Pidge!" Tramp encouraged her. "Jump on!"

Lady jumped onto the sledge, and Tramp pulled her down the snow-covered street and up to the top of a nearby hill. "What a view, huh?" he said.

"What a view indeed," Lady agreed. "What now?"

"Now, we ride," Tramp said. He pushed the sledge forwards and took a running leap onto it, sending them racing down the hill.

"Oh dear!" Lady yelped as they went down the hill, the wind blowing her ears back.

"Just hold on!" Tramp instructed.

Lady squeezed her eyes shut, and Tramp barked with excitement. But suddenly they hit a patch of ice, the sledge spun, and they went flying – right into a giant pile of snow!

Tramp jumped to his feet. "Pidge, are you okay?" he asked anxiously.

"Okay?" Lady asked. She was already pulling the sledge back up the hill. "Hurry up, Tramp! Let's do it again!"

Dangerous Pearls

One day, when Bonnie had gone out with her mum, the toys found a box of multi-coloured beads in her room.

"Hey, guys, come look at this!" Dolly called, opening the box for everyone to see. "They are pearls to create jewels."

"I've always loved necklaces," swooned Mrs Potato Head, trying on one of the brightly coloured strands of beads. "How does it suit me?"

"Very well," replied Mr Potato Head. "You look like the Queen of Potatoes!"

"They are just so fashionable!" said Jessie, as she attached some of the beads to her cowboy hat to add a touch of glamour.

"And funny too!" added Woody. "You can even use them to play ball." He grabbed a red bead from the box and kicked it towards Mr Potato Head.

"Mine!" called Mr Potato Head, as he caught the bead. "Are you ready? I'm going to pass it to ... Buttercup!" He launched the bead into the air, but as Buttercup the unicorn leaped into the air to get it – *CLONK!* – the bead got stuck on his horn!

When the bead didn't land on the floor, Buttercup got confused. "Huh? Where has it ended up?" he asked. He couldn't see that the bead had got stuck!

Mr Pricklepants started giggling. "It's on your horn!"

Buttercup shook his head from side to side, trying to shake the bead free, but it was stuck tight. He started to worry it would never come off.

"Take it away from me," he said sadly.

Mr Pricklepants thought if they pulled hard enough the bead would come off, but even when he and the aliens pulled together, it still wouldn't budge! The toys eventually collapsed in a heap on the floor.

"Nothing is working," sighed Woody.

"Wait!" said Buzz suddenly. "There is a better way." Holding a bead between his fingers, he explained, "We can thread something into the opposite hole of the bead to push Buttercup's horn out!"

"We could use my tail," Rex suggested. Buzz thought this was a great idea. Carefully, he threaded Rex's tail into the bead and – *pop!* – the bead came off.

Buttercup was delighted. "Hurray, I'm free!" She smiled, galloping around in celebration.

"Well done! You did it!" shouted Buzz. All the toys whooped and cheered, except Rex ... who was staring at the bead that was now stuck on the end of *his* tail.

He sighed. "Who's going to free me?"

Pinocchio

The Greatest Gift

Pinocchio was the luckiest boy in the whole world – and he knew it. No longer a wooden puppet, at last he was a real, live boy! And Pinocchio knew he owed it all to Geppetto for believing in him.

"I wish I could give Papa something in return," Pinocchio said to himself one day.

Pinocchio didn't have any money, so he decided to make a gift for Geppetto.

"Perhaps I should use Papa's tools and carve a present for him out of wood!" said Pinocchio.

So, one day while Geppetto was out, Pinocchio sat down at the woodworking bench. The problem was, Pinocchio didn't know how to do woodwork.

"That looks dangerous," said Pinocchio, eyeing a chisel. "I don't think Papa would want me to use that on my own." He decided he needed another gift idea. "I know!" he said. "Maybe I can cook something for Papa!"

Pinocchio went over to the hearth, where Geppetto did all of the cooking.

But he soon realized that he didn't know how to cook either. "And Papa is always telling me to stay a safe distance away from the fire," he reminded himself.

Pinocchio looked around the little house and spotted Geppetto's accordion sitting on the table.

"Of course!" cried Pinocchio. "Papa loves music. I could write him a song as a gift and then perform it for him!"

So Pinocchio picked up the accordion and began to play. But it sounded ... well ... awful!

"*Hmph*," Pinocchio said in frustration. "I don't know how to play the accordion *or* write a song." He put the accordion down and stood in the middle of the room. Tears were welling up in poor little Pinocchio's eyes when Geppetto came in through the front door.

"My boy," Geppetto said, "what is the matter?"

Through his tears, Pinocchio explained how he had wanted to make a gift to show Geppetto how much he appreciated everything his father had done for him.

As Geppetto listened, his look of worry softened into a smile, and then *his* eyes welled up with tears. "My son," he said, "don't you know that you, and you alone, are the greatest gift a father could ever want?"

"I am?" Pinocchio asked.

"You are," replied Geppetto.

"Well, in that case," said Pinocchio with a sly grin on his face, as he hugged his papa, "you're welcome!"

Then Geppetto picked up the accordion and they sang and danced all evening!

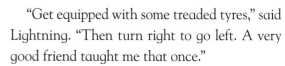

Rematch!

Lightning McQueen and Francesco Bernoulli had challenged each other to a race in Monza, Italy – Francesco's hometown.

"*Benvenuto!*" said Francesco. "Your plane was late, but this is no surprise. You will be late crossing the finish line, too."

Lightning smiled. Then he whispered to Mater, "I am so beating him – right here on his own turf!"

As they left the airport, the cars were surrounded by photographers.

"Everyone just loves Francesco. He has too many fans," said Francesco.

"Nobody has more fans than Lightning!" Mater piped up. He showed Francesco some bags overflowing with fan letters.

"Francesco has much, much more fan mail!" said Francesco.

Lightning cruised over to Francesco. "How about a warm-up before the big race – just you and me?" he asked.

Francesco nodded. "Ah, good idea, Lightning! Try to keep up, if you –"

Before Francesco could finish, Lightning was a red streak down the road! "Ka-*ciao*, Francesco!" yelled Lightning.

Francesco was just about to catch up when he nearly spun out of control on a left turn.

"How do you make those left turns so well?" Francesco asked Lightning.

"Get equipped with some treaded tyres," said Lightning. "Then turn right to go left. A very good friend taught me that once."

They finally stopped. Francesco sighed. "Ahh, Italia is beautiful, no?" he said, looking out over the landscape. "Just like Francesco!"

Lightning chuckled. "Do you always think about yourself?" he asked.

"Of course," Francesco replied. "On the track, Francesco only thinks about himself and doing his best. This is why he always wins!"

The next day was the big race. Francesco came out of the first left turn ahead. He showed off his new treaded tyres. "Perhaps Lightning has taught Francesco too well!"

As Lightning zoomed along, he was distracted by camera flashes and screaming fans. Suddenly Lightning remembered what Francesco had said about focusing on himself and doing his best. Lightning looked straight ahead and took the lead!

As the two cars crossed the finish line, the crowd gasped. The race was ... a tie!

The cars tried to figure out what to do. Then Francesco shouted, "No more talk! Talk is slow. What do we do? We race!"

Then the two fastest cars in the world zoomed away together!

RATATOUILLE
(rat·a·too·ee)

A Present Fit for a Chef

It was the day before Remy's birthday. Emile and Django were trying to decide what to give him as a present.

Django said they had to get his son a present that was fit for a rat, and suggested they get him a piece of rubbish. Emile insisted his brother would be much happier with something that was fit for a chef.

They decided to compromise, and set off to find a piece of rubbish that a chef would love. Emile led his dad up onto the street. They scurried between feet and dodged through the shadows, trying to stay out of sight.

They stopped outside a kitchen supplies shop. "I'm sure Remy would love one of these pieces of rubbish," Emile said, but Django said it wasn't the right sort of place for a rat. Sure enough, as they stared in the window they heard a scream from nearby. Both rats darted away as people threw things at them, trying to scare them off.

They headed for a rubbish tip and searched there, instead. For hours they dug through the rubbish, but while they found plenty of gifts suitable for a rat, there was nothing fit for a chef.

Emile decided there was only one thing to do. They needed help, and so he and Django went to see Linguini and Colette in the kitchen.

The two humans stared down in confusion as the rats waved their arms and squeaked, trying to explain their problem.

Eventually, Django decided enough was enough. He'd never trusted humans, and thought there was no way they'd ever understand what the rats were trying to do. They'd just have to find a present by themselves.

The next day, a crowd of rats gathered outside the restaurant. They sang "Happy Birthday" and presented Remy with cakes. Django and Emile gave him a gift-wrapped present, and when Remy opened it he couldn't believe his eyes.

It was a colander – a metal bowl with hundreds of tiny holes to let water drain through. It was a present fit for a chef!

Emile and Django shook hands. They'd done it. Remy loved his bowl, even if it did have all those holes in it.

As the rats celebrated, Linguini appeared at the door. He bent down and handed Remy a present wrapped in cheese-coloured paper.

Remy opened the gift and cheered when he saw the tiny chef's hat inside.

Django gasped in surprise. The humans had understood what they were trying to say. Maybe rats and humans weren't so different, after all....

Partysaurus Rex!

One day, Mr Potato Head and the other toys were having a bubble party. Everyone was having fun until Rex ran towards a bubble and – *pop!* – it burst. The other toys were annoyed and called him "Party-pooper Rex!" Rex was embarrassed.

Just then Bonnie grabbed him and hurried to the bathroom. "Bath time!" she called excitedly.

Rex was a little anxious because he'd never been in a bathtub before!

"Do you want to flood the house?" Bonnie's mum joked when she saw how full the tub was. She pulled the plug and helped Bonnie to get out, leaving Rex behind.

"Welcome aboard!" called Cap'n, a tugboat toy, after Bonnie and her mum had left. "What do they call ye, sailor?"

"Partysaurus Rex!" Rex exclaimed. He wanted these toys to think he was fun.

Just then, the last of the water gurgled down the drain and the bath toys fell onto their sides at the bottom of the bath. Without water, they couldn't move!

Rex wanted to help the bath toys. *Maybe I could turn the water on?* he thought. So he turned on the tap, pushed the plug into place and the bath began to fill. Then he pressed a button on a toy with flashing lights and music!

"Partysaurus, you rock!" said Ducky.

The toys tossed beads round Rex's neck. Then a toy squid jumped on his head, and Helga the soap dispenser put her Viking hat on top of the squid. Rex was really starting to look like a partysaurus!

But Rex was also nervous. The tub was full of toys now! Fearful that the water would overflow, Rex tried to turn the tap off, but it broke! So he pulled the stopper on top of the tap, instead. Everything was silent then the shower came on, filling the bathtub even faster!

Rex could see water creeping over the edge of the tub. "Overflow!" he cried. Helpless, Rex screamed as the water swept everyone over the edge!

Meanwhile, when Rex hadn't returned, Buzz, Woody and the rest of the gang had gone to the bathroom to look for him.

"I'm a partysaurus!" said Rex proudly, when his friends asked what he was doing.

"You?" scoffed Mr Potato Head.

Just then, a voice came through the window. "*Psst!* Partysaurus!"

Outside, water toys surrounded Bonnie's swimming pool.

"Rex! Rex! Rex!" they chanted.

Rex's friends were stunned.

"Duty calls!" said Rex, jumping out of the window. Partysaurus Rex was back!

Disney
101 DALMATIANS

Having a Ball!

"Ten days until Santa!" the spotted puppies barked, bouncing into one another as they tumbled down the hall.

"Ten days until presents!" Penny barked.

"And 10 days until Christmas dinner!" Rolly added, licking his lips.

"Ten days to stay out of trouble!" Pongo said with a smile.

"Do you puppies know what comes before Santa and dinner and presents?" Perdita asked.

"Umm ... stockings?" Lucky asked.

"No," Perdita said, laughing. "Before that."

Patch wasn't sure. He sat down on the hall rug to think.

"We have to decorate and sing carols," Perdita said, wagging her tail. At that very moment, Roger and Anita threw open the door to the study and invited all the dogs inside.

Patch blinked. He couldn't believe his eyes. "What's a tree doing in the house?"

"Just watch." Perdy gave Patch a quick lick.

While the dogs looked on, Roger and Anita began to decorate the tree. They hung lights and angels, snowmen and tinsel. Of all the decorations, Patch liked the glittering glass balls best. He could not take his eyes off them.

When the tree was ready, Anita brought in hot chocolate and dog biscuits. Munching on a biscuit in front of the fire, Patch didn't think the evening could get any better. Then Roger sat down at the piano, and everyone began to sing.

Patch howled along with the others, but he could not stop looking at the balls on the tree. A large red one was hanging near the floor.

Patch reached over and gave the ball a light tap with his front paw. It swung merrily above him. Looking at his reflection, Patch started to laugh. His nose looked huge!

"What are you doing?" Penny stopped singing to see what was so funny. Then Freckles joined them, then Lucky. The puppies took turns knocking the ball and watching it sway, then – CRASH! – it fell to the floor, shattering.

The singing stopped. Poor Patch was sure the special evening was ruined.

"Oh dear." Anita scooped the puppies out from under the tree. "Careful, now," she said. "Those balls aren't for playing with."

While Roger swept up the glass, Patch cowered. He knew he was in trouble.

"Maybe I should give you all one gift early," Anita smiled. Patch couldn't believe his luck. Instead of a firm talking-to, each puppy got to open a small package. Patch tore off the paper. Inside was a brand-new red rubber ball!

Red Alert!

"Nice work with the wheat husker," Flik said. He smiled with satisfaction as he watched a troop of ants lower the contraption that lightly smashed the wheat kernels. Flik wondered how the colony had ever got along *without* his clever inventions.

"How's it going with the berry masher?" called a voice. It was Atta, the colony's queen.

"I was just heading over to take a look," Flik said, smiling at Queen Atta. "Care to join me?"

"Sure," Atta said as she led the way to the berry-mashing area. Mashing berries was messy, so the ants did it in a special part of the anthill.

"Cowabunga!" called a large ant. Ten dozen ants leaped off a rock onto a giant lever. The lever lowered, pressing a flat rock onto a pile of berries. Sweet red juice squirted out from the sides and dripped into carved wooden bowls.

When all the juice was squeezed out of the berries, Atta dipped her finger into a bowl for a taste.

"Delicious," she said. Red juice stained her mouth and chin.

"The berries were especially sweet this year," Flik said modestly.

"And with your new invention we should have plenty of juice for this year's feast," Atta said. "As long as Dot and the Blueberries don't drink it all first," she added.

Flik laughed. Dot and her Blueberry friends loved berry juice and were always trying to dip into it before the feast. They had already been shooed away from the berry masher more than once in the last week.

"Good work, masher ants!" Flik called to the group climbing back up to their jumping rock. Another group was making a pile of fresh berries.

They had nearly finished piling a huge mound of berries, when suddenly the alarm sounded.

"Alert, alert!" a guard ant called through a megaphone made from a rolled-up leaf. "Red fire ants are storming the colony!"

Flik, Atta and the masher ants fled the food area as fast as their legs could carry them. Sure enough, they soon ran into half a dozen red ants. Flik was about to charge when he heard a familiar voice.

"Flik, it's me!" it said. The voice sounded like ... Dot's.

"Hold on!" Flik shouted. The ants stopped. Flik quickly wiped the first red ant's sticky face. "These aren't fire ants," Flik explained. "They're Blueberries – covered in berry juice!" He smiled at Atta. "Maybe we should call them Redberries, instead!"

Racing for Good

Early one morning in Radiator Springs, Lightning was showing around a special guest – racing superstar Jeff Gorvette.

"Thanks for helping me out with this charity race for Antique Auto Aid," Jeff said. "I hope we raise a lot of money to help older cars."

They headed towards the track.

"And it will be good to see some of our old racing buddies," said Jeff.

"You're right," replied Lightning. "In fact, I think I can see one now. *Ciao*, Francesco!"

"Francesco is happy to race for charity," said the Italian racing car. "Francesco is so generous and wonderful!"

Lightning laughed. "Ah, Francesco, you haven't changed."

Then more racers arrived. Shu Todoroki revved his motor. Carla Veloso showed off some quick turns and Nigel Gearsley, the suave English gentlecar, greeted friends with a wink.

Then a familiar green car pulled up. It was Chick Hicks! Lightning was suspicious.

"I guess my invitation got lost in the mail," said Chick.

"Well, Chick, we didn't think this type of race was your thing," said Jeff.

"Are you afraid I'll beat you guys?" Chick exclaimed.

Lightning sighed. "Fine, you can race. But you'd better be on your best behaviour."

But during the race, Chick was up to his usual dirty tricks. He smashed into Nigel and then made Carla and Shu spin out. "Ha-ha-ha ... OW!" Chick realized he had dented his side.

Chick tried to ram Francesco, but he swerved out of the way and Chick scraped up against the wall. "Yeooow!" he cried.

Chick caught up with Jeff and Lightning. The two friends winked at each other and slowed down, letting Chick pull out in front.

"Who's the big winner here today? It's ... AAHHHH!" Chick went into a tailspin – right over the finish line!

Chick hobbled up onto the winner's podium. "Well? Give me the money and trophy already!" he yelled.

Lightning presented a giant cheque to Chick. Then Lizzie, the charity spokescar, took the cheque straight back from him.

"Hey! What's going on?" exclaimed Chick.

"Chick, thanks for helping us raise so much money for charity," said Jeff.

Chick was stunned. "I did *what?*"

Lightning laughed. "That's right, Chick. You actually raced for a good cause. Next time, just don't beat yourself up over it!"

DISNEY
DUMBO
The Show Must Go On

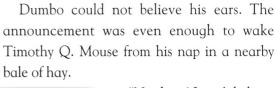

The wind whistled around the big top, pulling the canvas tent that Dumbo was holding out of reach of his small trunk. "I'll get it," Dumbo's mother said as the tent flapped over their heads.

If the weather hadn't been so terrible, Dumbo thought, *I could have flown up to grab the edge of the tent.* But the whipping wind was too much, even for Dumbo's wing-like ears.

At last, standing on her back legs, Mrs Jumbo caught the canvas in her trunk. She pulled it taut and let the roustabouts tie it off. But Dumbo noticed several new rips in the fabric.

"Quit your clowning!" the Ringmaster barked at the clowns. He had noticed the rips, too. He ordered the clowns to sew them up. "The repairs must be finished by showtime!"

Dumbo felt terrible. All the circus performers, animals and roustabouts were working hard in the storm. He had gone and made even more work, by letting the canvas get torn. And now the Ringmaster's mood was as foul as the weather!

Just then, Dumbo noticed another blast of cold air whirl the Ringmaster's black top hat off his head.

"That does it!" the Ringmaster shouted. "There will be no show tonight!"

Dumbo could not believe his ears. The announcement was even enough to wake Timothy Q. Mouse from his nap in a nearby bale of hay.

"No show? I can't believe it!" Timothy cried. The rest of the circus folk couldn't believe it either. They silently continued to set up.

"What a fuss over a hat," Timothy shook his head. "The show must go on."

Dumbo nodded. Then something caught his eye. The Ringmaster's hat was caught on the flagpole, high over the Big Top. Perhaps he could get it for him?

Bravely, Dumbo took off. The wind was strong, but he tucked his head down and flapped his ears hard. When the wind calmed for a moment, the small elephant saw his chance. He grabbed the top hat and flew back down.

Shyly, Dumbo held out the hat to the Ringmaster.

"Thank you, Dumbo." The Ringmaster took his hat gratefully. He looked around at all the people and animals still hard at work and felt a little embarrassed. Then, as he placed the hat on his head, he shouted, "The show must go on!"

Everyone cheered.

"What'd I tell ya?" Timothy asked, winking at Dumbo.

Old Man Octopus

"You're "It"!" Nemo tagged Sheldon, who was hiding next to a mollusc.

"Aw, man!" Sheldon swished his tail. "I'm going to get you next time, Nemo."

"Only if you can find me," Nemo teased. Then he called louder, "Olly, Olly, all swim free!" The rest of the fish, who were playing hide-and-seek, returned to the giant barnacle they were using as base. When they were all there, Sheldon began to count again.

Nemo swam away, scanning the reef for a good hiding spot. Sheldon would be out to get him for sure. Nemo swam past a large empty shell. "Hmm ... too easy," he muttered. He darted into an anemone. "Way too obvious." Finally he came to a dark cave in the coral. "Too dark," he shivered, looking into the spooky opening. "It'll be perfect."

Mustering his courage, Nemo swam inside. At first he couldn't see anything. Then, as his eyes adjusted to the dark, Nemo saw a large eye open on the cave wall. What could it be?

Another eye opened. Then the entire wall began to move.

"O-old Man Octopus!" Nemo stammered as eight long arms oozed off the cave wall. Nemo and his friends swapped stories about Old Man Octopus at sleepovers. In the stories, Old Man Octopus sneaked up on little fish and gave them a terrible scare.

"Sorry to disturb you," Nemo swam towards the cave entrance. Then he noticed something amazing. The octopus's arms were changing colour and texture! Instead of matching the brown bumpy cave wall, now they looked more like the reddish coral at the bottom of the cave.

"You didn't disturb me, boy. Tell me what brings you to this corner of the reef?" The octopus's voice was slow and kind, and Nemo's fear melted away.

"Hide-and-seek, sir," Nemo answered politely. "But I wouldn't need a cave if I could camouflage myself like you!"

Old Man Octopus laughed. "Hide-and-seek, eh? One of my favourites. The camouflage does come in handy, but nothing beats a cloud of ink when you want to make a break for the base!"

"You can shoot ink clouds, too?" Nemo was so excited he forgot to be quiet.

"I hear you, Nemo!" Sheldon shouted.

"Are you ready to swim for it?" Old Man Octopus whispered with a wink.

Nemo nodded. He high-fived one of Old Man Octopus's tentacles. Then, in a burst of inky blackness, he darted out of the cave, past Sheldon, and all the way back to the barnacle base. Safe!

Disney
The Fox and the Hound
Tod's Homecoming

Tod the fox wanted to show his fox friend Vixey where he grew up. He took her to the top of a hill where they could look down on a beautiful valley.

"I grew up on Widow Tweed's farm," said Tod, pointing with his paw at a farm nestled in the valley. "She took care of me when I was just a cub.

"And that's my best friend Copper," Tod said, pointing to a handsome hound. "Copper lives at Amos Slade's farm. His house is right next door to Mrs Tweed's."

As the two foxes watched, Widow Tweed, Amos Slade and Amos's cranky old dog, Chief, climbed into an old banger. With a puff of smoke, they drove off.

But Copper was still at home. He was near the fence, snoozing under an old barrel.

"Let's go visit Copper," said Tod.

"Not me!" Vixey declared. "I'm a fox, and I'm not fond of hounds. I'll catch some fish for our dinner. See you later."

Alone, Tod scampered down the hill, excited about seeing his old pal. But, when he got there, he spotted a strange man sneaking into Amos Slade's hen house.

"Wake up, Copper!" yelled Tod. "A chicken thief is raiding the hen house!"

Copper woke with a start and leaped into action. But the rope around his neck held him back.

"You'll have to stop that chicken thief yourself!" cried Copper.

"But I can't stop him alone!" Tod replied.

"We'll help," someone chirped. Tod looked up and saw Dinky the sparrow and Boomer the woodpecker sitting on the fence.

"Let's go!" said Tod.

Tod burst into the hen house first. The thief was there, holding a squawking chicken in either hand. Tod bit the man on the ankle.

"Ouch!" howled the thief.

Boomer flew through the window and pecked at the chicken snatcher's head. The thief dropped the chickens and covered his head.

Meanwhile, Dinky untied the knot that held Copper. Now, Copper was free – and angry, too! Barking, he charged at the burglar.

Eggs flying, the chicken snatcher screamed and ran. As he raced down the road, Dinky and Boomer flitted around his head, pecking him until he was out of sight. The fox and the hound trotted back to the farm.

"Good to see you, Tod," said Copper, wagging his tail. "What brings you here?"

"I just stopped by for a quiet visit," Tod replied.

"It was real quiet, all right!" said Copper.

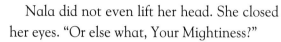

All Wet

Timon pounded his tiny chest and gave a mighty yell as he swung out over the lagoon. He let go of a vine and threw his arms out wide, hitting the water with a small but very satisfying smack. He popped to the surface, shouting, "Ta-da!"

Pumbaa was next. "Look out below!" he called. He backed up on the rock ledge, then charged. The warthog's splash sent water flying high into the air. The lagoon was still rippling when he surfaced.

"Not bad," Simba said. "But I bet Nala could do better." The Lion King looked up at Nala, who was sunning herself on a rock as far from the water as possible.

"Ha!" Nala laughed. "You know I don't like to get wet."

"Oh, come on, Nala. Give it a try. The water's fine!" Simba said.

"I know the water *is* fine ..." Nala replied slowly, rolling over and licking her paw, "... for drinking."

Pumbaa and Timon sniggered. Simba frowned. Nala was making him look silly in front of his friends. Was he King of the Pride Lands or not?

Using his most commanding voice, Simba gave Nala an order. "You will come swimming with us right now, or else!"

Nala did not even lift her head. She closed her eyes. "Or else what, Your Mightiness?"

Simba couldn't come up with anything, so the argument was over. And Nala, as usual, had won.

Accepting his defeat, Simba ran to the edge of the rocky ledge, sprang high in the air and tucked his paws in for a royal cannonball.

Pumbaa and Timon were drenched. Simba signalled to them as they came out of the water. He pointed at his dripping mane and then up at Nala's rock.

Timon winked, and he and Pumbaa began a noisy mock water fight to distract Nala. While they hollered and splashed, Simba climbed up to Nala's warm spot in the sun. He walked quickly but silently. Drawing closer, he crouched, his legs coiled to pounce. Nala did not move.

Then, with a triumphant roar, Simba jumped onto Nala's rock and gave his sopping mane a mighty shake. Nala was drenched.

Nala leaped to her feet with a snarl. Simba rolled onto his back, laughing.

"You're all wet, Nala!" Timon guffawed. Pumbaa was laughing so hard, he could barely breathe.

Nala tried to glare fiercely at Simba, but she couldn't. She had to laugh, too. "King of the practical jokers," she said.

Bambi
Night-time is for Exploring!

As the moon rose above the forest, Bambi snuggled close to his sleeping mother. What a day it had been! Exploring new places, learning new words and meeting new friends. Bambi yawned and closed his eyes....

"Bambi! Oh, Bambi!"

Bambi slowly opened his eyes. "Thumper?" he whispered. "Why aren't you asleep?"

"Asleep? Come on!" cried Thumper. "Sleep is for the birds! How can you sleep when there's so much to see and do at night?"

"But everybody knows that night-time is for sleeping," Bambi said.

"Oh, brother," Thumper said. "Do you have a lot to learn! Follow me, Bambi, and I'll show you how the night is a whole new day!"

And suddenly, at the prospect of a new adventure, Bambi's sleepiness disappeared. Quietly, he stood up and let Thumper lead the way.

Thumper was right – the forest was as busy at night as it was during the day, but with a whole new group of animals. Owls, opossums, raccoons and badgers – all those animals that Bambi thought spent most of their lives asleep – were now as lively as could be.

"Wh-wh-what's that?" Bambi exclaimed, as a dot of light landed on his nose.

"Don't worry, Bambi, it's just a firefly," Thumper said with a giggle.

"'Firefly'," Bambi said. Then suddenly, the little light disappeared. "Hey, where'd it go?"

"There it is!" cried Thumper, pointing to Bambi's tail. "No, wait. It's over there."

Happily, Thumper and Bambi chased the firefly as it flitted from one friend to the other. "I think he likes us!" Thumper cried.

But their game was soon interrupted by a flurry of sound. Thousands of leathery wings were suddenly beating overhead.

"Duck, Bambi!" hollered Thumper, just as the whole group swooped around their heads.

"Boy, that was close!" said Thumper.

"Were those fireflies, too?" Bambi asked.

"Naw," Thumper laughed. "They didn't light up! Those were bats."

"'Bats'," repeated Bambi. "They're really busy at night."

"You can say that again," agreed Thumper, trying to stifle a yawn. And, since yawns are contagious, Bambi's own yawn was not far behind.

"This was fun," Bambi told his friend. "But what do you say we go home and go to bed?"

But there was no answer ... Thumper was already fast asleep!

A Snowy Mission

One snowy winter morning when Bonnie was off at Sunnyside, Jessie looked out of the bedroom window and gasped. A little bird was hopping about in the snow, searching for something to eat.

"That bird seems so hungry," she said.

"I guess it's hard to find food in the snow," said Buzz.

The friends decided to help the bird. "We could get some crumbs from the bread box and feed it," suggested Woody.

"That's a galactic plan!" said Buzz, and Jessie was quick to agree.

The toys headed to the kitchen. Jessie and Woody held a bag open on the floor, while Buzz climbed up to the bread box to gather up the crumbs. "Are you ready, guys?" he asked, then he swept the crumbs off the shelf ...

... and missed the bag completely! Woody sighed as the crumbs rained down on his hat, then he and Jessie set to work scooping them all up into the bag.

Finally, when the bag was full, they pushed open the door and ventured out into the garden. The front step was slippery, and the garden was full of deep snow.

"Hold on!" said Jessie. "I don't want to get wet."

The others agreed. If they got wet, Bonnie would know they'd been outside. "We need some waterproof garments," said Buzz, spotting Bonnie's welly boots beside the door.

Jessie knew just what to do. "Ta-dah!" she said, bringing a roll of cling film from the kitchen.

"What do you want to do with that?" Woody asked, confused.

Jessie winked. "You'll find out," she said, and she set to work wrapping each of Buzz and Woody's legs in the clear plastic wrap. She did her own legs next, and soon all three of them were wearing a home-made waterproof outfit.

Safe from getting wet, the toys stepped out into the snow. It was hard to walk, and by the time they reached the middle of the garden their legs ached. As they began to spread the crumbs, Jessie spotted the little bird swooping in.

The bird chirped with delight as it spotted the crumbs, and began to hungrily peck at them. The toys smiled at a job well done. "Finally, we can go back inside and get some rest," said Buzz.

"Um ... yeah," said Woody, looking up. The branches of a nearby tree were full of birds, all cheeping and chirping hopefully.

Woody and the others got back to their aching feet. "But first, we've got to feed some more friends!"

Mickey's Night Before Christmas

'Twas the night before Christmas, and all through the town, most creatures were stirring and scurrying 'round.

The stockings were hung by the chimney with care, while Mickey sat back in his big comfy chair.

When out on the lawn there arose such a clatter, Mickey sprang from his chair to see what was the matter. Away to the door Mickey flew in a flash. Had Goofy arrived with his usual crash?

Then what to his wondering eyes should appear, but a jingle-bell sleigh – were those really reindeer? And a little old driver so cheerful and bright, could this be Uncle Scrooge? Yes, it was! What a sight!

"Yoo-hoo!" called out Minnie. "May we join the fun?" And Morty and Ferdie showed up on the run.

"Hiya, pal!" called a voice from a Pluto-led sleigh.

"It's Goofy!" cried Huey. "Grab snowballs! Let's play!"

Just then, "Time for dinner!" rang out through the house. Every creature was stirring – each dog, duck and mouse!

Pass the turkey and stuffing and cranberries, please! Mashed potatoes, gravy, carrots and peas! Seconds for anyone? Now, don't be shy. Did you get enough food? Did you save room for pie?

When they'd filled themselves up from their heads to their shoes, they all settled down for a short winter snooze. Each found a spot and soon dozed in their beds, while visions of Christmas treats danced in their heads.

Then out of the sky flew a wonderful sight – it was jolly St Nick on his Christmas Eve flight! St Nick crossed the roof with a leap and a bound, and sprang to the chimney, not making a sound.

On the hearth down below, Pluto thought, *What is this?* as a clump of wet snow doused the fire with a hiss. Then all of a sudden, a man all in red, plopped right down that chimney … and patted his head!

"Merry Christmas!" he said, giving Pluto a hug. Then he left a big sack on the living room rug. And laying a finger aside of his nose, and giving a nod – up the chimney he rose.

The clock chimed at midnight and on the last stroke … "It's Christmas!" yawned Grandma. Those nappers awoke!

"Let's open the presents!" the kids called with glee.

"What's this?" Mickey asked. "There's a sack by the tree! Now we all have our gifts, so let's give a big cheer! Merry Christmas to all, and a happy new year!"

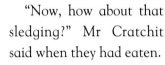

A Merry Christmas

"Merry Christmas!" Ebenezer Scrooge crowed as he watched the Cratchit children open the gifts he'd brought.

"A teddy bear!" Tiny Tim exclaimed. His sister had a new doll, and his brother was busy playing with a new train set.

"And there's another present, too," Scrooge said with a twinkle in his eye. "I'll be right back." A moment later, he reappeared, holding a big package wrapped in red paper and tied with a giant green bow.

The children squealed in delight as they opened it.

"Father, it's a sledge!" they cheered.

"I can see that," Bob Cratchit replied, looking up from the turkey he was carving. Scrooge had brought the turkey over that very morning.

"Can we go sledging? Can we? Can we?" the children chorused.

"Of course," Cratchit replied. "But not until after dinner."

"And dinner is ready right now," Mrs Cratchit said.

"Dinner!" the children shouted as they scrambled to their seats at the table.

Mrs Cratchit sat down at the table. "I can't remember when we've had such a feast, Mr Scrooge," she said happily. "Thank you."

Scrooge raised his glass in the air. "That's what Christmas is all about," he said warmly. "Happiness and goodwill."

Everyone clinked glasses in agreement, then got busy eating.

"Now, how about that sledging?" Mr Cratchit said when they had eaten.

Minutes later, everyone was wrapped up warm. Scrooge pulled the children through town, singing Christmas carols at the top of his lungs.

"Why is everyone staring at Mr Scrooge?" Tiny Tim asked his father.

Mr Cratchit smiled at his son. "Because they like him," he said.

"I like him too," Tiny Tim said, as Scrooge pulled the sledge to the top of a hill. Everyone climbed off to look at the steep slope.

Scrooge picked up the sledge and walked several paces away from the top of the hill. Then, taking a running start, he jumped onto the sledge and raced to the bottom.

"Whoopeeee!" he cried.

Then Scrooge pulled the sledge back up the hill. "Who's next?" he asked, panting.

"Me!" Tiny Tim shouted. Everyone else got a few turns, too.

Later, as he pulled the children back to their house, Scrooge felt warm despite the chill in the air. This was the merriest Christmas he could remember.

Stanley Claus

Radiator Springs was a glorious sight. Fairy lights covered buildings. Christmas stockings hung from shop windows. Even the statue of Stanley proudly wore a Santa hat.

"Everyone's going to be amazed with all these decorations, Ramone," said Lightning McQueen.

Ramone was busy using his spray paints against a brick wall, creating a mural of Santa in his sleigh – cars pulling him through the sky instead of reindeer. "My painting will be the best part of all!"

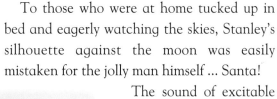

Sarge looked at Ramone's work curiously. "Don't be sparing with the red, soldier," he advised, with his critical eye for detail.

"I've brought buckets of it, Sarge." Ramone reversed to admire the job so far....

SPLOSH! Ramone accidentally sent the paint barrels tumbling like dominoes. Red paint flooded the road and sloshed all over Stanley's statue.

Ramone turned to see the damage, but felt his wheels sliding in the paint puddles.

BASH! "Ouch!" Ramone moaned as he struck Stanley's podium. The cars all gasped as Stanley was knocked flying into the air.

Like a shooting star, Stanley soared through the night sky, getting tangled in the hanging decorations and lights.

To those who were at home tucked up in bed and eagerly watching the skies, Stanley's silhouette against the moon was easily mistaken for the jolly man himself ... Santa!

The sound of excitable cries could be heard across Radiator Springs.

Then Stanley landed in a pile of tyres.

"Luckily he didn't get damaged," said Lightning McQueen, as they dragged Stanley back.

"I gotta clean this mess up before Doc finds out what I've done," Ramone said, frantically cleaning up puddles of paint.

The next morning, the cars yawned with exhaustion. Everything was clean again with not a speck out of place.

Just then, Doc approached. "Well, it looks like something happened last night," Doc said.

"It wasn't my fault!" Ramone cried. "We were just –"

"Unable to sleep!" cut in Sarge. "I went to the window and saw Santa Claus fly by!"

All the cars watched Doc's face as he mulled this over. Santa Claus? In the sky?

"Amazing," Doc murmured at last, admiring the decorations around Stanley's podium.

Ramone sighed with relief and Sarge grinned. No one else needed to know about Stanley's little adventure among the stars....

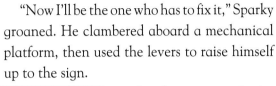

Disaster Zone

Barbara and Brody, owners of the Landing Zone motel, were heading off for the day, leaving Sparky and Dusty in charge.

"It's very kind of you to fill in for us while we're gone," said Barbara. She and her husband set off, promising they'd be back later that evening.

Dusty and Sparky were excited to have been left in charge. As they checked the first few guests in, they both came to the conclusion that running a motel wasn't all that difficult.

There was one thing Dusty was desperate to do – turn on the big neon sign above the building. Sparky didn't see the point. After all, it was still daytime, and the sign could only be seen at night.

"But I've always wanted to do it!" Dusty said. He pressed the button and gazed up at the sign ... but the light didn't come on.

"Don't you see? It's not plugged in," Sparky said, pointing towards where the sign's plug lay on the ground next to the power socket.

Dusty knew just how to sort that. Using his fuel-filling arm, he scooped up the plug and carefully pushed it into the socket.

Suddenly, there was a flash and a loud bang. The sign above the motel flashed and fizzed, as it short-circuited in a spectacular shower of sparks.

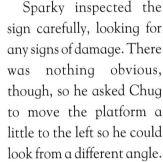

"Now I'll be the one who has to fix it," Sparky groaned. He clambered aboard a mechanical platform, then used the levers to raise himself up to the sign.

Sparky inspected the sign carefully, looking for any signs of damage. There was nothing obvious, though, so he asked Chug to move the platform a little to the left so he could look from a different angle.

Chug tried shoving the platform, but it was stuck. "It won't budge!" he said.

Sparky realized too late that the platform was caught on the sign. As Chug gave it a final big push, the platform broke the sign in half. The friends both watched in horror as the broken sign smashed against the ground.

"We've got to put it back up before Barbara and Brody get back," Chug gasped, but it was too late. He and Sparky looked up and spotted the motel owners swooping in for a landing.

"Oh, we forgot to tell you not to turn on the sign," Brody said before Chug and Sparky could tell them what happened. "It's broken. The technician's coming tomorrow to put up a new one."

Sparky and Chug sighed with relief. Thanks to them, the technician wouldn't have to take the old sign down first!

DISNEY · PIXAR

FINDING NEMO

The Secret of Skull Cove

In a quiet corner of the reef, there was a twisted coral formation that looked like the open-mouthed skeleton of an angry clownfish.

"My dad said Mean Old Man Crab lives in there. He's been chasing kids away for an eternity!" said Nemo.

"No one has seen Mean Old Man Crab in years. Let's go! It will be an adventure," said Tad, his fins wiggling in excitement.

Nemo and his three friends cautiously entered the mouth of the cove.

Sheldon sneezed loudly, startling Pearl. She rounded on him in annoyance, but froze when she saw something emerging from a dark corner.

"Ahh!" she screamed, as a giant crab with pincers as big as her body came bursting out.

"What are you kids doing?" the crab screeched with a click of his claws. "Maybe one or two pinches will teach you a lesson!"

"It's Mean Old Man Crab!" exclaimed Nemo. "Swim for your lives!"

Pearl squirted ink in the crab's scary face as they dashed off, tearing up the seaweed garden in their haste.

"You're trampling my plants!" the crab wailed. "Wait until I get my claws on you!"

Back home, Marlin was wondering where his son could be, when Nemo came racing up with his frightened friends in tow.

"Dad! A crab!" he screamed.

"Crab?" everyone at the reef choked in fear.

"Use the coral as camouflage!" Marlin instructed them.

"I'm sorry I went to Mean Old Man Crab's cove," Nemo apologized, as they hid.

"That's the crab that's chasing you?" asked Marlin. He seemed less afraid now.

Mean Old Man Crab scurried over the hill with his pincers raised.

"Hey!" Marlin yelled, as he raced out. "Keep those claws to yourself, crabby!" He pointed an orange fin directly into the crab's face. "Remember me? You chased me from Skull Cove when I was little, but I went back anyway and warned you about the shark. You were almost dinner until I saved you!"

Mean Old Man Crab's angry frown melted. He lowered his claws thoughtfully. "That was you?" he gasped.

Marlin nodded.

Later, the sea creatures emerged from their hiding places to find Mean Old Man Crab smiling at them!

"Swim by the cove tomorrow," the crab said. "We can talk about old times!"

"You got it, crabby," promised Marlin.

"Dad's a super-fish." Nemo grinned in pride, as Mean Old Man Crab waved goodbye.

The Acting Lesson

"Wow! I love this castle!" said Buttercup the unicorn, admiring the cardboard castle Bonnie and her mum had built.

"It looks so royal," gasped Mr Pricklepants. "I guess Bonnie will be playing knights and princesses today!"

Buttercup bowed his head, "I'll be the perfect prince unicorn."

"You'll be great in that role," Mr Pricklepants agreed. But as Buttercup looked over at the other toys, who were excitedly reading a space adventure, he wasn't so sure they were ready to take on their royal roles. "They all need a good acting lesson," Mr Pricklepants decided. "And I'm just the toy who can help!"

Buttercup and Mr Pricklepants rushed over to the other toys. "Hey! You know Bonnie's going to play with the castle, don't you?" shouted Mr Pricklepants.

"I'll be the tower dragon," roared Rex.

"Yes, but only after my acting lesson, Rex!" replied Mr Pricklepants.

Buzz was shocked. "We don't need any acting lessons. We are professional toys!"

But Mr Pricklepants wouldn't change his mind. "You're wrong!" he said. "A toy always needs to prepare, so he can give his best!"

Mr Pricklepants called the other toys when he had set up an acting training session for

them. He had one of Bonnie's fairy-tale books to read from, and watched as the toys acted out different parts of the story.

"Let's see the brave knight battle the terrible dragon!" called Mr Pricklepants.

Buzz, pretending to be the brave knight, rode in on Bullseye. Just then, Rex the dragon stormed in. Buzz fired his space laser at Rex, "You've lost, dragon!"

Mr Pricklepants sighed.

"Knights don't use space lasers," Buttercup said helpfully.

Next, Jessie pretended be a princess but then she started swinging from the castle turrets using her lasso. "No!" cried Mr Pricklepants. "A princess doesn't move like that."

"But I'm a cool princess!" replied Jessie.

Later, all the toys acted out the final part of the story. But just as brave Buzz was about to rescue princess Jessie, Bonnie came home!

All the toys froze when she came into the room. Bonnie picked up the toys, ready to play. They had been preparing for knights and princesses all day, but Bonnie had another idea. "Let's pretend this castle is a space base!"

"All that work for nothing," sighed Mr Pricklepants.

Jessie giggled. "See, you should have read the space adventure with us!"

Disney · PIXAR

Cars

Rally to the Finish!

German racing superstar Max Schnell invited Lightning McQueen to the Black Forest Rally Race Invitational. Lightning was thrilled! He asked Mater, Luigi and Guido to come along as his race crew.

When Team Lightning arrived in Germany, they were greeted at the airport by Max, then whisked off to a pre-race party. Lightning was happy to see two more World Grand Prix buddies there – Spanish racer Miguel Camino and French rally car Raoul ÇaRoule.

Later, Lightning told Mater he wanted to head to the Black Forest to practise on the racetrack.

An old gentlecar overheard their plans. "Black Forest at night, eh? Just beware of that Waldgeister Monster."

"A m-m-monster?" stammered Mater.

"I'm sure that 'monster' is just a legend," said Lightning. He and Mater revved their engines and drove out to the forest.

"Whee-hoo!" yelled Mater, as he raced down a tree-lined path. "This here's fun!"

The buddies drifted down roads and across bridges until ... Mater got lost.

"Lightning? Hellooooo?" yelled Mater.

Suddenly, Mater felt something snag his tow hook. "Who's there?" he gasped as he spun around. A huge figure loomed over him.

"Ahhh!" Mater screamed, taking off backwards. "The monster's *real!*"

But no one believed him. The next day was race day. Lightning and the other racers pulled up to the starting line.

Mater drove out onto the track. "You guys aren't still gonna race, are you? There's a monster!"

"There's nothing to worry about, buddy," Lightning said.

The green start flag dropped. Lightning sped around a tricky curve with Max, Raoul and Miguel right on his bumper.

Suddenly, the racers heard a low grumbling sound that shook the forest floor. It grew until a roar echoed everywhere! They stopped in their tracks, panic-stricken.

"It's the Waldgeister Monster!" yelled Lightning. "He's real!"

The cars raced for their lives! They sped down a rocky slope and skidded around turns. They raced full speed towards a river and leaped over it! The audience couldn't believe what they were seeing. All four racers crossed the finish line at the same time and they had all broken the rally record for the fastest time!

"What motivated all of you to race your best today?" asked a reporter later.

"Well, we couldn't have done it without the Waldgeister Monster," giggled Lightning.

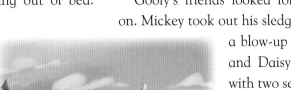

Goofy's Sledging Contest

One chilly morning, Goofy woke up to find snow outside his window.

"Yahoo!" he yelled, jumping out of bed. "Winter is here!"

Goofy loved winter – getting bundled up in his warmest clothes, building snowmen and the crunch of snow. But Goofy's favourite thing was sledging!

Goofy had lots of sledges, but he wondered if there was a faster way down the hill. He looked for something that could work and found just the thing ... his surfboard!

Goofy ran outside and up a hill. He put the surfboard down, jumped on it and ... it sank!

"Gosh," said Goofy. "I guess I need to find something lighter."

Then he got two bananas and put the peels on his feet. He took a step forward and – *BAM!* – Goofy slipped and fell into the snow.

"Ouch!" he said. "I guess I slip on banana peels, but they don't slip on snow."

Just then, Mickey came along. "Why are you lying in the snow?" he asked.

"I'm trying to find the fastest way down the hill," Goofy explained. "Any ideas?"

"Hmm," Mickey said. "I have a racing sledge that is very fast. You could try that."

"I wonder if it is faster than my sledges? We should all have a race!" said Goofy.

He called Minnie, who called Daisy, who called Donald. Everyone was very excited!

Goofy's friends looked for things to race on. Mickey took out his sledge, Donald found a blow-up raft and Minnie and Daisy chose a sledge with two seats.

Maybe a sledge is best, after all, Goofy thought.

But which one should he use? Goofy couldn't decide. So he piled his sledges into a washing basket and dragged them all to the hill.

The friends headed to the top of the hill and got ready to race. Goofy took out all the sledges, but he still couldn't decide!

"Everybody ready?" Mickey asked. "On your marks, get set...."

But Goofy wasn't ready! He turned ... and accidentally fell right into his washing basket!

"GO!" yelled Mickey.

The race had started without Goofy! But then the basket started to slip down the hill. It moved faster and faster until Goofy slid past his friends!

"Yahoo!" he yelled, as he raced to the bottom of the hill. Goofy had won!

"You were so fast!" Mickey said.

"What made you use the wash basket?" asked Minnie.

Goofy smiled. "I guess you could say I just fell into it!"

See you
next year!